section A
PCA SKIN® philosophy

section B
patient consultation

section C
skin physiology

section D
skin conditions

section E
daily care products

section F
daily care solutions for specific conditions

section G
daily care regimens

section H
PCA SKIN® peel fundamentals

section J
business development

section K
reference materials

section L
notes

A

PCA SKIN® philosophy

A

our vision

We will improve people's lives.

For us to deliver on this promise, we must truly understand the wants and needs of our customers and patients. We do that by hiring and retaining the very best and brightest to our team and giving them the tools they need to be successful.

This then extends to our customers — physicians, nurses, medical and licensed skin care professionals, and students — who attend our educational sessions, developing the knowledge base, skill set and tools to build their practices.

Our vision extends even further to patients who are treated by highly qualified physicians and clinicians with products that work to help them correct an undesired skin condition such as acne, hyperpigmentation, sensitive skin and aging or sun-damaged skin.

our mission

PCA SKIN® will hire and retain the most talented professionals in the industry.

We will continuously improve ourselves and our research efforts in order to provide our clinicians with the most innovative and effective products to improve the health and appearance of their patients' skin.

We will ensure the success of our clinicians' practices by exceeding expectations with the best education, customer service and technical support in the industry.

PCA SKIN will always practice the highest ethical and professional standards.

fulfilling our vision and mission

Acknowledged in prominent medical textbooks as the originator of modified and enhanced Jessner's chemical peel formulations, PCA SKIN® remains the trusted healthcare industry leader in the development of gentle, yet highly effective professional treatments and daily care products.

The physician's choice
PCA SKIN is a healthcare company whose clinically researched and scientifically formulated products have been designed to work in treating such skin conditions as acne, aging skin, sensitive skin and hyperpigmentation. A true industry pioneer, we were the first to provide these products to the medical and clinical aesthetics markets. Our peels are viewed as the gold standard in the industry. From the beginning, we have supported our peel technology with daily care products that are combined in customized regimens specific to the individual patient's skin needs and goals.

Today, after over two decades of leading the way in the clinical skin care industry, PCA SKIN remains the healthcare industry leader in the development of gentle, yet highly effective professional treatments and daily care products. We are the trusted educational resource to physicians and clinicians the world over.

Founded as Physician's Choice of Arizona, Inc., by an aesthetician working with a handful of physicians, the company has evolved into Physicians Care Alliance, LLC, a global organization serving over 5,000 medical practices in the United States and in 70 countries around the globe. Throughout our history, we have consistently been referred to as PCA SKIN, a company dedicated to the science of healthy skin.

Smart skin solutions
Our philosophy starts with the basic premise that healthy skin is beautiful skin. We believe strongly in the importance of pre- and post-treatment for the skin, preparing it properly for in-office procedures, then keeping it hydrated and calm afterwards. This allows the patient to achieve outstanding results.

We also know that everyone's skin is unique and requires a customized regimen that addresses all of their issues simultaneously. Our professional treatment protocols focus on penetrating the stratum corneum (the outer layer of the skin) to nourish the underlying epidermis and dermis, as opposed to simply stripping away the surface. The PCA SKIN peels' progressive approach leads to dramatic results without unnecessary and unwanted trauma or downtime.

Our educators have their own practices and conduct over 500 seminars and workshops annually. They have an intimate working knowledge of PCA SKIN professional treatments and daily care regimens, and fully support our philosophy for achieving healthy, beautiful skin. This highly trained team of medical professionals goes through a rigorous training process to ensure that they are delivering top-quality education so that physicians and clinicians can, in turn, deliver outstanding results to their patients.

Part of the team

Although they are customers, PCA SKIN® Certified Professionals are an extension of our organization. Much like our own team, these professionals are intellectually curious, have a high standard of values and ethics, and are enthusiastic about serving others. Their aim is to deliver the best possible results to their patients, and we support them every step of the way. Once a physician or clinician has invested the time and resources necessary to achieve certification, we are prepared to work closely with them to build their practice, continue building their knowledge base, and develop the tools and skill set needed for treating their patients.

We have a highly trained and knowledgeable Practice Development Group and Advanced Educators ready to assist physicians and clinicians with any questions regarding ordering, treatment protocols, product ingredients, disease pathways, industry news and marketing tools. Also, when calling in to our offices, clinicians have access to our medical practice and the PCA SKIN management team.

We are excited to partner with you in helping your patients reach their skin care goals and look forward to helping you build your business with PCA SKIN. Thank you for selecting us to help your patients achieve healthy, beautiful skin.

A

PCA SKIN® formulating philosophy

At PCA SKIN we use rigorous research and science to develop safe, highly effective products that deliver healthy, beautiful skin. We accomplish this while maintaining a deep respect for human health and the environment.

All finished products are tested in clinical trials with patients in our medical practice.

We do not perform or condone animal testing.

Our broad spectrum SPF products are recommended by The Skin Cancer Foundation.

Our products are free of:

- synthetic dyes
- synthetic fragrances
- mineral oil
- petrolatum
- lanolin
- phthalates
- parabens

These ingredients are used in conjunction with best-in-class support and delivery vehicles to ensure optimum results.

Chirality

PCA SKIN® has provided only chirally correct products since the company was founded two decades ago.

D-ascorbic acid   L-ascorbic acid

Chirality refers to the "handedness" of an asymmetrical molecule. These "hands" are considered mirror images of each other. All cells in the body will prefer or use more effectively one hand versus the other. Using the incorrect side of a molecule can cause sensitivity, irritation or just ineffectiveness.

A helpful analogy is the fact that your right hand cannot comfortably fit into a left-handed glove.

On any of our packaging, our ingredient listings do not include the L- and D- isomer indications, as the International Nomenclature for Cosmetic Ingredients (INCI) dictionary does not include these isomer designations in the official name of an ingredient. The Personal Care Products Council (formerly known as the Cosmetic, Toiletry and Fragrance Association or CTFA) is an independent organization that designates the accepted international name for each ingredient that will be used in cosmetic and drug products. The U.S. FDA uses this dictionary of ingredient designation as the acceptable and appropriate source for correct label listings.

In other written materials aside from packaging, the only ingredient name that includes its isomer designation is L-ascorbic acid. Ascorbic acid written without its L- indicates a mixture of both L- and D- ascorbic acid. Only the L- portion of ascorbic acid is, in fact, vitamin C. Although we do not label all ingredients in this manner, we always use the chirally correct form of any ingredient, where applicable.

PCA SKIN® treatment philosophy

Healthy skin is beautiful skin
As the largest organ of elimination, the skin is an outer reflection of the health of the body and its systems. Regular use of topical products that preserve, promote and protect healthy skin will lead to a radiant and youthful appearance. Through the elimination of skin issues by fighting free radicals and inflammation, increasing cell turnover and collagen production, we achieve skin wellness. Generally, healthy skin naturally glows from the inside, resulting in beautiful skin.

Customizing for optimal results
Each patient's skin represents a unique combination of their DNA, environment, lifestyle choices and product usage. Customizing regimens for each of your patients is the best way to address multiple skin issues simultaneously. PCA SKIN provides sets of trial-size products grouped together to address specific skin challenges. These solutions are a great place for the patient to start their introduction to PCA SKIN. Once the patient returns to purchase full-size products, you can further customize their regimen for them.

Importance of pre-treatment
Having your patients on PCA SKIN daily care prior to a professional treatment has many benefits. First, the patient's skin is properly prepared for a peel, increasing the likelihood of a positive treatment outcome. Dispensing the trial-size solutions at the consultation allows the patient to determine preferences, thus minimizing product returns. Additionally, the patient is typically ready to purchase full-size products at their first appointment.

Progressive approach
Consumers are often mistaken that if a little of something is good, more is better. This is especially untrue when it comes to treating the skin. Inflammation is the cause of many skin conditions we work to treat, and causing irritation and inflammation in the skin with overly aggressive treatments and products will only worsen, not correct, the situation. Gentle treatment delivers more dramatic and consistent outcomes. If the goal is healthy, beautiful skin, then a progressive approach is usually the best choice.

Layer and leave on
PCA SKIN peels are not timed, neutralized and removed from the skin. Instead, they are self-neutralizing and are left on the skin, with the exception of the masks, which are removed with moist cotton pads. The strength and depth of the treatment is controlled by the trained professional based on the number of layers applied during treatment. After peel application, nutritive topicals and calming, broad spectrum SPF products are applied, and the patient leaves with a glowing, healthy complexion. This makes the experience much more relaxed and pleasant for both the clinician and patient.

Important peeling ingredients

We use blends of well-tolerated, safe and effective peeling ingredients in our peel solutions. Alpha hydroxy acids (AHA), beta hydroxy acids (BHA), trichloroacetic acid (TCA) and retinoids are used in strategic combinations to address a wide variety of skin concerns. These ingredients work to break down surface buildup and loosen the desmosome bonds holding the keratinocytes together. Ancillary ingredients that nourish, strengthen and protect the skin are incorporated into the formulas so the skin is flooded with these beneficial actives during treatment. A more detailed discussion of each peeling ingredient can be found in the **PCA SKIN® peel fundamentals** section of this textbook.

Importance of post-treatment care

When it comes to ensuring dramatic results, the way patients take care of their skin post-treatment is almost as important as the peel formulation itself. Each peel manufacturer's post-procedure recommendations vary, but the basics remain the same: keep the area clean, calm inflammation, protect from UV rays and keep the area hydrated. Gentle products that protect the skin are critical for excellent results. We recommend dispensing **The Post-Procedure Solution** after any in-office treatment to be certain that patients use only beneficial products during this post-treatment period. It also reinforces the importance of quality daily care products. They should use these post-procedure products until flaking has resolved, typically three to five days; then the patient can return to their recommended skincare routine.

B

patient consultation

initial consultation

The consultation is a vital part of achieving success with your patients. The initial consultation sets the tone for your relationship with your patients and is the key to your success. Trust between you and your patient builds loyalty as well as compliance. Educating your patients about their skin works to further solidify that relationship.

We recommend charging for your consultation and building the cost of a trial solution into your fee. During the consultation you can provide these trial products to the patient at no charge, and go through each product and direction for their use using your **Rx Treatment Plan**. Consider washing their face and applying their recommended products. This teaches application technique and demonstrates the immediate benefits of using quality skincare products. A condition-specific trial-size solution of PCA SKIN® products allows the patient to try products prior to their first peel. This is highly recommended 10 to 14 days prior to an in-office superficial chemical peel to prepare the skin. This is a suggestion, not a requirement, but it will increase results and minimize reactions. Use of the trial solutions prior to their first treatment also minimizes product returns and increases full-size retail product purchases at the initial treatment appointment.

The initial consultation should typically be limited to 45 minutes. A **Patient Profile** should be completed thoroughly by the patient prior to consultation.

creating comprehensive patient files

PCA SKIN provides you with essential forms to be used in creating patient files. Using these forms will help build your relationship with the patient, gather necessary information to develop effective daily care regimens and treatment plans, and most importantly, ensure patient results. The following consultation forms are available from PCA SKIN:

- **New Patient Procedure Checklist** – highlights important information to be covered prior to a treatment and gives the clinician the order in which each step should take place (analyzing the skin, determining the appropriate daily care regimen, scheduling the patient's first treatment, etc.). We recommend that you charge for a consultation. Following this checklist ensures that patients get the most out of their consultation and that you are armed with all the necessary information to make the best daily care and professional treatment recommendations for your patients.

- **Patient Profile** – provides for full disclosure of pertinent patient information, which will enable the clinician to determine an appropriate treatment plan and daily care regimen. Have your patients review this prior to each treatment to ensure they have not changed medications, topicals, procedures, etc.

- **Consent Form** – the patient signs and dates prior to their appointment, stating they consent to the treatment that will be performed on them that day. An oral agreement to treatments is not sufficient for your protection. In addition, they agree to have a clear understanding of expectations and have followed all pre- and post-procedure recommendations. Have patients review prior to each appointment, and initial and date to re-consent.

- **Face Diagram** – used to document specific areas of concern or areas the clinician has addressed. It is best to take before and after photographs. The **Face Diagram** can be used in addition to photos or in place of them if photographic equipment is not available to the clinician.

- **Preparation for a Peel Treatment** – educates the patient on lifestyle considerations prior to their scheduled treatment. This will help ensure patient compliance and reduce the incidence of complications following treatment.

- **Rx Treatment Plan** – helps you customize a regimen using this prescription pad, or you can start a patient on one of the condition-specific daily care trial-size kits.

- **Patient Treatment Log** – used to document data regarding the treatment performed (the specific products used in the treatment protocol, number of layers applied of the chemical peel, sensitivity of patient during the treatment, any visible signs of trauma, etc.).

- **Post-Procedure Skin Treatment Tips** – provided to the patient following treatment. It is important to review these important tips with the patient prior to their leaving the practice. This will help ensure they have a clear understanding of their post-procedure process.

new patient procedure checklist ☑

Patient Name:_____ Date:_____

Clinician Comments

Discuss Peel Treatments with Patient:

❑ **Patient Profile** form

❑ expectations

❑ possible reactions

❑ mandatory sunscreen use

❑ have patient sign the **Consent Form** and give them a copy

Analyze the Skin:

❑ visually

❑ UV light devices (Wood's Lamp, Visia®, Skin Scanner)

❑ magnifying lamp

❑ take "before" pictures/use **Face Diagram** when a camera or UV light device is not available

Daily Care Regimen:

❑ trial-size kits

❑ customized regimen with instructions

❑ patient brochure

❑ **Preparation for a Peel Treatment** instructions

Peel Appointment:

❑ date of first treatment

❑ **Post-Procedure Skin Treatment Tips**

❑ **Post-Procedure Daily Care Regimen**

What is your daily care regimen? _____

_____

What are the cosmetic improvements you would like to see in your skin?_____

Treatment recommendation: _____

Patch Test Date:_____Solution:_____Test Area:_____Result:_____

patient profile

Name:_____ DOB:_____ Age:_____ Sex:_____

Address:_____

City:_____ State:_____ Zip:_____

Phone:_____ E-mail:_____

About You:
- What is your hereditary background? (circle all that apply) Nordic / Scandinavian / Irish / English / Asian / Mediterranean / Hispanic / Native American / Middle Eastern / African American / Other _____
- Natural eye color: _____
- Natural hair color: _____
- Do you consider your skin (circle the best option): Sensitive / Resilient / Unsure
- Describe your skin (circle all the apply): Normal / Dry / T-Zone/Combination / Thick / Thin / Saggy / Firm / Oily / Acne / Comedones/Blackheads / Milia / Cysts / Breakouts / Acne-scarred / Large pores / Small pores / Rosacea / Eczema / Freckled / Sun-damaged / Melasma / Hyperpigmentation / Hypopigmentation / Uneven/Blotchy / Mature / Wrinkled / Patchy dryness / Sallow / Psoriasis / Dehydrated/ Lacking moisture / Asphyxiated / Telangiectasia/Broken surface capillaries
- What are the changes you'd most like to see in your skin?

_____

_____

_____

Lifestyle:
- Are you pregnant or lactating? ❏ No ❏ Yes
  (**Please consult with your obstetrician.** Only the Oxygenating Trio®, Detox Gel Deep Pore Treatment, Hydrate: Therapeutic Oat Milk Mask, Detoxify: Therapeutic Charcoal Mask or Revitalize: Therapeutic Papaya Mask are appropriate.)
- Do you wear contact lenses? ❏ No ❏ Yes
  (**Remove contacts** if eyes are sensitive or if having microdermabrasion.)
- Do you currently have a sunburned/windburned/red face? ❏ No ❏ Yes
  Why? _____
- Are you in the habit of going to tanning booths? ❏ No ❏ Yes
  (If within past 14 days, decline treatment. This practice should be discontinued due to increased risk of skin cancer and signs of aging.)
- Do you participate in vigorous aerobic activity or sports? ❏ No ❏ Yes
  What type? _____
- Do you smoke or use tobacco? ❏ No ❏ Yes
- What kind of work do you do? _____
- On average, how many hours per week do you spend outdoors? _____

Medical/Treatment History:

- Do you currently use depilatories or wax?   ❏ No ❏ Yes
  (Discontinue use five days pre- and post-treatment.)

- Have you had a chemical peel or any type of procedure with a medical device?   ❏ No ❏ Yes
  Within the last 14 days?   ❏ No ❏ Yes
  What type? _____

- Do you have regular collagen, Botox® or other dermal filler injections?   ❏ No ❏ Yes
  (Peels should precede or follow injections by two days to prevent movement of the filler
  or stinging at the injection site.)

- Have you recently had laser resurfacing or facial surgery?   ❏ No ❏ Yes
  Describe _____
  When? _____

- Are you currently taking any medications, topical or otherwise?   ❏ No ❏ Yes
  (Tretinoin/Retin-A®/Renova®/Differin®/Tazorac®/Avage®/ EpiDuo®/Ziana®)
  Which one(s)?_____
  For how long? _____
  What strength? _____
  (High percentages of certain ingredients may increase sensitivity. Discontinue use five days
  before and after treatment. Consult your physician before discontinuing use of any prescription.)

- Have you ever undergone Accutane® therapy (isotretinoin)?   ❏ No ❏ Yes
  **(If you are currently using Accutane® therapy (isotretinoin), please consult with your
  dispensing physician.)**
  (If you are no longer using Accutane® therapy (isotretinoin) it is OK to apply ONE layer of
  Ultra Peel® I, Sensi Peel®, Advanced Treatment Booster, Oxygenating Trio®, Hydrate: Therapeutic
  Oat Milk Mask, or Revitalize: Therapeutic Papaya Mask or Detoxify: Therapeutic Charcoal Mask.)

- Do you develop cold sores/fever blisters?   ❏ No ❏ Yes
  Last breakout? _____

- Are you allergic/sensitive to (circle all that apply) milk / apples / citrus / grapes /   ❏ No ❏ Yes
  aloe vera / aspirin / perfumes / latex / hydroquinone / mushrooms?
  If any other allergies, what?_____

- Have you ever used any other products that caused a bad reaction?   ❏ No ❏ Yes
  Describe _____

Patient Signature:_____ Date:_____

Clinician Signature:_____ Date:_____

consent form

Prior to receiving treatment, I have been candid in revealing any condition that may have bearing on this procedure, such as: pregnancy (if so, consult your physician prior to treatment), recent facial surgery, allergies, tendency to cold sores/fever blisters, or use of topical and/or oral retinoid treatments such as: tretinoin, Retin-A®, isotretinoin, Accutane®, Differin®, Tazorac®, Avage®, EpiDuo® or Ziana®.

I understand there may be some degree of discomfort such as stinging, pin-prickling sensation, heat or tightness.

I understand there are no guarantees as to the results of this treatment, due to many variables, such as: age, condition of skin, sun damage, smoking, climate, etc.

I understand I may or may not actually peel and that each case is individual. I understand that the amount of peeling does not correlate with degree of improvement.

I understand this treatment is a cosmetic treatment and that no medical claims are expressed or implied.

I understand that to achieve maximum results, I may need several treatments.

I understand that although complications are very rare, sometimes they may occur and that prompt treatment is necessary. In the event of any complications, I will immediately contact the physician/clinician who performed the treatment.

I agree to refrain from tanning in tanning beds or outdoors while I am undergoing treatment, and during the 14 days prior to and following the end of treatment. This practice should be discontinued due to the increased risk of skin cancer and signs of aging.

I understand that extended direct sun exposure is prohibited while I am undergoing treatment, and the daily use of sunscreen protection with a minimum SPF of 30 is mandatory.

I have not had any other chemical peel of any kind within 14 days of this treatment. I understand I cannot have another chemical peel within 14 days of this treatment, whether it is performed at this location or any other location.

I understand that I should follow my clinician's recommendations for post-procedure skin care to minimize side effects and maximize results.

I hereby agree to all of the above and agree to have this treatment performed on me. I further agree to follow all post-peel care instructions as I am directed.

Signature: _____ Date:_____

Initials: _____

Signature of Clinician: _____

Signature of Witness:_____

Continued Treatment Consent

Date	Initials

face diagram

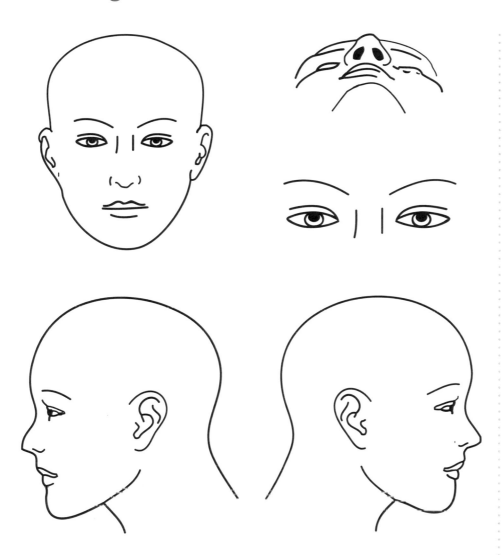

preparation for a peel treatment

You will be having a light peel treatment on the day of your appointment. Please follow the outline below to prepare.

- Use of PCA SKIN® daily care products prior to your peel will prepare the skin, allow for better treatment results and reduce the risk of complications. This is recommended but not mandatory. Please consult your physician or skin care clinician for appropriate recommendations for your skin type and condition.

It is recommended that you take the following into consideration:

- For best results and to reduce the risk of complications, it is recommended that you use PCA SKIN daily care products 10 to 14 days prior to treatment.

- If you are lactating, pregnant or may be pregnant, only **Oxygenating Trio®, Detox Gel Deep Pore Treatment**, **Hydrate: Therapeutic Oat Milk Mask, Detoxify: Therapeutic Charcoal Mask** or **Revitalize: Therapeutic Papaya Mask** is appropriate. Consult your OB/GYN before receiving any treatment.

- Do not go to a tanning bed two weeks prior to treatment. This practice should be discontinued due to the increased risk of skin cancer and signs of aging.

- It is recommended that extended sun exposure be avoided, especially in the 10 days prior to treatment.

- It is recommended to delay use of tretinoin, Retin-A®, Renova®, Differin®, Tazorac®, Avage®, EpiDuo®, Ziana® and high-percentage AHA and BHA products for approximately five days prior to treatment. Consult your physician before temporarily discontinuing use of any prescription medications.

PCA SKIN superficial peels result in little to no downtime but create dramatic and visible results. Treatments may cause slight redness, tightness, peeling, flaking or temporary dryness. Most patients find it unnecessary to apply makeup, as the skin will be smooth, dewy and radiant following your treatment. If you would like to apply makeup, allow approximately 15 minutes for the pH of the skin to stabilize before applying foundation.

your daily regimen

PCA SKIN's line of daily care products can be customized into a regimen unique to each person's skin. The **Rx Treatment Plan** is designed to help simplify every patient's daily care regimen.

Rx Treatment Plan

This prescription pad allows you to indicate exactly what the patient is to use and how. This is a convenient and easy-to-use format. It provides a copy for the patient to take home with them to follow as they get used to their new regimen. The pad provides space for the clinician to indicate specific products for the patient to use, and outlines key products in the following categories:

- Shows key, featured products that most patients will see benefit from

- Offers space for professional treatment details, daily care instructions and additional product recommendations

- Can be provided to the client to take home

- Works alongside the **Patient Treatment Log** to provide every PCA Certified Professional with a comprehensive record of each patient's care

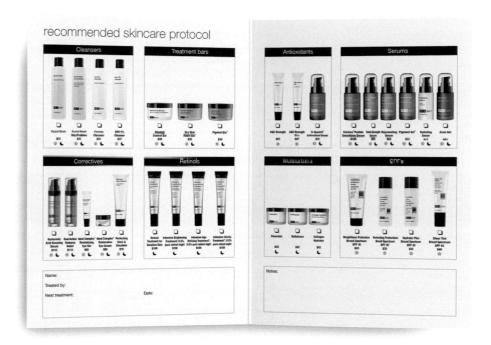

patient treatment log

PCA skin®

Patient name:_____ Treatment #:_____ Date:_____

Next scheduled treatment:_____

Area treated: face   neck   chest   hands   arms   feet   other_____

Scale of one to ten: 1 2 3 4 5 6 7 8 9 10

Comments: _____

_____

Protocol:

Cleanse
❑ Facial Wash
❑ Facial Wash Oily/Problem
❑ Total Wash Face & Body Cleanser
❑ Creamy Cleanser
❑ BPO 5% Cleanser
❑ Blemish Control Bar
❑ Dry Skin Relief Bar®
❑ Pigment Bar®

Prep/degrease
❑ Smoothing Toner
❑ Nutrient Toner

Treat

Enhanced Jessner's peels
❑ PCA Peel® Hydroquinone Free   _____layers
❑ PCA Peel® with Hydroquinone   _____layers
❑ PCA Peel® with Hydroquinone & Resorcinol   _____layers

TCA peels
❑ Sensi Peel®   _____layers
❑ Ultra Peel® I   _____layers
❑ Ultra Peel Forte®   _____layers
❑ Smoothing Body Peel®   _____layers

Retinoid treatments
❑ Advanced Treatment Booster   __1__layer
❑ 4% Pure Retinol Peel   __1__layer
❑ 6% Pure Retinol Peel   __1__layer

Therapeutic masks
❑ Hydrate: Therapeutic Oat Milk Mask   __1__layer
❑ Detoxify: Therapeutic Charcoal Mask   __1__layer
❑ Revitalize: Therapeutic Papaya Mask   __1__layer
❑ Clarify: Therapeutic Salicylic Acid Mask   __1__layer
❑ Retexturize: Therapeutic Pumpkin Mask   __1__layer

Peel alternatives
❑ Detox Gel Deep Pore Treatment   __1__layer
❑ Oxygenating Trio®   __1__layer

Treatment enhancements
❑ Replenishing Gel   _____layers
❑ Calming Balm   _____layers

Correct
❑ Gentle Exfoliant
❑ Pore Refining Treatment
❑ Purifying Mask
❑ Detoxifying Mask
❑ Revitalizing Mask
❑ ExLinea® Peptide Smoothing Serum
❑ Pigment Gel®
❑ Pigment Gel® HQ Free
❑ Acne Gel
❑ Acne Cream
❑ C-Quench® Antioxidant Serum
❑ A&C Synergy Serum®
❑ Total Strength Serum
❑ Hydrating Serum
❑ Rejuvenating Serum
❑ Anti-Redness Serum
❑ Retinol Renewal with RestorAtive Complex
❑ Retinol Treatment for Sensitive Skin
❑ Intensive Clarity Treatment®: 0.5% pure retinol night
❑ Intensive Age Refining Treatment®: 0.5% pure retinol night
❑ Intensive Brightening Treatment: 0.5% pure retinol night
❑ Intensive Pigment Eraser
❑ C&E Strength
❑ C&E Strength Max
❑ Hyaluronic Acid Boosting Serum
❑ Dual Action Redness Relief
❑ Ideal Complex® Revitalizing Eye Gel
❑ Ideal Complex® Restorative Eye Cream
❑ EyeXcellence
❑ Perfecting Neck & Décolleté
❑ CliniCalm™ 1%
❑ Peptide Lip Therapy

Hydrate
❑ Clearskin
❑ ReBalance
❑ Apres Peel® Hydrating Balm
❑ Collagen Hydrator
❑ Silkcoat® Balm
❑ Body Therapy

Protect
❑ Weightless Protection Broad Spectrum SPF 45
❑ Perfecting Protection Broad Spectrum SPF 30
❑ Protecting Hydrator Broad Spectrum SPF 30
❑ Hydrator Plus Broad Spectrum SPF 30
❑ Active Broad Spectrum SPF 45: Water Resistant
❑ Sheer Tint Broad Spectrum SPF 45

Daily care product recommendations:

_____   _____

_____   _____

_____   _____

post-procedure skin treatment tips

For two days post-procedure:

- Stay as cool as possible. Overheating internally can cause hyperpigmentation.
- Do not put the treated area directly into a hot shower spray.
- Do not use hot tubs, steam rooms or saunas.
- Do not go swimming.
- Do not participate in activities that would cause excessive perspiration.
- Do not use loofahs or other means of mechanical exfoliation.
- Do not direct a hair dryer onto the treated area.
- Do not apply ice or ice water to the treated area.

General guidelines:

- After receiving a PCA SKIN® professional treatment, you should not necessarily expect to "peel". However, light flaking in a few localized areas for several days is typical. Most patients who undergo these treatments have residual redness for approximately one to 12 hours post-procedure.
- As with all peels and treatments, it is recommended that makeup not be applied the day of treatment, as it is ideal to allow the skin to stabilize and rest overnight; however, makeup may be applied 15 minutes after the treatment if desired.
- To minimize side effects and maximize results use **The Post-Procedure Solution** for three to five days or until flaking has resolved.
- If the skin feels tight, apply **ReBalance** for normal to oily skin types or **Silkcoat® Balm** for drier skin types to moisturize as needed. For maximum hydration, you can apply **Hydrating Serum** under **ReBalance** or **Silkcoat® Balm.**
- Moisturizer should be applied at least twice a day, but can be applied more frequently for hydration and to decrease the appearance of flaking
- It is recommended that other topical, over-the-counter medications or alpha hydroxy acid products not be applied to the skin seven days post-procedure, as they may cause irritation.
- It is recommended to delay use of tretinoin, Retin-A®, Differin®, Renova®, Tazorac®, Avage®, EpiDuo® or Ziana® five days post-procedure. Consult your physician before temporarily discontinuing use of any prescription medications.
- Avoid direct sun exposure and excessive heat. Use **Weightless Protection Broad Spectrum SPF 45**, **Perfecting Protection Broad Spectrum SPF 30**, **Protecting Hydrator Broad Spectrum SPF 30**, **Hydrator Plus Broad Spectrum SPF 30** or **Sheer Tint Broad Spectrum SPF 45** for broad spectrum UV protection.
- Do not go to a tanning bed for at least two weeks post-procedure. This practice should be discontinued due to the increased risk of skin cancer and signs of aging.
- Do not pick or pull on any loosening or peeling skin. This could potentially cause hyperpigmentation.
- Do not have electrolysis, facial waxing or use depilatories for approximately five days.

Do not have another treatment until your clinician advises you to do so.

new patient procedure

Skin analysis

- Review the **Patient Profile** with the patient, noting any unusual problems, allergic conditions, use of medications or contributing stress factors.

- Ask the patient to describe their skin and have them specify areas of concern.

- Assess the patient using the Fitzpatrick scale and Global Heritage Model.

- Cleanse the skin thoroughly with **Facial Wash Oily/Problem**.

- Tone with **Smoothing Toner**. This product will sting or tingle mildly on most individuals. Ask, "On a scale of one to ten, ten being extremely active, how do you rate this sensation?" Make note of their response, as this is an indication of patient sensitivity.

- Analyze the skin visually utilizing available tools such as: Visia,® Skin Scanner, Wood's Lamp or a 5-diopter magnification lamp. Note skin type and conditions on the **Patient Profile** form.

- **Face Diagram** – used to document specific areas of concern or areas the clinician has addressed. It is best to take before and after photographs. The **Face Diagram** can be used in addition to photos or in place of them if photographic equipment is not available to the clinician.

- Take "before" photos using either a camera or available imaging technology. If using a camera, a tripod and chin rest are useful to ensure consistent facial positioning at each appointment. These photos serve to remind the patient of their skin's condition prior to treatments; as a way to track treatment progress; and, with their written consent, to build a portfolio of visible treatment results for your practice.

- Select the appropriate trial-size solution or customized regimen for the patient and educate them on the chosen product regimen.

- If planning to use hydroquinone, patch test a small area at this time in front of or behind the ear to verify they have no allergy or hypersensitivity to this ingredient.

- Apply the advanced treatment products from the **correct** category that are included in the trial-size solution you have selected for them. This allows the patient to experience your recommended products.

- Complete the analysis with the application of the appropriate SPF product for their skin type and condition; either **Weightless Protection Broad Spectrum SPF 45**, **Perfecting Protection Broad Spectrum SPF 30**, **Protecting Hydrator Broad Spectrum SPF 30**, **Hydrator Plus Broad Spectrum SPF 30** or **Sheer Tint Broad Spectrum SPF 45**.

- Review their recommended daily care regimen using either the **Rx Treatment Plan** or one of the PCA SKIN® condition-specific regimens.

how to analyze the skin using UV light devices

Ultraviolet light is a very useful tool for accurate skin analysis. The violet rays of the lamp enable you to "see" into the deeper layers of the skin in order to help identify certain skin conditions and recommend a proper treatment protocol. Different conditions are determined by the various colors as shown through the magnification glass of the Wood's Lamp, by looking into a machine such as Visia® or a Skin Scanner, or reviewing captured digital UV images. Some technologies have different settings for viewing various skin issues. If using a Wood's Lamp, it must be used in a completely dark room. Consistent low light is best for most other technologies.

To assist you with reading the colors seen in the skin through a UV light device, please refer to the guide below:

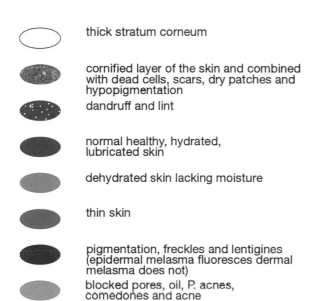

thick stratum corneum

cornified layer of the skin and combined with dead cells, scars, dry patches and hypopigmentation

dandruff and lint

normal healthy, hydrated, lubricated skin

dehydrated skin lacking moisture

thin skin

pigmentation, freckles and lentigines (epidermal melasma fluoresces dermal melasma does not)

blocked pores, oil, P. acnes, comedones and acne

In general, the lighter/whiter the color, the thicker the skin is. For example, you will see a lighter color in the cheeks.

Thinner skin, such as the eyelids appear darker. Appropriate lubrication and hydration appears in purple tones. Dehydrated skin appears lighter and brighter in color, and less purple compared to hydrated skin.

The standard Wood's Lamp is available through PCA SKIN®: 60 hertz, .17 amps, 115 volts, two 4 watt bulbs.

before and after photo tips

Visual records of a patient's history have many benefits. "Before" pictures help patients remember how far they have come in their course of treatment and they can greatly increase patient compliance. Also, with a patient's written consent, before and after photographs may be used as a great way to market your practice and the services you offer. In order for photographs to be useful to you in your practice, they must be taken according to some basic guidelines.

- Use a high mega pixel camera or one of the many excellent imaging technologies available like Visia® or a Skin Scanner.

- Have your camera set up in a consistent location with a tripod, chin rest and markings on the floor where a patient should sit/stand. This ensures that each set of photos is taken from the same distance and angle. Many imaging technologies provide this consistent environment as part of the device.

- Document the settings of your lighting. Using brighter lights in an "after" picture can lead people to believe that the picture was intentionally highlighted to make the results seem more dramatic. In face-forward photos the intensity of the lighting can be easily detected in the patient's pupils.

- At each visit take face-forward, left-side and right-side photos.

- Remove all makeup to match the first photo. Dramatic lipstick or eye makeup can detract from the results you are attempting to document.

- Have patients remove all jewelry prior to taking any photographs.

Building a portfolio of the dramatic patient outcomes you can achieve using PCA SKIN® daily care and professional treatments is an excellent way to build your practice and increase your credibility.

ensuring patient compliance

- Send your patients home with their daily care products and the **Rx Treatment Plan**. Give them instructions for product use and a **Preparation for a Peel Treatment** form.

- Determine the length of time between treatments according to each patient's skin type and condition, ethnicity and actinic damage (refer to **Frequency of Treatment** chart). Educate the patient on the importance of treating at the specified intervals to achieve the best possible outcome. Suggest a minimum of three treatments to start.

- Schedule the first peel treatment approximately two weeks after the initial consultation. This allows the patient to prep their skin with the PCA SKIN® daily care regimen you have recommended.

- Call your patient three to five days following the consultation to ensure the patient is responding well to the daily care regimen and to answer any questions.

useful patient education tools

Patient brochure

This informative brochure is written with the patient in mind. With pictures and easy-to-understand descriptions of PCA SKIN® daily care products, it makes educating patients about their daily regimens effortless. Use this brochure during your patient consultations in conjuction with the **Rx Treatment Plan** so patients can get the most out of their daily regimens.

initial in-office procedure

At this initial appointment, review the **Patient Profile** with your patient to be certain that nothing has changed in the two weeks since the consultation. Give the patient the opportunity to review their signed consent form, and have them initial and date it to re-consent for that treatment. Review their expectations and desired outcome. Educate the patient about superficial peels, how they work on the skin, possible reactions and what the professional treatments can realistically accomplish for their condition. Inform the patient that dryness, flaking and a possible breakout would be considered normal, yet temporary reactions to a superficial chemical peel. Everyone's skin is different, so it is important not to guarantee specific results.

Peel treatments are not to be performed on pregnant or lactating women, or patients who use tanning booths. However there are several peel alternative treatments that are appropriate, which can be found in the **Professional Treatments: Facts and Protocols** section of this textbook.

- Administer the selected procedure with a customized peel treatment that you determined to be appropriate for the skin type and condition of that particular patient.

- Watch for unusual reactions, such as excessive erythema (redness), edema (swelling) or blanching (protein coagulation).

- During and throughout the procedure, be sure to have the patient tell you how the procedure feels to them using the scale of one to ten (as described in the **Peel Fundamentals** section of this textbook).

- Always end your treatments with an application of the appropriate broad spectrum SPF product: **Weightless Protection Broad Spectrum SPF 45, Perfecting Protection Broad Spectrum SPF 30, Protecting Hydrator Broad Spectrum SPF 30, Hydrator Plus Broad Spectrum SPF 30** or **Sheer Tint Broad Spectrum SPF 45**.

- Document all data on the **Patient Treatment Log,** including number of peel layers, visible reactions or comments made by the patient. Chart the highest number on the scale of one to ten reached by the patient at any time during the treatment for future reference.

- Recommend the patient use **The Post-Procedure Solution** for three to five days following the treatment (the cost of this product may be included in the price of the procedure) to ensure the skin remains calm and hydrated following treatment.

- Let the patient know that if their **The Post-Procedure Solution** is used as recommended until flaking has resolved, typically three to five days, they will be able to use it after their next professional treatment.

- Book the patient's next appointment, and let the patient know you are available if they have any questions or concerns following the treatment.

- Call the patient the following day and document any comments or feedback.

skin physiology

the structure of human skin

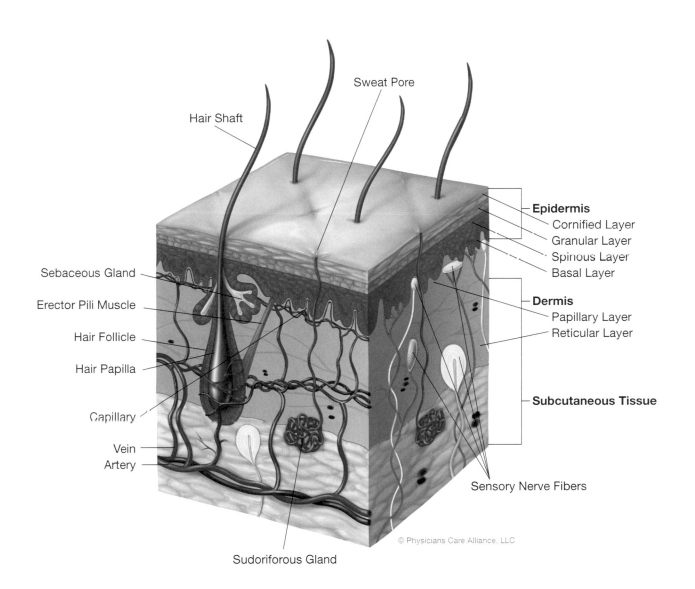

Hair Shaft

Sweat Pore

Epidermis
Cornified Layer
Granular Layer
Spinous Layer
Basal Layer

Dermis
Papillary Layer
Reticular Layer

Subcutaneous Tissue

Sebaceous Gland

Erector Pili Muscle

Hair Follicle

Hair Papilla

Capillary

Vein
Artery

Sensory Nerve Fibers

Sudoriforous Gland

© Physicians Care Alliance, LLC

structure and functions of the skin

The skin is the largest organ of the body. It is an elastic protective covering, which is thinnest on the lips and eyelids, and thickest on the palms of the hands and soles of the feet.

Structure of the skin: three major divisions

- **Epidermis** - the outermost layer of the skin
- **Dermis** - the inner corneum made up of connective tissue
- **Subcutaneous** - the deep layer of adipose (fatty) tissue

Epidermis

This is the outermost layer of the skin, which forms the protective covering of the body. Keratinocytes, or squamous cells, are produced in the basal layer (stratum germinativum) of the skin. These cells then migrate up through the epidermis until they complete their life cycle in the dead stratum corneum. The epidermis contains the following layers:

Basal layer (stratum basale) – consists of keratinocytes that undergo cell division and are responsible for growth of the epidermis. This layer also contains melanocytes that protect the cells from the UV rays of the sun.

Spinous layer (stratum spinosum) – consists of multiple layers of square-shaped cells. The desmosomes that hold the cells together have a spiny or prickle-like appearance when viewed under a microscope. As cells move upward during natural cell turnover, they become more flat. This layer also contains Langerhans cells that assist in the skin's immune function.

Granular layer (stratum granulosum) – consists of dying cells that contain distinct granules.

Clear layer (stratum lucidum) – is a barrier composed of transparent cells through which light can pass. These cells are only present in thick skin, such as the palms of the hands and soles of the feet.

Cornified layer (stratum corneum) – is composed of tightly packed dead cells, which are constantly being shed and replaced. This layer contains the skin's natural moisturizing factor (NMF) and is responsible for maintaining hydration of the stratum corneum. NMF exists inside the corneocytes (dead keratinocytes).

The NMF includes a combination of:

- amino acids
- sodium PCA
- lactate
- urea
- ammonia
- uric acid
- glucosamine
- creatinine
- organic acids
- citrate
- sodium potassium
- calcium
- magnesium
- phosphate
- chlorine
- sugar
- peptides
- other unidentified substances

A decrease in the NMF results in an increase in transepidermal water loss (TEWL), causing dryness and inflammation. The protein keratin and the lipid bilayer around each cell also assist in hydration by acting as occlusives, waterproofing the skin and preventing water evaporation. A small amount of TEWL is constantly taking place within the cornified layer and is critical to skin health; however, TEWL increases when the epidermis is compromised and may result in sensitivity.

Dermis

The dermis is the layer lying underneath the epidermis, consisting of highly sensitive and vascular connective tissue, collagen, elastin and reticular fibers. It consists of two layers: the papillary layer and the reticular layer.

Papillary layer – is composed of small conical elevations called "papillae," which push up into the epidermis and contain blood vessels and nerve fibers called tactile corpuscles. The epidermis receives its nourishment through this blood supply. Through these nerve fibers, we gain our sense of touch.

Reticular layer – contains the extracellular matrix (ECM), blood vessels, lymph nodes, nerves, sebaceous and sudoriferous glands, and fibrous and elastic tissue.

Extracellular matrix (ECM) – is a complex group of biomolecules designed to support and protect the cells. The ECM consists of structural proteins, such as collagen; adhesive proteins, such as fibronectin; glycosaminoglycans (GAG), such as hyaluronic acid; and elastin. A healthy ECM provides the skin with a firm and youthful appearance; however, environmentally-induced enzymes in the skin known as matrix metalloproteinases (MMP) break down and recycle proteins and can prematurely degrade this structure.

Matrix metalloproteinases (MMP) – are enzymes such as collagenase and elastase, and are responsible for the breakdown and recycling of proteins like collagen and elastin. MMP are beneficial to a certain extent and fight environmental factors such as pollution and other free radicals. When too many of these enzymes are present, the result is an unwanted breakdown of healthy proteins and extrinsic aging.

Matrix metalloproteinases inhibitors (MMPi) – are ingredients that maintain the correct balance within the extracellular matrix by inhibiting the activity of the enymes responsible for the breakdown of its structure (MMP). Examples of common MMPi are antioxidants such as resveratrol, epigallocatechin gallate (EGCG), and vitamins C and E.

Sebaceous glands – are small oil-producing glands that consist of little sacs whose ducts open into the hair follicles. They secrete sebum, which lubricates and prevents moisture loss from the skin. These glands are found in all parts of the body with the exception of the palms of the hands and soles of the feet. These glands respond to androgen hormones (male hormones) and increase the production of sebum during adolescence.

Sudoriferous glands – are tubular glands that are abundant in most parts of the body, but are more predominant on the palms, soles, forehead and underarms. The sudoriferous glands regulate body temperature and help eliminate waste products from the body. There are two types of sudoriferous glands found in the skin: eccrine and apocrine glands.

- **Eccrine glands** – secrete a watery sweat that is a mixture of 99% water, and 1% salts and fats. They are not associated with the hair follicle and respond to temperature to keep the body cool.

- **Apocrine glands** – become active at puberty. These glands are larger and deeper than eccrine glands and are associated with the hair follicle. Apocrine glands produce thicker secretions than eccrine glands and contain pheromones, which emit odor.

Subcutaneous layer

This is the fatty layer lying directly below the dermis, which is composed of fat cells, blood, nerves and lymph supply. It gives smoothness and contours to the body, contains fat that is utilized by the body for energy and acts as a protective cushion for the outer skin.

Functions of the skin

The following are the six primary functions of the skin:

1. **Heat regulation**
   The skin regulates the body temperature by sweating. Sweat is produced by the sudoriferous glands. The evaporation of the moisture enables the body to cool itself. Surface capillaries dilate, resulting in flushing and the release of heat.

2. **Absorption**
   The epidermis contains an acid mantle layer, which limits the amount of substances entering through the skin. Cosmeceutical treatment products must be formulated at an appropriate pH with chirally correct ingredients for optimal penetration and absorption.

3. **Secretion**
   The sebaceous glands excrete sebum to lubricate and maintain the health of the skin.

4. **Protection**
   The fat cells in the adipose layer provide insulation and protection against trauma to the internal organs. The skin also protects itself from the harmful effects of UV rays and light, and acts as a barrier against the invasion of bacteria.

5. **Excretion**
   Perspiration is the process by which the sudoriferous (sweat) glands excrete waste materials, water and salt.

6. **Sensation**
   Nerve endings in the skin allow us to feel heat, cold, touch, pleasure, pressure, itch and pain.

skin conditions

aging skin

Visible aging is characterized by changes in the skin due to degradation of its structure and elasticity over time. These changes are due to a combination of multiple physiological and environmental factors.

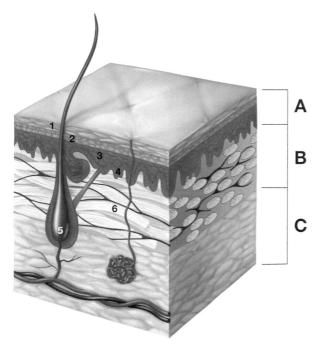

Younger skin

A. Epidermis

   1. Cornified layer (stratum corneum)

   2. Granular layer

   3. Spinous layer

   4. Basal layer

B. Dermis

   5. Hair follicle

   6. Collagen and elastin fibers

C. Subcutaneous tissue

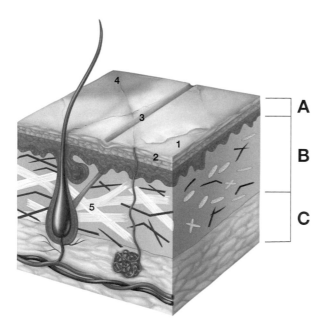

Older skin

A. Thinning epidermis

   1. Dry stratum corneum due to decreased NMF

   2. Decreased desquamation leading to dull surface appearance

   3. Visible fine lines and wrinkles

   4. Discolorations and lentigos

B. Dermis

   5. Cross-linking of collagen fibers, loss of elasticity and reduction of collagen distribution

C. Loss of subcutaneous tissue

Types of aging

- **Intrinsic aging** refers to the physiological breakdown that occurs naturally due to genetics and the passage of time. As skin ages, there is a natural loss of adipose (fat) tissue and a shrinking of the bones. The dermis thins by an average of 20% as we age and there is also a decrease in the thickness of the epidermis. Desquamation slows while the cellular renewal process is reduced, leading to a buildup of dead surface cells and therefore a dull appearance.

  Intrinsic factors are also responsible for the natural slowing of collagen, elastin and glycosaminoglycan (GAG) production. Elastic fibers responsible for skin's flexibility may develop small cysts or gaps, leading to a loss of flexibility. This natural aging process leads to a reduction of the distribution of nutrients to the dermis and epidermis.

  The onset of visible intrinsic aging is determined by a person's genetics. Because of this, those of differing ethnic backgrounds will typically experience the visible signs of aging at different times throughout life.

- Although generally thought to be responsible for up to 85% of the visible signs of skin aging, **extrinsic aging** is considered to be preventable. Sun exposure, an unhealthy lifestyle, gravity, environmental pollutants and chronic inflammation contribute to a breakdown of the skin's extracellular matrix (ECM), including collagen, elastin and GAG. Over-exposure to any of these offenders increases the production of matrix metalloproteinases (MMP), the enzymes responsible for the breakdown of the skin's support system.

  Common results of extrinsic aging include a degradation of collagen, elastin and GAG, leading to laxity, wrinkling and dehydration. Collagen becomes disorganized and cross-linked, disrupting the structure necessary for firm, healthy skin, resulting in wrinkles. Depending upon the severity of UV damage, the epidermis displays abnormal thickening and coarsening. An increased number of melanocytes and abnormal dilation of the blood vessels, usually due to sun exposure, is typical. These UV-related changes are responsible for uneven pigmentation, as well as increased facial redness and telangiectasias.

  Extrinsic aging can present at various chronological ages depending upon exposure to these destructive factors, always becoming more apparent with time. Those who protect themselves from the elements from a young age can significantly reduce many of the avoidable visible signs of aging.

Presentations of aging skin

- **Sagging/laxity** is caused by both intrinsic and extrinsic factors. Shrinking of the bones and loss of adipose (fat) tissue allows the skin to sag naturally over time. Gravity, along with the cross-linking and loss of collagen, also contributes.

- **Loss of elasticity** occurs naturally with age as gaps and cysts form on elastic fibers. Additionally, UV rays, free radicals and inflammation trigger MMP, which can break down elastin.

- **Fine lines** form naturally over time as collagen production slows and skin hydration decreases.

- **Thinning of skin** can occur due to a drop in estrogen levels during menopause. It is also exacerbated by UV exposure.

- **Dryness/dehydration** occurs naturally over time as the skin's proteoglycan production slows. Proteoglycans, such as hyaluronic acid, are responsible for attracting and holding moisture in the skin. Dryness will increase with prolonged use of aggressive topical products, improper cleansing and moisturization practices, reducing the skin's barrier function. Time and sun exposure also lead to an impacted stratum corneum and increased surface dryness.

- **Increased transparency** is a result of the natural and UV-induced thinning of the skin. This transparency causes capillaries to become more visible, leading to an increase in skin redness and visible telangiectasias.

- **Deep/abnormal wrinkling** are caused primarily by extrinsic factors. UVA rays cause an accelerated breakdown and cross-linking of collagen. Lipid oxidation, caused by free radical damage, triggers MMP enzymes to break down both elastin and collagen. Smoking creates abnormal vertical lines around the mouth. Facial expressions, such as frowning and smiling, are responsible for deeper lines in the glabella, forehead and around the mouth, as well as "crow's feet" around the eyes.

The density of melanocytes actually decreases with the natural aging process, although hormonal shifts during menopause can increase the number and activity level of melanocytes. Actinic damage, pregnancy and menopause will increase the number of melanocytes and increase pigment deposits in the keratinocytes.

- **Thickening of the epidermis** occurs in certain cases of sun damage, commonly referred to as an orange peel or leather-like appearance.

- **Hyperpigmentation** is a result of sun exposure, hormones and inflammation.

- **Telangiectasias** become more visible as the skin thins and becomes more transparent with age. UV exposure causes dilation of capillaries along with a thinning of their walls, making blood vessels more visible and more prominent.

- **Enlargement of pores** is a result of a reduction of collagen in the skin caused by actinic damage. Pores appear larger as the support of the surrounding collagen decreases.

- **Coarsening of skin** is caused by a buildup of dead skin cells in the stratum corneum; proliferation and desquamation decreases with time and with exposure to the elements.

Controlling aging skin

Gently exfoliate and increase cell turnover
With sun exposure and natural chronological (intrinsic) aging, the stratum corneum becomes impacted. Superficial exfoliating treatments will gently remove surface buildup, leading to a smoother appearance. The PCA SKIN® professional treatments recommended for age control include bioavailable alpha and beta hydroxy acids, retinoids, skin-firming polysaccharides, and hydrating and plumping phytohormones.

The cellular turnover cycle slows considerably with age. Daily use of topical products designed to increase cell turnover is imperative for patients concerned with visible aging. Professional treatment options may also be used to increase visible exfoliation and cellular turnover. Vitamin A derivatives (retinoids) help to increase cellular proliferation and turnover, bringing healthy cells to the surface more quickly. The agent used must be chosen carefully, as some of the more popular retinoids (Retin-A®) can be irritating. Retinol is a more gentle vitamin A derivative that is highly effective, yet non-irritating. Certain botanicals, such as vigna aconitifolia seed extract, increase cell turnover without irritation. The use of superficial chemical peels will also help to increase cell turnover, revealing a more youthful appearance.

Increase matrix proteins
Multiple studies support that the topical application of certain alpha hydroxy acids (AHA), peptides, botanicals and vitamins trigger collagen production, increasing skin firmness and decreasing fine lines. Using products that contain multifaceted ingredients, such as retinol and vigna aconitifolia seed extract, increase collagen and cell turnover. Combining peptides with intensive hydration will naturally plump the skin while decreasing the appearance of lines. Daily application of these advanced topical solutions is imperative to reducing the signs of aging.

Inhibit melanogenesis
Many melanogenesis inhibitors not only discourage the pigmentation response, but also have been shown to fade current discolorations. Ingredients such as retinol and L-ascorbic acid inhibit melanogenesis, brighten skin tone and provide anti-aging benefits. It is recommended to use daily care products containing melanogenesis inhibitors such as hydroquinone, kojic acid, lactic acid, azelaic acid, arbutin, retinol or L-ascorbic acid to stave off any future discoloration, even after success has been achieved with in-office treatments.

Increase hydration

Topical products designed to increase hydration must contain a combination of humectants to draw moisture to the epidermis and occlusive agents to hold it in. Over-use of AHA with small molecular size (e.g. glycolic acid) should be avoided in the treatment of aging skin, as they penetrate too quickly and cause undue redness and inflammation. A better choice is to utilize hydrating AHA, such as lactic and citric acids, that support the needs of aging skin more effectively. Astringent products containing a high concentration of alcohol should also be avoided to prevent unnecessary dehydration.

Protect from UV rays and other inflammatory stimulants

Sun protection is particularly important to age control skin care regimens, as continued UV exposure will negate the anti-aging effects treatments and daily care products have accomplished. Everyone is advised to use an SPF of 30 or greater every day on any exposed skin. Remember that the SPF rating of a product only relates to its ability to protect the skin from UVB rays. Patients should always use a product that also offers protection from long and short wave UVA rays. PCA SKIN® achieves this broad spectrum UVA/UVB protection with the addition of zinc oxide to our sun protection products. Also consider recommending that your patients wear protective clothing and wide-brimmed hats, and avoid prolonged UV exposure during the midday hours of 10 a.m. and 4 p.m.

Aging skin frequency of treatment:
every 3 weeks

PCA SKIN® daily care solutions

The Anti-Aging Kit

ExLinea® Peptide Smoothing Serum

C&E Strength Max

Intensive Age Refining Treatment®: 0.5% pure retinol night

Hydrator Plus Broad Spectrum SPF 30

Collagen Hydrator

Available as a trial-size solution.

hyperpigmentation

Hyperpigmentation is the deposition of melanin (pigment) due to the stimulation of melanogenesis. Melanogenesis is the process by which pigment is produced and duplicated in the skin. It is the end result of the immune system triggering an inflammatory response, which then triggers melanocyte activity to protect the skin's DNA from damage and mutation. This process is instigated by any hormonal trigger or cutaneous inflammation, such as heat, trauma and sun.

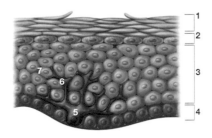

1. Cornified layer (stratum corneum)
2. Granular layer
3. Spinous layer
4. Basal layer
5. Melanocyte
6. Dendrite (arm of melanocyte)
7. Keratinocyte

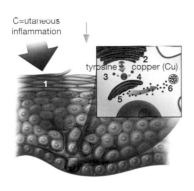

C=utaneous inflammation

1. Cutaneous trauma/inflammation occurs
2. Enzyme tyrosinase is produced and released from the rough endoplasmic reticulum (RER)
3. Tyrosinase acts on the amino acid tyrosine
4. Tyrosinase binds with copper (Cu)
5. Melanin is produced and released from the golgi apparatus (GA)
6. Melanin-filled melanosome is formed

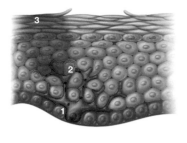

1. Melanin-filled melanosomes travel along the melanocytic dendrites
2. Melanosomes are transferred to the keratinocytes and congregate, forming a barrier over the keratinocyte's nucleus to protect the DNA
3. Faint hyperpigmentation appears on the skin surface and darkens as pigmented cells rise

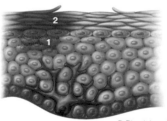

1. Melanin-filled keratinocytes rise with the natural cell turnover cycle
2. Hyperpigmentation darkens as cells move closer to the skin surface

Melanogenesis and the pigmentation response

Melanocyte stimulating hormone (MSH) is triggered and released in response to cutaneous inflammation or hormonal fluctuations. Within the melanocyte, a chain of events is triggered that begins with the enzyme tyrosinase being released from the rough endoplasmic reticulum (RER) and acting on the amino acid tyrosine to convert it to L-DOPA. Then, tyrosinase binds with copper and acts on the L-DOPA, converting it into melanosomes. These melanosomes are transported along the dendrites (arms) of the melanocyte and transferred into the keratinocyte, creating an umbrella-like pattern to protect the DNA within the cell, resulting in hyperpigmentation.

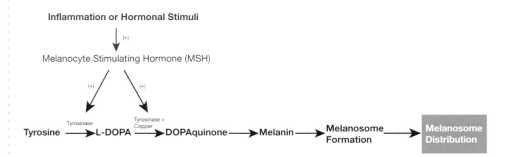

Inflammation or Hormonal Stimuli

↓ (+)

Melanocyte Stimulating Hormone (MSH)

Tyrosine →(Tyrosinase) L-DOPA →(Tyrosinase + Copper) DOPAquinone → Melanin → Melanosome Formation → Melanosome Distribution

Types and causes of hyperpigmentation

UV-induced hyperpigmentation

Hyperpigmentation that is considered UV-induced can be caused by overexposure to sun, tanning beds, and fluorescent and ambient lighting. This type of hyperpigmentation usually presents as diffuse spots or macules that are evenly distributed around the face. This is also referred to as actinic hyperpigmentation.

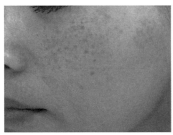

Hormonally induced hyperpigmentation: melasma

Any hormone fluctuation can induce hyperpigmentation. The term melasma comes from the Greek word "melas," which means black. It is commonly associated with a fluctuation of hormones (pregnancy, oral contraceptives, thyroid dysfunction, menopause or hormone replacement therapy (HRT)) and will worsen with UV exposure. It appears as large symmetrical bilateral patches with jagged borders typically around the jawline, upper lip, cheeks and forehead.

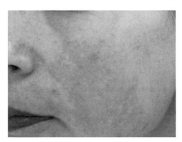

- Melasma affects five to six million American women annually.

- While the exact cause is unknown, melasma is thought to be a result of an increase in the formation and distribution of melanosomes (packets of melanin pigment) among the keratinocytes, along with increased branching of melanocytic dendrites.

- Research shows that elevated estrogen levels experienced during pregnancy and while taking birth control pills will increase both the number of melanocytes and the activity of tyrosinase.

- Studies indicate that androgen dominance, which can occur during menopause when the ovaries cease to produce estrogen, is also responsible for an increase in tyrosinase activity.

- It should be noted that hormonally induced hyperpigmentation may or may not subside once the hormone imbalance is normalized, and has the potential to recur with future fluctuations and with UV exposure.

Post-inflammatory hyperpigmentation (PIH)

PIH is pigment deposited as a result of surface irritation, inflammation or abrasion of the epidermis. It is characterized by darkened areas at the sites of the trauma.

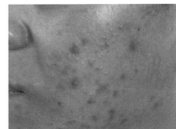

- Acne, dermatitis, psoriasis, eczema and bug bites are common triggers.

- Manipulating the nose because of allergies can result in a line of pigment across the bridge of the nose, called the "salud line," which may worsen the appearance of under-eye circles.

- PIH may appear after shaving-related ingrown hairs or as an overall darkening of the affected area (beard, underarms, bikini line, etc.).

- Darkening of knees and elbows can come from flexural friction.

- Ill-fitting undergarments and other clothing friction may cause discoloration such as "bra burn."

Controlling hyperpigmentation

Gently exfoliate

The closer pigment lies to the surface of the skin, the darker it appears to the naked eye. Many are fooled into thinking that the problem has been corrected after one treatment of microdermabrasion or one superficial peel, because pigment will appear lighter to the naked eye. With natural cell turnover, it is only a matter of time before deeper pigment will rise to the surface, making the area appear dark once again. It is for this reason that it is usually necessary to have multiple treatments to lift pigmentation.

Using gentle peeling agents that do not cause undue trauma to the skin in conjunction with melanogenesis inhibitors is a more effective treatment path than simple exfoliation because you not only lift the pigment, but you also are inhibiting the production of new pigment by the melanocytes. Many of the PCA SKIN® professional treatments are formulated with melanogenesis inhibitors to make this process even easier.

Increase cell turnover

It is helpful to have these patients use topical agents that help to increase the skin cell-turnover rate. A group of ingredients that are quite effective at this are retinoids. This family of vitamin A derivatives helps to increase cellular proliferation and turnover, bringing healthy cells to the surface more quickly. The agent used must be chosen carefully, as some of the more popular retinoids (e.g. Retin-A®) can be irritating to some skin types and actually create more hyperpigmentation. A safer bet is retinol, as it is a more gentle vitamin A derivative that is highly effective, yet non-irritating. Using a daily care product with low level retinol is beneficial in the battle against hyperpigmentation. The addition of superficial chemical peels helps to not only remove the darkened surface cells, but it also allows for better skin function and improved cell turnover rates.

Inhibit melanogenesis

In an attempt to discourage melanin, we recommend using melanogenesis inhibitors in daily care products and professional treatments. This family of ingredients helps to stop the chain reaction that results in melanin deposition. Melanogenesis inhibitors are especially important for those who are genetically predisposed to hyperpigmentation.

It is wise for these patients to use a product daily that contains gentle melanogenesis inhibitors to stave off any future discoloration, even after success has been achieved with their treatment. Some common and effective melanogenesis-inhibiting ingredients include:

- **Hydroquinone** is synthetically produced or naturally found in wheat, berries, coffee and tea. It inhibits the binding of copper to tyrosinase and induces melanocyte-specific cytotoxicity.

- **Arbutin** is naturally found in wheat, pears, bearberries, blueberries and cranberries. It suppresses the activity of tyrosinase and inhibits melanosome maturation.

- **Kojic acid** is naturally found in soy, mushrooms and rice bran. It chelates copper bound to tyrosinase and decreases the number of melanosomes and dendrites.

- **Retinoids** are synthetically produced. They suppress the activity of tyrosinase, decrease the amount of melanosomes and inhibit melanosome transfer.

- **L-ascorbic acid** is naturally found in many botanical sources, such as citrus fruit and corn. It converts DOPAquinone back to L-DOPA, preventing melanin formation.

- **Lactic acid** is naturally found in milk and sugars, and suppresses the formation of tyrosinase.

- **Azelaic acid** is naturally found in many grain products and castor beans. It provides anti-proliferative and cytotoxic effects on melanocytes, but not the surrounding healthy cells, and inhibits tyrosinase activity.

- **Glycyrrhiza glabra root extract** (licorice root) suppresses the tyrosinase activity of melanocytes without cytotoxicty.

- **Morus alba root extract** (mulberry root or white mulberry tree) inhibits tyrosinase activity, particularly the conversion of tyrosinase to L-DOPA.

- **Rumex extract** is naturally found in various herbs. It inhibits the activity of tyrosinase with no irritation.

- **Phenylethyl resorcinol** is synthetically produced. It inhibits the conversion of tyrosinase to L-DOPA.

- **Resveratrol** is synthetically produced. It prevents the synthesis of the melanocyte stimulating hormone (MSH) and, as a result, the formation of tyrosinase, melanin and melanosome transfer.

- **Phytic acid** is found naturally in various types of grains, bran and seeds. It inhibits the activity of tyrosinase while also inducing the exfoliation of superficial melanin-filled skin cells.

- **Niacinamide** reduces redness, yellowing of the skin due to glycation and melanosome transfer.

- **Hexylresorcinol** helps to promote an even skin tone and reduce the inflammation that can lead to discoloration.

- **Hydroxyphenoxy Propionic Acid** inhibits the release of melanin by melanocytes and provides photoprotective effect.

Protect from UV rays and other inflammatory stimulants

Everyone should be using broad spectrum SPF of 30 or greater **every** day on any exposed skin. This is particularly important for those trying to rid themselves of hyperpigmentation. If the skin is exposed to UV rays on a daily basis (even walking to and from your car or exposure to fluorescent light bulbs) the process of evening the complexion will be slowed, if not halted. Remember that the SPF rating of a product only relates to its ability to protect the skin from UVB rays. Patients should always use products that also offer protection from long and short wave UVA rays. Also consider recommending that your patients wear protective clothing and wide-brimmed hats, and avoid prolonged UV exposure during the midday hours between 10 a.m. and 4 p.m. Allow sun protection to absorb for 30 minutes prior to daytime exposure. Reapply after two hours of sun exposure and repeat every two hours as needed.

Melanogenesis inhibitors reduce the melanin content of the epidermis, making it potentially more susceptible to UV-induced matrix metalloproteinases and free radical damage. This makes the regular use of topical antioxidant and MMPi ingredients critical additions to the regimens of patients fighting hyperpigmentation.

Hyperpigmentation frequency of treatment:
every 3 weeks

PCA SKIN® daily care solutions

The Discoloration Kit

Pigment Gel®

C&E Strength Max

Intensive Brightening Treatment: 0.5% pure retinol night

Perfecting Protection Broad Spectrum SPF 30

ReBalance

Available as a trial-size solution.

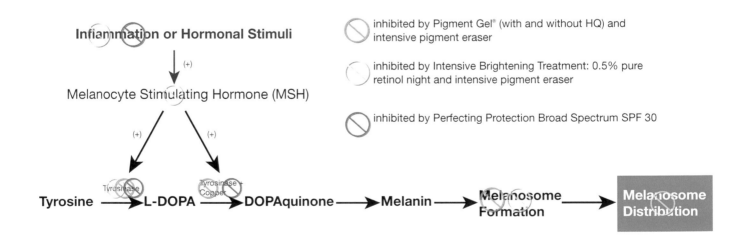

Inflammation or Hormonal Stimuli

(+)

Melanocyte Stimulating Hormone (MSH)

(+)   (+)

Tyrosine →(Tyrosinase)→ **L-DOPA** →(Tyrosinase + Copper)→ **DOPAquinone** → **Melanin** → **Melanosome Formation** → **Melanosome Distribution**

⊘ inhibited by Pigment Gel® (with and without HQ) and intensive pigment eraser

◯ inhibited by Intensive Brightening Treatment: 0.5% pure retinol night and intensive pigment eraser

⊘ inhibited by Perfecting Protection Broad Spectrum SPF 30

Hypopigmentation

Hypopigmentation is the result of a reduction in melanin production or the complete cessation of melanocyte function. In general, hypopigmentation is incredibly difficult to treat, often with little to no success.

Types of hypopigmentation

UV-induced hypopigmentation

This type of hypopigmentation is typically intermingled with hyperpigmentation. There are no available treatments to re-pigment the white lesions, but the reduction of the surrounding hyperpigmentation will usually make the hypopigmentation appear less noticeable.

Post-traumatic hypopigmentation

Burns, cuts and other trauma to the skin can result in melanotoxicity (melanocyte death) in that area, resulting in pigment loss of the scar. This type of pigment loss is usually permanent, but over a long period of time, it could re-pigment partially or totally. There are no topical treatments for this type of hypopigmentation.

Vitiligo

An autoimmune disorder in which the melanocytes are damaged, causing smooth, white patches of hypopigmentation. It can be localized or appear all over the body. There is no cure for vitiligo, but the topical use of prescription products like tacrolimus (Protopic®), pimecrolimus (Elidel®) or topical steroids can occasionally trigger re-pigmentation of the affected areas.

Albinism

An inherited disorder caused by an abnormal gene that causes a partial to complete absence of melanin in skin, hair or eyes. There is no cure for albinism.

acne/breakout-prone skin

Acne is a disorder of the skin marked by papules, comedones or cysts. Increased sebaceous activity or inflammation are often present as well.

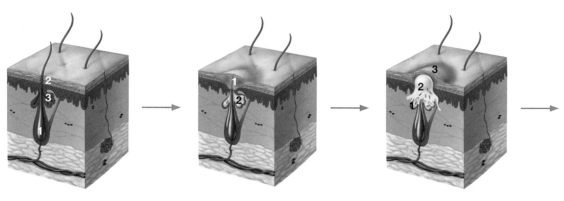

Normal follicle

1. Hair follicle
2. Open pore
3. Sebaceous gland produces oily sebum

Closed comedone

Androgen hormones increase the adherence of keratinocytes to the follicle wall and increase sebum production, resulting in a plugged pore.

1. Keratinocytes adhere to follicle wall
2. Sebum production increases

Papule

Increased sebum and P. acnes bacteria build up behind the plug and trigger an inflammatory response.

1. Sebum increases
2. Bacteria and sebum build up under the plug
3. Inflammatory response

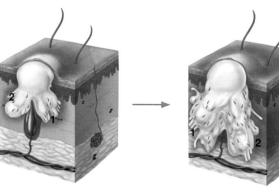

© Physicians Care Alliance, LLC

Pustule

The number of P. acnes increases, and breaks down sebum into irritating free fatty acids which stimulate an immune response. White blood cells weaken the follicular wall resulting in rupture and increased inflammation.

1. P. acnes proliferates
2. Follicle wall can rupture

Nodule

Ruptures in follicle wall with marked inflammation and tissue destruction with possible scarring.

1. Follicular wall ruptures
2. Inflammation and tissue destruction

Grades of acne

Acne simplex

- **Grade I** – considered acne simplex and may include open or closed comedones. Inflammatory lesions and cysts are not typically seen. Scarring is unlikely in acne simplex as the lesions tend to be superficial; however, patient excoriation may lead to hyperpigmentation or texture changes.

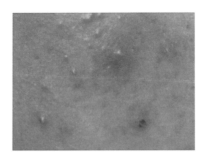

- **Grade II** – also considered acne simplex and will include the open or closed comedones seen in grade I, as well as papules and pustules. Cystic lesions and scarring are uncommon.

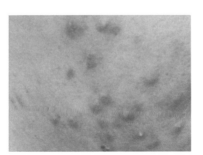

Acne vulgaris

- **Grade III** – a form of acne vulgaris, where inflammation and bacterial lesions are typical. Open and closed comedones may also be seen and scarring will be more likely than with the lower acne grades. Medical prescription intervention may be necessary.

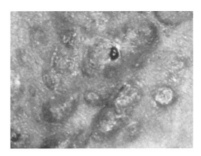

- **Grade IV** – sufferers experience deeper cystic and nodular lesions, as well as papules, pustules and comedones. Scarring is very common due to the depth of the lesions. Medical prescription intervention is recommended.

Four main causes of acne

- increased keratinization within the follicle
- increased sebum production
- proliferation of Propionibacterium acnes (P. acnes) bacteria
- inflammation

Common presentations

Hormonal acne is common in adolescence and is typically accompanied by an overproduction of sebum. Cyclical breakouts are often seen in females in the perioral area and hormonal acne may present itself at any stage in life when hormones fluctuate (e.g. pregnancy, introduction of oral contraceptives, menopause).

Acne cosmetica is triggered by comedogenic or irritating ingredients in everyday products. Certain makeup, laundry detergents and hair care products may clog the pores and lead to breakouts. Regularly changing pillow cases and cleaning makeup applicators will help treat acne cosmetica.

Inflammatory acne is red and inflamed, and may be uncomfortable for the patient.

Asphyxiated acne is characterized by a rough surface keratolytic buildup and reduced cell turnover with sebum and other debris trapped beneath. Asphyxiated acne is more common in dry environments and may be caused by the use of drying ingredients, such as alcohol, without the use of a daily hydrator.

Bacterial acne may be the result of an over-production of bacteria within the follicle or pore. P. acnes is the bacteria responsible for acne. It is anaerobic (cannot live in the presence of oxygen) and flourishes in warm, humid environments. Topical oxygen sources, such as benzoyl peroxide, help to control bacteria distribution and proliferation.

Cystic acne sufferers experience large, painful nodules beneath the surface of the skin, which can remain for weeks or months. The depth and inflammation associated with cystic acne can destroy the follicle, resulting in scarring.

Systemic acne usually appears as acne vulgaris, may involve other areas of the body (arms, chest, back and shoulders) and may be brought on by disease, illness, medication or other diet-related issues.

Controlling acne

Gently exfoliate and increase cell turnover
The initial trigger in the production of acne papules is the increased adherence of keratinocytes to the follicle wall and increased sebum production, resulting in a plugged pore. Skin cells often do not shed enough on their own, creating a buildup of surface cells that traps oil and bacteria, allowing the bacteria to proliferate. Using well-rounded, blended peeling agents that control bacteria and oil production, as well as loosen impacted stratum corneum, not only opens the pores but also allows treatment products to penetrate more effectively. Ingredients that act as keratolytics, such as salicylic acid, resorcinol, sulfur and benzoyl peroxide, are particularly helpful in the treatment of acne because of their ability to dissolve follicular buildup. Products and treatment formulations containing benzoyl peroxide, gluconolactone, salicylic acid, azelaic acid, alpha hydroxy acids, sulfur and retinoids are all excellent options.

Retinoids, the family of vitamin A derivatives, help to increase cellular proliferation and turnover, bringing healthy cells to the surface more quickly. The agent used must be chosen carefully, as prescription strength retinoids like Retin-A® (retinoic acid/tretinoin) can be irritating to some skin types, but they may be necessary in more severe grades of acne. Retinol is a more gentle vitamin A derivative that is effective, yet non-irritating. Retinol is converted to retinoic acid in the skin. Using a daily care product with low-level retinol, in conjunction with anti-inflammatory exfoliating treatments, allows for better skin function and improved cell turnover rates with minimal irritation.

Control sebum production
In acne-prone skin, increased sebum and P. acnes bacteria build up behind the plug and can trigger an inflammatory response. It is imperative to understand that over-drying a patient's skin, even if they are oily, will cause the skin to compensate by producing an excessive amount of sebum. This will cause even more breakouts as opposed to addressing the problem. Use of natural astringents that also moisturize will avoid this over-production of sebum. Professional treatments containing a combination of the following will most effectively help control sebum production: salicylic acid, ginger root, green burnet root, licorice root, cucumber extract and cinnamon bark. In addition, there are several beneficial oils important in the treatment of acne, as they contain beneficial, naturally derived fatty acids. These include, but are not limited to, borage seed oil, grape seed oil and essential wheat germ oil, which all help balance oily and acneic skin.

Acne frequency of treatment:
every 2 weeks

Decrease P. acnes proliferation

Using antibacterial and antimicrobial topical agents, and oral or topical antibiotics (when applicable) are suitable ways to control the bacteria population. Topical oxygen sources, such as benzoyl peroxide and hydrogen peroxide, effectively deliver oxygen to the follicle, killing the anaerobic bacteria. Acne patients who use topical agents that help to increase the cell turnover rate of their skin, combined with gentle exfoliation, ensure that P. acnes will not be trapped in a deoxygenated environment and allowed to proliferate.

In-office treatments that increase circulation and blood flow will deliver oxygen, leading to a decrease in P. acnes, and assist in the clearing of active lesions. A light massage during application of products will also increase circulation. Avoid massage in grades III and IV acne, where cross contamination may occur.

Protect from UV rays and other inflammatory stimulants

Inflammation is both a cause and result of acne. When the number of P. acnes increases, sebum is broken down into irritating free fatty acids, which stimulate an immune response. White blood cells weaken the follicular wall, resulting in rupture and increased inflammation. Utilizing anti-inflammatory topical ingredients will soothe current irritation and help to avoid undue future inflammation. Aloe vera, salicylic acid, bisabolol, panthenol, licorice extract, boldine extract, resveratrol and EGCG from green tea are all extremely effective in helping to control inflammation. Over-drying and over-stimulation will lead to further breakouts.

With inflammatory acne, do not treat more often than the recommended frequency of treatment and avoid the daily use of irritating ingredients. Many of the products that help treat acne make the skin more sun-sensitive, thereby increasing the risk for damage and post-inflammatory hyperpigmentation (PIH). Everyone should be using a broad spectrum SPF of 30 or greater every day on any exposed skin. Exposure to UV rays on a daily basis (even walking to and from your car or exposure to fluorescent light bulbs) will cause greater inflammation, slowing the process of treating acne. Remember that the SPF rating of a product only relates to its ability to protect the skin from UVB rays. Patients should always use products that also offer protection from long and short wave UVA rays. PCA SKIN® broad spectrum SPF products also have the benefit of containing antioxidant ingredients. Wearing protective clothing and wide-brimmed hats, and avoiding prolonged UV exposure during the midday hours between 10 a.m. and 4 p.m. is recommended.

PCA SKIN® daily care regimens

The Acne Control Regimen

BPO 5% Cleanser

Acne Cream

Intensive Clarity Treatment®: 0.5% pure retinol night

Clearskin

Available as a two-month supply kit.

The Acne Kit

BPO 5% Cleanser

Acne Cream

Intensive Clarity Treatment®: 0.5% pure retinol night

Weightless Protection Broad Spectrum SPF 45

Clearskin

Available as a trial-size solution.

sensitive skin

Sensitive skin is a heightened intolerance to topical products or external factors.

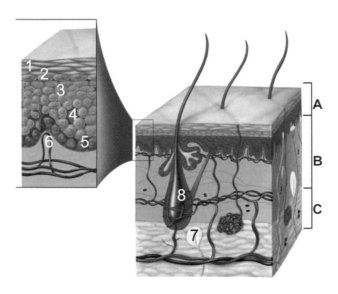

Normal skin

A. Epidermis

1. Cornified layer comprised of flattened corneocytes, their natural moisurizing factor (NMF) and lipid bilayers

2. Granular layer

3. Spinous layer

4. Langerhans cell (immunologic mediators)

5. Basal layer

B. Dermis

6. Capillaries

7. Sensory nerves

8. Hair follicle

C. Subcutaneous tissue

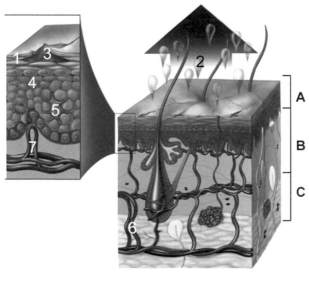

Sensitive skin

A. Epidermis

1. Abnormally functioning stratum corneum with decreased NMF and interruption of lipid bilayer leading to excessive dryness

2. Increased transepidermal water loss (TEWL)

3. Decreased desquamation resulting in dry flaky surface

4. Inflammation in lower epidermal layers as a result of pro-inflammatory cytokines

5. Inflammation-activated langerhans cell

B. Dermis

6. Increased vascularity

7. Hyperpermeable and dilated capillaries

C. Subcutaneous tissue

Types of sensitive skin

- rosacea

- impaired barrier function

- atopic dermatitis

- psoriasis

Rosacea

Rosacea is a chronic sensitive skin condition often involving inflammation of the cheeks, nose, chin and forehead. Rosacea sufferers may experience sensitivity, excessive flushing, persistent redness, broken capillaries or breakouts.

- Rosacea is seen more frequently in women aged 30-50; however, it typically affects men more destructively.

- Compared to others, rosacea sufferers may get red easier and remain red longer when participating in any activity or behavior that causes general flushing (exercise, steam, stress, etc.).

- Dry skin and barrier dysfunction are common among certain rosacea sufferers. Not addressing this dryness/dehydration will worsen the symptoms of rosacea.

- If left untreated, rosacea tends to worsen.

- Rosacea may be more common in certain hereditary backgrounds, such as Irish, English, Scottish, Welsh, Russian, Polish, Czech, Native American and Asian, or it may be due to genetic predisposition.

Rosacea subtypes

- **Subtype one (erythematotelangiectatic rosacea)** - flushing and persistent redness of the central third of the face, typically with visible telangiectasias

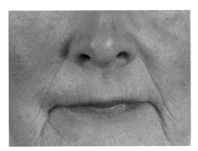

- **Subtype two (papulopustular rosacea)** – persistent redness of the central third of the face accompanied by papules and pustules

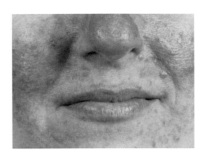

- **Subtype three (phymatous rosacea)** – thickening of the skin, irregular surface nodularities and enlargement; most commonly presented as rhinophyma (enlargement of the nose), but may affect other locations, such as the glabella and chin

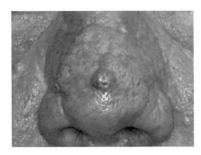

- **Subtype four (ocular rosacea)** – irritation of the eye area, including watery, bloodshot eyes, foreign body sensation, burning, stinging, dryness, itching and frequent styes, that may result in blepharitis, conjunctivitis or irregularity of the eyelid margins

© 2003 Elsevier - Bolognia, Jorizzo and Rapini: Dermatology - www.dermtext.com

Potential causes of rosacea

Studies performed on rosacea patients demonstrate a variety of potential contributors to the rosacea pathway. There have been no conclusive findings as to the cause of rosacea. The most common theories are listed below, although some are more substantiated than others:

- **Vascular dysfunction**
  Studies have shown that people with rosacea may experience increased blood flow to the vessels of the face. There is an increase in the number of blood vessels and blood vessels may be closer to the surface of the face, making redness and visible superficial capillaries more common. Certain pro-inflammatory mediators found naturally within the skin may be more prominent or active in rosacea sufferers.

- **Vascular endothelial growth factor (VEGF)**
  VEGF stimulates the growth and development of new blood vessels, which is proven to play a role in the pathogenesis of rosacea. VEGF also encourages microcapillary hyperpermeability (leakiness). Studies suggest that plasma leaking to surrounding tissues may induce an inflammatory response, causing redness and irritation.

- **Prostaglandin E$_2$ (PGE$_2$)**
  This group of hormone-like substances participates in the dilation of blood vessels. PGE$_2$ is released by blood vessel walls in response to inflammation.

- **Pro-inflammatory cytokines**
  Also known to be involved in rosacea, they are part of the flushing and chronic inflammatory responses. There are many potential cytokines involved in this inflammatory pathway.

Common rosacea triggers

Certain environmental and dietary elements act as triggers for rosacea. Avoiding the following will not cure rosacea, but can help keep it less irritated, red and inflamed:

Temperature-related triggers:

- drinking alcoholic beverages
- using alcohol-based products topically
- eating spicy foods
- drinking hot beverages such as coffee and tea
- using saunas, steam rooms and hot tubs
- exercising
- experiencing extremes in temperature

Other triggers:

- using aggressive mechanical exfoliation (e.g. loofahs, nut-based scrubs)
- smoking
- certain medications, cosmetics and foods
- leading a stressful lifestyle

Impaired barrier function

Improper function of or damage to the stratum corneum results in moisture loss, irritation, redness and hypersensitivity.

Common causes and characteristics

- overuse of aggressive products, and use of products with excessive perfumes and preservatives

- harsh climate

- removal of the skin's natural moisturizing factor (NMF), the substances that are responsible for maintaining the skin's hydration and pliability, by attracting and holding moisture; removal of the NMF will result in excessive transepidermal water loss (TEWL)

- interruption of intracellular lipids found between the dead surface cells and responsible for trapping water in the stratum corneum; this lipid bilayer provides an occlusive, impermeable barrier and prevents the loss of water and NMF

- TEWL from inside the body through the epidermis to the surrounding atmosphere; a small amount of TEWL is critical to skin health, yet excessive TEWL may result in skin sensitivity; TEWL is increased when the epidermis is compromised and the NMF is decreased

- keratin denaturation, an alteration of the protein's shape through some form of external stress (e.g. application of heat, acid or alkali), may prevent the keratin from carrying out its normal cellular functions

Atopic dermatitis

Atopic dermatitis, a disease that is commonly referred to as eczema, typically starts in early infancy and is usually genetic. It is characterized by pruritus (itchiness), xerosis (dry skin) and lichenification on the skin (thickening of the skin and increase in skin markings).

Common characteristics

- personal history of allergies
- sensitivity to allergens, such as dust mites, pollen, animal dander and molds
- food allergies, including cow's milk, eggs, peanuts and soy
- history of asthma or hay fever
- commonly occurs in three stages and may lie dormant between each stage (infancy, childhood, adulthood)

Psoriasis

Psoriasis involves chronically recurring rash-like lesions (thick red scaly patches) accompanied by pruritus (itchiness), irritation, redness, impacted surface cells or hypersensitivity. It is most common on the scalp, elbows, knees, hands and feet. The majority of cases see onset before the age of 40.

Common causes

- genetic predisposition
- trauma
- infection
- medications

Controlling sensitive skin

Gently exfoliate and increase cell turnover
Gentle exfoliating treatments will remove surface buildup without causing irritation. Each of the PCA SKIN® recommended treatments for rosacea include anti-inflammatory components to soothe inflammation and redness. Mechanical exfoliants such as microdermabrasion should be avoided in the treatment of rosacea and irritated sensitive skin conditions.

It is also helpful to have these patients use topical agents that increase the cell turnover rate in their skin. A group of ingredients that are quite effective at this are retinoids. This family of vitamin A derivatives helps to increase cellular proliferation and turnover, bringing healthy cells to the surface more quickly, especially with sensitive skin. The agent used must be chosen carefully, as some of the more popular retinoids (Retin-A®) can be very irritating to some sensitive skin types. Retinol is a more gentle vitamin A derivative that is highly effective, yet non-irritating at lower percentages. Using a daily care product with low-level retinol in conjunction with anti-inflammatory exfoliating treatments allows for better skin function and improved cell turnover rates. The use of anti-inflammatory, superficial chemical peels will also help to increase cell turnover, allowing for better skin and barrier function.

Decrease redness and inflammation

Each in-office treatment and daily care regimen should be customized using anti-inflammatory ingredients that will combat redness and discomfort. Prescription intervention may be necessary in some cases. Topical ingredients that are effective in reducing the appearance of redness are often anti-inflammatory agents that have an effect on microcapillary function. Many work by interrupting the inflammatory process. Several specific red and brown algae extracts suppress the pro-inflammatory mediators, VEGF and PGE_2, while caper bud extract inhibits the production of inflammatory cytokines.

Anti-redness ingredients:

- **Ascophyllum nodosum (brown algae) extract** reduces VEGF* and PGE_2** expression when combined with asparagopsis armata extract.

- **Asparagopsis armata (red algae) extract** reduces VEGF* and PGE_2** expression when combined with ascophyllum nodosum extract.

- **Capparis spinosa (caper bud) fruit extract** inhibits the production of pro-inflammatory cytokines (immune-activated cells involved in the amplification of inflammatory reaction).

  Ingredients containing high levels of omega-3 and omega-6 essential fatty acids provide powerful anti-inflammatory characteristics. Some common sources are grape seed oil, evening primrose seed oil, borage seed oil, wheat germ oil and black currant seed oil. Support ingredients such as bisabolol, aloe vera and evening primrose calm and soothe the skin.

  * VEGF stimulates the growth of new blood vessels and promotes hyperpermeability.
  **PGE_2 are prostaglandins that work to dilate blood vessels.

Anti-inflammatory and skin-soothing ingredients:

- **Hydrocortisone** is used to relieve the itching, redness, dryness, crusting, scaling, inflammation and discomfort of various skin conditions. Limit use to seven-day intervals.

- **Aloe vera extracts** are rich in choline salicylate, which offers anti-inflammatory benefits.

- **Panthenol (pro-vitamin B-5)** reduces inflammation while increasing the moisture-retention capacity of the skin.

- **Oenothera biennis (evening primrose) seed oil** is an excellent source of omega-3 gamma linolenic acid (GLA), and provides anti-redness and anti-inflammatory capabilities.

- **Bisabolol** is the anti-inflammatory component of chamomile.

- **Menthyl lactate** is used to soothe discomfort while creating a cooling effect.

- **Melissa officinalis (balm mint) extract** is used as a natural topical pain reliever and skin soother.

- **Salix alba (willow bark) extract** is a natural analgesic or pain reliever related to aspirin.

Increase hydration to control excessive dryness
Products must contain humectant ingredients that draw moisture to the epidermis and occlusive ingredients that hold it in.

Humectant ingredients:

- glycerin
- AHA
- lecithin
- urea
- hyaluronic acid
- sorbitol
- collagen
- honey
- sodium PCA
- pseudoalteromonas ferment extract

Occlusive ingredients:

- silicones (dimethicone and cyclomethicone)
- shea butter
- titanium dioxide
- olive oil
- zinc oxide
- niacinamide

every 4 weeks

Decrease possible bacterial factors
Utilizing products containing multifaceted ingredients, such as salicylic and azelaic acids, will help to control both the bacteria and inflammation involved with subtype 2 papulopustular rosacea. The clinician should be familiar with the differences between subtype 2 rosacea and acne. It is important to avoid more aggressive antibacterial agents, like benzoyl peroxide, on rosacea patients, which may induce further inflammation. The location of the breakouts (most commonly affecting the central third of the face in rosacea sufferers versus the hormonal acne typically seen in adults, which tends to present on the jawline and chin) and the presence of persistent redness can assist in determining the underlying cause.

Protect from UV exposure (SPF)
Everyone should be using an SPF of 30 or greater everyday on any exposed skin. Studies suggest that the inflammation associated with chronic photodamage significantly contributes to rosacea pathology. Even walking to and from your car, and fluorescent light bulbs can increase the production of nitric oxide and other free radicals within the skin cells. An increased production of these offenders can lead to vasodilation and broken capillaries. Remember that the SPF rating of a product only relates to its ability to protect the skin from UVB rays. You should always use a product that also offers protection from long and short wave UVA rays. Also consider recommending that your patients wear protective clothing and wide-brimmed hats, and avoid prolonged UV exposure during the midday hours between 10 a.m. and 4 p.m.

PCA SKIN® daily care solutions

The Sensitive Skin Kit

Hydrating Serum

Anti-Redness Serum

Retinol Treatment for Sensitive Skin

Protecting Hydrator Broad Spectrum SPF 30

ReBalance

Available as a trial-size solution.

skin cancer

Skin cancer occurs when DNA becomes irreparably damaged, resulting in the growth of abnormal skin cells capable of invading and destroying surrounding normal skin cells and tissues. As the damaged cells multiply, a visible tumor is typically formed. They are divided into melanoma and non-melanoma skin cancer (basal and squamous cell carcinomas).

Types of skin cancer

| Melanoma | Basal Cell Carcinoma | Squamous Cell Carcinoma | Actinic Keratosis |

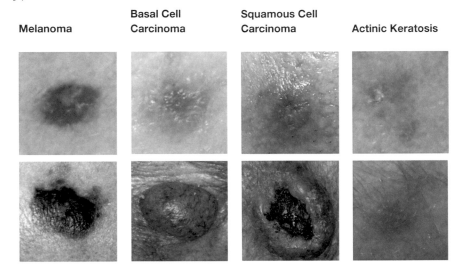

Melanoma is a malignancy of the melanocyte, usually darkly pigmented. This is the most dangerous form of skin cancer due to its ability to metastasize and spread to lymph nodes, blood, distant tissues and organ systems. If detected and treated early while it is still thin, melanoma can typically be cured. If left untreated, the malignancy may grow downward from the skin's surface and invade healthy tissue. Once it spreads, melanoma can be extremely difficult to treat and often leads to death. Because it is made of pigment producing cells (melanocytes), melanoma is dark in color and may be raised or even with the skin's surface. Refer to the **ABCDEs of melanoma detection** chart for examples of characteristics to look for in melanoma. If any mole has any of these characteristics, or is changing in size, shape, color or texture, the mole should be evaluated by a dermatologist.

ABCDEs of melanoma detection

Asymmetry

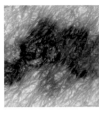

One half unlike the other

Border

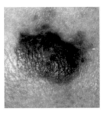

Irregular, blurred or scalloped

Color

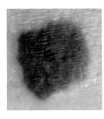

Coloring varies from one area to another or is blue to black

Diameter

Larger than 1/4 inch (the size of a pencil eraser)

Evolution

Any change in size, shape, color, texture or elevation

Non-melanoma skin cancer is a malignant growth of the epidermal keratinocytes. It typically originates from the squamous cells of the spinous layer (squamous cell carcinoma) or basal layers (basal cell carcinoma) and does not involve melanocytes.

Basal cell carcinoma (BCC) is the most common form of skin cancer in the U.S. Presentation can be as simple as a tiny clear or flesh-colored bump, or may be more apparent, such as an open sore or shiny red, pink, brown or black lesion that could be mistaken for a mole. It is considered the most benign form of skin cancer as it grows the slowest and is the least likely to metastasize. Although BCC rarely spreads to surrounding tissues, making fatality rates exceptionally low, removal can lead to scarring.

Squamous cell carcinoma (SCC) primarily affects the superficial layers of the epidermis. This type of skin cancer has a red, rough or flaky appearance and causes thickening of the skin; ulcerations may occur and cause a chronic open sore. Approximately 97% of SCC do not spread; however, if metastasis does occur, scarring, disfigurement or death is possible.

Actinic keratosis (AK) is considered a pre-skin cancer. It is an abnormal growth resulting from over-exposure to UV rays and, if left untreated, can develop into SCCs. Their appearance is rough and scaly, and they can be tan, red, pink or flesh-colored. Studies show that up to 60% of squamous cell carcinomas began as actinic keratoses that were never treated. AK can be treated by physicians in several ways, including cryotherapy (freezing), cutterage, photodynamic therapy (PDT), surgical excision and topical destructive cream medications. Clinical studies have also shown chemical peels, such as Jessner's solutions and trichloroacetic acid (TCA) preparations, to be effective treatments as well.

Causes of skin cancer

Ultraviolet radiation (UVR) is responsible for 90% of all skin cancers and is the most preventable risk factor for this potentially deadly disease. UVR is broken down into three categories: UVC (200 - 280NM), UVB (280 - 320NM) and UVA (320 - 400NM). The proof of the link between skin cancer and sun exposure dates back to the early 1900s, and as the atmospheric ozone depletes, the number of cases increases each year. UVA rays penetrate deep into the dermis and are responsible for the acceleration of aging (photoaging) associated with **sun exposure**. UVB radiation primarily affects the epidermis, and is responsible for sunburn and tanning. Both UVA and UVB have been proven to cause DNA damage and mutation, leading to abnormal cell proliferation and cancer. Sun bathing increases this risk significantly. A tan is the visible result of the melanocyte producing pigment to protect the DNA of the keratinocyte. Upon stimulation from UV rays, the melanocyte transfers packets of pigment (melanosomes) to the keratinocytes throughout the epidermis. The melanosomes are distributed as a cap over the nucleus of the cell where the DNA is stored. DNA damage, induced by UV rays, leads to all forms of skin cancer.

Unfortunately, the frequent erroneous claims regarding the biological need for sun exposure for vitamin D production can be confusing for patients. Although there is no doubt that vitamin D is essential to overall health, adequate amounts can be obtained through food and milk consumption, vitamin supplementation and through the amount of sun exposure received during normal daily activities, even while wearing sunscreen. The recommended dose of vitamin D for an adult is about 1,000 international units (IU) per day. Additional exposure is never warranted and leads to negative effects, such as accelerated aging, decreased immune function and skin cancer.

In a survey involving 8,000 Americans, 68% felt that they looked better and healthier with a tan. Unfortunately, this thought process has the use of artificial UV exposure rising steadily each year. **Tanning beds** are considered even more dangerous than natural sun exposure because of the strength and type of UV rays used. Studies show that 20 minutes in a tanning bed is equivalent to two to three hours of natural sun exposure. In addition, tanning beds use not only high amounts of UVA rays, but also more UVB radiation than currently received from the sun, and even UVC rays which are completely absorbed by the ozone in outdoor exposure. Tanning beds also promote year-round exposure regardless of the season. Undisputable research has linked tanning beds with basal cell, squamous cell and melanoma skin cancers, and the use of tanning beds is contributing to the staggering skin cancer rates worldwide. The chances of developing melanoma have increased nearly 2,000% in the last 75 years, with nearly 60,000 new cases reported annually. BCC is not only the most common form of skin cancer, but the most common form of cancer in the United States, and with 71,000 deaths attributed to excessive sun exposure in the year 2000 alone, experts have declared a skin cancer epidemic. These risks have physicians and scientists comparing tanning bed use to cigarettes and lung cancer, and because of this, strictly enforced regulations are likely to be introduced in the near future. Certain states currently limit the use of tanning beds on those under 18 years of age.

Preventing skin cancer

Sun protection through the daily application of broad spectrum sunscreen is imperative to the prevention of skin cancer. The myth that sun protection only needs to be utilized when spending long periods outdoors or during peak hours is just that, a myth. Although UVB rays do peak between the hours of 10 a.m. and 4 p.m., UVA rays remain constant throughout the day and are able to penetrate windows, clouds and clothing. In addition, UV radiation is emitted from fluorescent and halogen bulbs found in most offices and homes. It is for this reason that everyone must wear sunscreen everyday regardless of the amount of time spent outdoors.

Consumers are often not aware that the sun protection factor (SPF) label only indicates the amount of UVB protection provided by a product. Certain ingredients must be utilized in order to receive UVA protection as well. In order for a product to provide broad spectrum UVA/UVB protection, zinc oxide, titanium dioxide, avobenzone or ecampsule (Mexoryl™) must be included. Extremely high ratings of SPF can also be deceiving, as SPF protection does not increase proportionally with an increased SPF number (e.g. an SPF 15 sunscreen protects the skin from 93% of UVB radiation, an SPF 30 sunscreen provides 97% protection and an SPF 65 provides approximately 98% protection). There are no sun protection products that block out 100% of UV rays. Unfortunately, higher SPF products can be less cosmetically elegant and could decrease patient compliance. Some ingredients are more stable than others, although all sunscreens break down over time regardless of water resistance, SPF rating or ingredients used. Sunscreen products should be reapplied every two hours and following swimming or vigorous activity. As skin care professionals it is important to educate our patients on the importance of adequate daily sun protection.

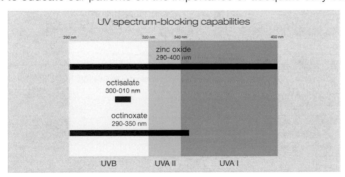

Ultraviolet rays are measured in nanometers. The higher the number of nanometers, the deeper through the earth's atmosphere they travel. All PCA SKIN® broad spectrum SPF products provide hydration and UV protection against 270-400 nanometers (NM), the entire range of the UVA and UVB rays that reach the earth. Each sunscreen is formulated to be cosmetically elegant. PCA SKIN offers multiple options to suit a variety of skin types and conditions. These broad spectrum SPF products not only protect the skin from UV exposure, but they also promote daily use:

- **Weightless Protection Broad Spectrum SPF 45**: This broad spectrum sunscreen provides UVA/UVB protection with the technology of ultra-sheer zinc oxide and a blend of additional sunscreen ingredients. Silybin, also known as milk thistle, and caffeine provide antioxidant action. Its unique quick-absorbing and light finish makes **Weightless Protection Broad Spectrum SPF 45** ideal for patients with oily or breakout-prone skin and those who dislike the feel of traditional sunscreen products.

- **Perfecting Protection Broad Spectrum SPF 30**: This revolutionary broad spectrum UVA/UVB product combines the protective benefits of ultra-sheer zinc oxide and other potent sunscreen agents with licorice, mulberry and bearberry extracts to encourage an even skin tone. In addition, silybin, also known as milk thistle, and caffeine provide antioxidant action. **Perfecting Protection Broad Spectrum SPF 30** is suitable for all skin types and is also recommended following peels, lasers and other in-office procedures.

- **Protecting Hydrator Broad Spectrum SPF 30**: This non-oily daily hydrator with SPF is formulated with aloe vera and panthenol to provide light moisture with a matte finish. It provides broad spectrum UVA/UVB coverage with the protective benefits of ultra-sheer zinc oxide and additional sunscreen agents. Silybin, also known as milk thistle, and caffeine provide antioxidant action. **Protecting Hydrator Broad Spectrum SPF 30** is best for patients with normal to oily skin types.

- **Hydrator Plus Broad Spectrum SPF 30**: This nourishing moisturizer with SPF is formulated with a blend of UV-protecting ingredients, including ultra-sheer zinc oxide, that provides broad spectrum UVA/UVB protection. It is specifically formulated with moisturizing hyaluronic acid and sodium PCA for dry or dehydrated skin. Silybin, also known as milk thistle, and caffeine provide antioxidant action.

- **Active Broad Spectrum SPF 45: Water Resistant**: This revolutionary formulation provides water-resistant broad spectrum protection with a light finish. The blend of UVA/UVB protecting sunscreen agents, including ultra-sheer zinc oxide, provides sun-shielding benefits. Tested to protect for 80 minutes in water, it is the perfect choice for an outdoor lifestyle. Silybin, also known as milk thistle, and caffeine provide antioxidant action.

- **Sheer Tint Broad Spectrum SPF 45**: This universally tinted broad spectrum sunscreen provides UVA/UVB protection in a purely physical formula. It's water resistant for up to 80 minutes, this formula smooths the skin's tone and texture outdoors. Ubiquinone (CoEnzyme Q10) provides added antioxidant protection.

All PCA SKIN® broad spectrum SPF products also provide multiple antioxidants to fight the free radical damage caused by UV exposure and have been awarded The Skin Cancer Foundation Seal of Recommendation for Daily Use or Active Use.

In addition to daily sunscreen products, wearing **protective clothing**, **hats** and **sunglasses** can significantly increase protection from UV exposure. Sunglasses should have specific UV coating to ensure adequate protection, and hats should be wide enough to provide shade for the entire face, ears and neck. Certain companies have developed protective clothing and detergents that provide UV protection. Even wearing darker rather than lighter-colored clothing will increase the amount of protection.

Antioxidants are molecules that are able to slow or prevent the oxidation of other molecules. Oxidation produces free radicals, which trigger a chain reaction in the body that damages cells, potentially leading to skin cancer. Multiple studies have been conducted regarding the protective benefits of topical antioxidants, and results indicate that the addition of antioxidants to daily sunscreen usage may play an important role in skin cancer and photoaging prevention. Those antioxidants that have demonstrated not only radical scavenging capabilities, but also chemo-protective activity include epigallocatechin gallate (EGCG) from green tea, resveratrol from grapes, genistein from soy, caffeine, and silybin from milk thistle, which also may be particularly beneficial for the skin cancer patient.

Early detection is key to the prevention of metastasis in every type of skin cancer. Self inspections should be performed monthly, and should include examination of the face, scalp, torso, back, arms, hands, legs, feet and nails. The presence of any new growth or formation should be reported to a physician immediately. In addition to self examinations, yearly visits to a dermatologist should be scheduled for a thorough, full-body exam. Aestheticians should develop a relationship with a trusted dermatologist close to their facility and a mutual referral process for their clients. Until skin cancer affects a patient personally or someone close to them, they may not understand the importance of prevention and detection. Education is the most valuable tool the skin care professional can provide. If at any time a patient has any type of questionable lesion, immediately refer them to a dermatologist for evaluation and, if necessary, treatment.

If a lesion appears suspicious to a physician, they will remove a portion and perform a biopsy. If skin cancer is diagnosed there are several available **treatment** methods, and the physician will choose the most appropriate option for each individual case based on type of tumor and location. Treatment options include electrodesiccation and curettage (burning and scraping off the tumor), topical chemotherapy and several different methods of surgical excision.

Mohs micrographic surgery is considered the most effective treatment method for cosmetically sensitive areas, with the highest cure rate of up to 97% and least likely to scar. Mohs surgeons are highly trained and remove as little tissue as possible, testing each layer for malignancies and halting surgery once the tissue is tumor-free. Once the tumor has been completely removed, cosmetic reconstructive surgery can be done.

chemotherapy and the skin

According to a yearly report from the American Cancer Society, it is estimated that nearly 1.7 million new cancer cases were diagnosed in 2016. There were approximately 596,000 cancer deaths. Although mortality rates are going down for many cancers, these numbers are still staggering. With these statistics, it becomes increasingly likely that some of our patients will undergo some type of chemotherapy. As we know, chemotherapy is necessary to eradicate various types of cancers, but it undeniably wreaks havoc on the skin. As the largest organ of elimination, the skin of those undergoing chemotherapy has an overwhelming task. In addition to simply trying to process the drugs that are introduced into the body during these necessary treatments, the skin is also reacting to the unavoidable increase in emotional stress that a cancer diagnosis will cause.

Different cancers necessitate varying combinations of chemotherapeutic drugs. Each combination comes with its own risks of side effects. The skin of those going through chemotherapy becomes extremely stressed.

Common dermatological side effects of treatment

- sensitivity or allergic reactions
- severe dryness
- flushing
- hyperpigmentation
- photosensitivity
- rashes
- folliculitis, an acne-like skin rash

Through good skincare, we can help these patients look and feel better. It is wise to select skincare products that do not contain synthetic fragrances, colors or other known sensitizers and irritants to avoid instigating any reactions. Peels should be avoided during the course of chemotherapy, except **Detox Gel Deep Pore Treatment** for acne breakouts/folliculitis. Cancer patients should consult their oncologist prior to beginning any new regimens.

Caring for the skin during chemotherapy

One important component to healthy, functioning and resilient skin is proper hydration. Having skin well hydrated prior to starting a series of chemotherapy treatments is an enormous help. Extremely **dehydrated skin** is a common side effect. These patients' daily regimens should include products that contain urea, glycerin, hyaluronic acid, sodium PCA and other humectants. These types of ingredients draw moisture from the dermis up into the epidermis, plumping and hydrating the skin while improving overall function. It is equally important to ensure that light occlusive agents like squalane, niacinamide, dimethicone and cyclomethicone are applied to bind and retain this increased moisture within the skin. Well-hydrated skin will be poised to handle the chemotherapy with fewer complications.

Typically what appear to be acne breakouts during chemotherapy is actually **folliculitis**, an inflammation or infection in the hair follicles. Unlike acne, increased sebum and bacteria production are not part of the underlying cause, rather the drugs are believed to be the trigger in the development of these follicular irritations. Folliculitis can appear on the face, the scalp or anywhere on the body. Inflammatory cells inside the follicles create irritation that draws leukocytes, or white blood cells, to the follicle. Folliculitis needs to be addressed gently, as this compromised skin is hypersensitive and prone to reactions. Traditional drying and surface-stimulating acne treatments will prove too harsh for this condition, and could result in greater reactivity and follicular distress. Gentle products that clear the follicles of cell debris, such as low percentage salicylic acid, will help shorten the duration of the outbreak.

Also important for clearing folliculitis is reducing the inflammation with ingredients like hydrocortisone, resveratrol, bisabolol, willowherb and white willow bark, while fighting any local infection with sulfur, salicylic acid, azelaic acid and antibacterial botanicals, like calendula and tea tree oil. Products containing these types of antibacterial, anti-inflammatory and keratolytic ingredients are a great choice for clearing folliculitis, wherever it appears on the body, including the scalp.

Hyperpigmentation is a common side effect of chemotherapy. For this reason it is important to use gentle melanogenesis inhibitors before, during and after treatment. Because many of the common melanogenesis inhibitors can be irritating, it is absolutely critical to only use ingredients that are not drying, stimulating or irritating. One must be especially careful with hydroquinone, because it is likely to irritate this sensitive skin. We recommend using products that also contain anti-inflammatories and are hydrating.

Sensitivities and allergic reactions are also a common side effect of chemotherapy. It is especially important for the chemotherapy patient to avoid the use of products containing synthetic colors, fragrances or other known sensitizers. Additionally, good hydration, anti-inflammatory ingredients and topical steroids can bring relief and be soothing to this severely stressed skin.

PCA SKIN® is an ideal choice for soothing and supporting the skin of those undergoing treatment. We offer many advanced daily care products that provide gentle, non-irritating cleansing, soothing and strengthening benefits for stressed skin.

PCA SKIN daily care solutions

The Solution for Chemotherapy Support

Creamy Cleanser

Hydrating Serum

Anti-Redness Serum

Perfecting Protection Broad Spectrum SPF 30

CliniCalm™ 1%

ReBalance

Silkcoat® Balm

Peptide Lip Therapy

Rehabilitating the skin after completion of treatment

Using gentle products during treatment can help keep hyperpigmentation at bay, but once the skin recovers, blended superficial chemical peels can help to rid the skin of any unwanted pigmentary deposits. Protocols should focus on a progressive approach to allow the skin to adjust and regain equilibrium.

This textbook contains several helpful daily care regimens and professional treatments for cancer patients. Our highly educated Practice Development Group is also available to help you customize regimens and treatments for them.

daily care products

PCA SKIN® daily care products

Dermatologist-approved and clinically researched, PCA SKIN daily care products contain advanced ingredients, such as alpha and beta hydroxy acids, MMP inhibitors, peptides, antioxidants and botanicals. These sophisticated products are available exclusively through physicians and PCA SKIN Certified Professionals. Each PCA SKIN product is scientifically formulated to target and treat troublesome skin conditions at the cellular level using a progressive, not aggressive, philosophy. We believe healthy skin is beautiful skin.

While professional treatments are important for keeping skin healthy, nothing is more important than daily care. Whereas a clinician will treat the skin once a month, we each are responsible for caring for our skin at least twice a day in the morning and evening. This being the case, choosing the best products to care for skin daily is essential. Utilizing daily care products in the same line will lead to the best results, as a single line will be formulated to assure each product blends well with the next. When picking and choosing products from different lines, it's possible that some of the ingredients in one product will counteract those in the next, or that a reaction is caused that worsens the skin concern being treated. By using professional treatments from PCA SKIN and recommending daily care from the PCA SKIN line of products as well, you and your clients can be sure that their skin is being treated optimally, both at home and in your office.

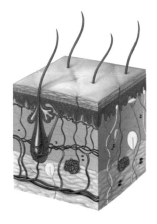

Explanation of INCI
(International Nomenclature for Cosmetic Ingredients)

INCI stands for the International Nomenclature for Cosmetic Ingredients. These are the names that are used in ingredient listings on product packaging. The Personal Care Products Council (formerly known as the Cosmetic, Toiletry and Fragrance Association or CTFA), an independent organization, designates the accepted international name for each ingredient that will be used in cosmetic and drug products. The U.S. FDA uses this dictionary of ingredient designation as the acceptable and appropriate source for correct label listings.

ingredient categories

Below are brief descriptions of some important ingredient categories and their purposes in formulations. You will hear us refer to these types of ingredients throughout this course, as well as in our other materials and seminars.

Humectants

Humectant, or hygroscopic, agents attract water. When applied topically, these ingredients draw moisture from the dermis to hydrate the epidermis. In some cases they draw moisture from the environment, but this is much less common. Humectants are important to both dry and oily skin types. Maintaining the skin's natural moisture balance keeps dry skin from becoming dehydrated and uncomfortable, and oily skin from over-producing oil. If the skin becomes moisture depleted, it will attempt to make more sebum to compensate for the deficit. Humectant action makes this excess sebum production unnecessary. Certain humectants, such as hyaluronic acid, do not penetrate the stratum corneum but work by drawing moisture upward. Ingredients such as glycerin and urea are able to penetrate the stratum corneum and travel through the skin cells' aquaporins (water channels) to increase hydration within the cells. Many other ingredients function as humectants, including panthenol, sodium PCA and honey.

Occlusives

Occlusive agents are a class of ingredients that form a film on the surface of the skin to prevent moisture loss. Occlusives work in conjunction with humectant ingredients. Humectants draw moisture up from the dermis to hydrate the epidermis, and occlusives create a barrier to keep that moisture within the skin. All effective moisturizing products must contain both occlusive and humectant agents. Occlusives are either heavy ingredients such as petrolatum, shea butter, zinc and titanium dioxide, or light oils such as squalane, rose hip seed oil and borage oil. Silicones are among the most commonly used occlusive agents because of their light feel and lack of comedogenicity. Some commonly used silicones are dimethicone and cyclomethicone.

Glycosaminoglycans (GAG)

GAG are responsible for keeping collagen and elastin fibers in good condition, as well as promoting their ability to hold moisture. GAG are also essential to the epidermal and dermal cells' metabolism. GAG consist of hyaluronic acid, mucopolysaccharides and chondroiton sulphates. Their main function is to maintain and support the collagen, elastin and turgor within cellular spaces.

Alpha hydroxy acids (AHA)

AHA are a class of chemical compounds that are derived from food products or synthesized in a lab. They have the ability to break down the bonds between the cells (desmosomes) to allow for easier exfoliation of impacted skin cells. Some examples of AHA are glycolic acid (sugar cane or rhubarb), lactic acid (sour milk or sugars), malic acid (apples), citric acid (citrus fruits), mandelic acid (bitter almonds) and tartaric acid (grapes).

Beta hydroxy acids (BHA)

Beta hydroxy acids are lipid-soluble carboxylic acids. The beta hydroxy acid that is typically used in cosmeceuticals is salicylic acid. It is able to penetrate into the pore, which contains sebum, and exfoliate the dead skin cells that are built up inside. Salicylic acid also has anti-inflammatory properties, making it highly effective for treating acne and breakout-prone skin.

Polyhydroxy acids (PHA)

Polyhydroxy acids have properties similar to AHA. Due to their structure, PHA are less irritating when compared to AHA of the same concentration, while still delivering the same type of benefits, including exfoliation, moisturization, improvement of skin laxity and uneven skin tone, and helping with skin roughness and pore size. PHA have also shown the ability to strengthen skin barrier function, improve photodamaged skin and quench free radicals. PHA are naturally occurring in the body and have a favorable safety profile.

Gluconolactone is a PHA that shows significant benefits in reducing skin keratinization and improving acne by reducing the number of both inflamed and non-inflamed lesions (one study compares 14% gluconolactone and 5% benzoyl peroxide with similar outcomes). It has the additional antioxidant benefit of acting as a metal chelating agent and free radical scavenger, thereby protecting skin from some of the damaging effects of UV radiation.

Retinoids

Retinoids are one type of vitamin A; carotenoids being the other. Retinoic acid, retinol, retinyl palmitate and retinaldehyde are all considered retinoids. All have similar functions but different levels of irritancy. If formulated correctly, products containing retinoids are able to increase cell turnover, stimulate collagen and elastin production, inhibit melanogenesis and increase skin hydration without irritation. The only retinoid capable of binding with retinoic acid receptor (RAR) is retinoic acid; however, this form can be irritating and not suitable for all patients. Fortunately, other retinoids such as retinol and retinyl palmitate are converted to retinoic acid when applied topically and deliver similar benefits without the risk of inflammation.

Peptides

A peptide is a compound consisting of two or more amino acids, the building blocks of proteins. Peptides act as transmitters from the brain to the body, telling muscles and nerves to perform specific functions. There are multiple peptides available that will achieve different topical results. The following are a few examples of different peptides and their functions:

- Palmitoyl Tripeptide-38 is a three amino acid chain designed to increase collagen I, III and IV; fibronectin; hyaluronic acid; laminin 5; and heat shock protein 47.

- Palmitoyl Tripeptide-5 stimulates collagen production to strengthen skin and minimize wrinkling.

- Palmitoyl Oligopeptide- Palmitoyl Tetrapeptide-7 (Matrixyl® 3000) is a blend of two peptides that activates the synthesis of the skin's extracellular matrix (ECM) and provides a visible anti-wrinkle activity.

- Palmitoyl Pentapeptide-4 (Matrixyl®) is a peptide consisting of five amino acids that provides an increase in the synthesis of collagen I, collagen IV and fibronectin.

- Palmitoyl Tetrapeptide-7 is a peptide consisting of four amino acids that improves skin firmness and elasticity, and decreases inflammation.

- Dipeptide-2 is a peptide consisting of two amino acids that improves lymphatic circulation to more effectively remove toxins in the skin.

- Acetyl Hexapeptide-8 (Argireline) is a peptide consisting of six amino acids that works by relaxing the facial muscles that cause repeated facial expression wrinkling (crow's feet, laugh lines, etc.).

- Palmitoyl Oligopeptide stimulates collagen production.

- Copper Peptides stimulate the synthesis of collagen and elastin.

- Polypeptide is a single chain of amino acids (general term).

- Oligopeptide is a polypeptide less than 50 amino acids long (general term).

- Protein is a polypeptide more than 50 amino acids long.

Antioxidants

Antioxidants are molecules that are able to slow or prevent the oxidation of other molecules. Oxidation produces free radicals, which trigger a chain reaction in the body that damages cells. Some examples of antioxidants are L-ascorbic acid, beta-carotene, tocopherol and tocotrienols, resveratrol, glutathione, silymarin, epigallocatechin gallate (EGCG) and caffeine. The best antioxidant protection is typically achieved by using a combination of these types of ingredients.

Epidermal growth factor (EGF)

All cells have growth factor receptors on their surface into which specific growth factors fit. They are similar to a lock and a key. When the growth factor binds to the growth factor receptor, it stimulates cell division. Growth factors play an enormous role in the health and function of our bodies. There are many different types of growth factors that have specific functions in different parts of our bodies. Epidermal growth factor works specifically to stimulate tissue growth and epithelial cell proliferation. The INCI name for our epidermal growth factor is rh-Oligopeptide-1.

Matrix metalloproteinase inhibitors (MMPi)

MMP are enzymes, such as collagenase and elastase, which are responsible for the breakdown and recycling of older and unusable protein fragments. MMP are beneficial to a certain extent, as they rid the skin of this protein 'waste.' However, because MMP production increases with exposure to UV rays, pollution, free radicals and other external factors, they can be responsible for an unwanted breakdown of healthy proteins.

MMPi are ingredients that maintain the current balance within the extracellular matrix by inhibiting the activity of the enzymes responsible for the breakdown of its structure (MMP). These ingredients allow for MMPs to rid the skin of the unwanted proteins, but maintain the healthy and necessary ones, including collagen and elastin. Examples of common MMPi are resveratrol, epigallocatechin gallate (EGCG), and vitamins C and E.

Sun protection

When selecting a sunscreen, one important factor is the product's ability to guard against both UVA and UVB wavelengths. The SPF (Sun Protection Factor) number only refers to UVB protection. The FDA does not currently require sunscreen packaging to indicate levels of UVA protection, although there are new regulations in deliberation. Before purchasing a sunscreen, check the ingredient list to ensure that it contains one of the four currently approved UVA-protecting ingredients: zinc oxide, titanium dioxide, avobenzone (Parsol 1789) and ecamsule (Mexoryl).

Sunscreen agents are classified as physical or chemical. A physical sunscreen is an inorganic ingredient that sits on the surface of the skin and reflects or scatters UV radiation before it can cause cellular damage. In contrast, a chemical sunscreen is an organic substance that penetrates the corneocytes and absorbs UV rays before they affect the skin. A combination of organic and inorganic sunscreen ingredients offers the best overall protection. Many avoid chemical sunscreens out of concern for sensitivities. In actuality, reactions are typically in response to a product's base rather than its active ingredients; therefore, even patients with sensitive skin can find an effective sunscreen.

In the past, although physical sun protection was effective, it was often associated with thicker product consistency and a white appearance on the skin. It is well-documented that zinc oxide provides excellent UV protection, providing more complete UVA protection and less whitening than titanium dioxide. By using zinc oxide of a smaller particle size (micronized) in the newest available bases, we have been able to deliver on our promise to provide our customers and their patients with cosmetically elegant, highly effective sun protection. A blend of physical and chemical ingredients combined with powerful antioxidants will minimize sunburn cell formation, and greatly reduce the chance of developing skin cancer and premature skin aging.

Waterproof/sweat-proof claims are false and irresponsible. There aren't any waterproof or sweat-proof products, and these terms are misleading to the patient. Products can however be water- or sweat-resistant, meaning that they are able to maintain their protection after a pre-determined amount of time in dynamic water. A water-resistant product will remain active for up to 40 minutes in dynamic water, and a very water-resistant product will maintain results for up to 80 minutes of submersion. Regardless of a product's claims, all sunscreens should be reapplied after swimming, sweating, toweling off or vigorous outdoor activity.

Daily compliance with SPF usage is critical. We strongly believe that patient compliance with daily use of SPF is directly connected to a product's cosmetic elegance. Now we can provide an even better family of sun protection products that provides appealing and quick-absorbing textures, hydration, antioxidant protection, melanogenesis inhibition and protection during outdoor sports or activities. We also have a formulation available that disappears into the skin and leaves no surface residue, for those patients that do not want to wear any sunscreen or moisturizer. Our sunscreens are suitable for all skin types, including those with sensitive skin.

Weightless Protection Broad Spectrum SPF 45

This broad spectrum sunscreen provides unsurpassed UVA/UVB protection with the ultra-sheer technology of zinc oxide and a blend of additional UV-absorbers. Its unique quick-absorbing and light finish makes **Weightless Protection Broad Spectrum SPF 45** ideal for patients with oily or breakout-prone skin and those who dislike the feel of traditional sunscreen products. Silybin, also known as milk thistle, and caffeine provide superior antioxidant action to help maintain skin health during exposure.

Perfecting Protection Broad Spectrum SPF 30

This revolutionary broad spectrum UVA/UVB product combines the superior protective benefits of ultra-sheer zinc oxide and other potent sunscreen agents with licorice, mulberry and bearberry extracts to encourage an even skin tone. In addition, silybin, also known as milk thistle, and caffeine provide superior antioxidant action to help maintain skin health during exposure. **Perfecting Protection Broad Spectrum SPF 30** is suitable for all skin types and is also recommended following peels, lasers and other in-office procedures.

Protecting Hydrator Broad Spectrum SPF 30

This non-oily daily hydrator with SPF is formulated with aloe vera and panthenol to provide light moisture with a matte finish. It provides optimal broad spectrum UVA/UVB coverage with the ultra-sheer protective benefits of zinc oxide and additional sunscreen agents. Silybin, also known as milk thistle, and caffeine provide superior antioxidant action to help maintain skin health during exposure. **Protecting Hydrator Broad Spectrum SPF 30** is best for patients with normal to oily skin types.

Hydrator Plus Broad Spectrum SPF 30

This nourishing moisturizer with SPF is formulated with an outstanding blend of UV protecting ingredients, including ultra-sheer zinc oxide, an effective barrier that provides superior broad spectrum UVA/UVB protection. It is specifically formulated with moisturizing hyaluronic acid and sodium PCA for dry or dehydrated skin. Silybin, also known as milk thistle, and caffeine provide superior antioxidant action to help maintain skin health during exposure.

Active Broad Spectrum SPF 45: Water Resistant

This revolutionary formulation provides water-resistant broad spectrum protection with a light finish. The superior blend of UVA/UVB protecting sunscreen agents, including ultra-sheer zinc oxide, provides superb sun-shielding benefits. Tested to protect for 80 minutes in water, it is the perfect choice for an outdoor lifestyle. Silybin, also known as milk thistle, and caffeine provide superior antioxidant action to help maintain skin health during exposure.

Sheer Tint Broad Spectrum SPF 45

This universally tinted broad spectrum sunscreen provides UVA/UVB protection in a purely physical formula. It's water resistant for up to 80 minutes, this formula smooths the skin's tone and texture outdoors. Ubiquinone (CoEnzyme Q10) provides added antioxidant protection.

The entire line of PCA SKIN® broad spectrum SPF products has been awarded The Skin Cancer Foundation Seal of Recommendation for Daily Use or Active Use. When used regularly, these SPF products help to reduce the potential risk of skin cancer and premature skin aging caused by over-exposure to UV rays.

To receive The Seal of Recommendation, our products were put through rigorous testing and met stringent criteria for safety and efficacy:

1. Photobiology (SPF determination) – this test confirms that the product not only meets, but also exceeds the SPF number listed on the package.

2. Phototoxicity – this test determines whether the product will cause any type of acute light-induced skin response. This ensures that the product is not sensitizing, even in extreme UV conditions.

3. RIPT (Repeat Insult Patch Test aka Contact Irritancy Testing) – this test places our product under occlusion on test participants' skin for six weeks to prove that there is no chance of the product being an irritant. With the passing of this test, we know that our products are not irritating or sensitizing, even on sensitive skin types.

Cleanse, tone, correct, hydrate & protect

Designing and using a PCA SKIN® daily care regimen is easy. The products are grouped into four categories: **cleanse**, **tone**, **correct** and **hydrate & protect**.

Cleanse

Our cleansers are all pH appropriate, meaning that they cleanse the skin without disrupting the delicate pH environment of the stratum corneum. In many traditional lines, it is considered necessary to use a toner after cleansing to restore the skin's pH balance. This is unnecessary with PCA SKIN. All of our cleansers are pH balanced so it is completely acceptable to skip the toner altogether for patients wanting to simplify their routines.

Tone

Our toners function more as liquid treatment products, rather than simple astringents or pH adjusters.

Correct

The wide variety of products that fall within the **correct** category allows you to customize even more to address each patient's particular mix of skin care needs. The spot treatment products are listed first and then the remainder of the products are listed from thinnest to thickest consistency; application in this order allows for maximum penetration and efficacy of each active ingredient.

Hydrate & protect

Last, and most certainly not least, the **hydrate & protect** category provides options from light hydration to intense moisture, as well as broad spectrum protection from damaging UV rays. PCA SKIN also provides a quick-absorbing and cosmetically elegant very water-resistant formulation.

PCA SKIN® condition-specific correctives

	Aging	Discoloration
Antioxidant	**C&E Strength Max** Morning antioxidant (vitamins C and E) ☀	**C&E Strength Max** Morning antioxidant (vitamins C and E) ☀
Targeted	**ExLinea® Peptide Smoothing Serum** ☀ 🌙	**Pigment Gel®** ☀ 🌙
Retinol	**Intensive Age Refining Treatment®: 0.5% pure retinol night** Evening retinol (vitamin A) 🌙	**Intensive Brightening Treatment: 0.5% pure retinol night** Evening retinol (vitamin A) 🌙

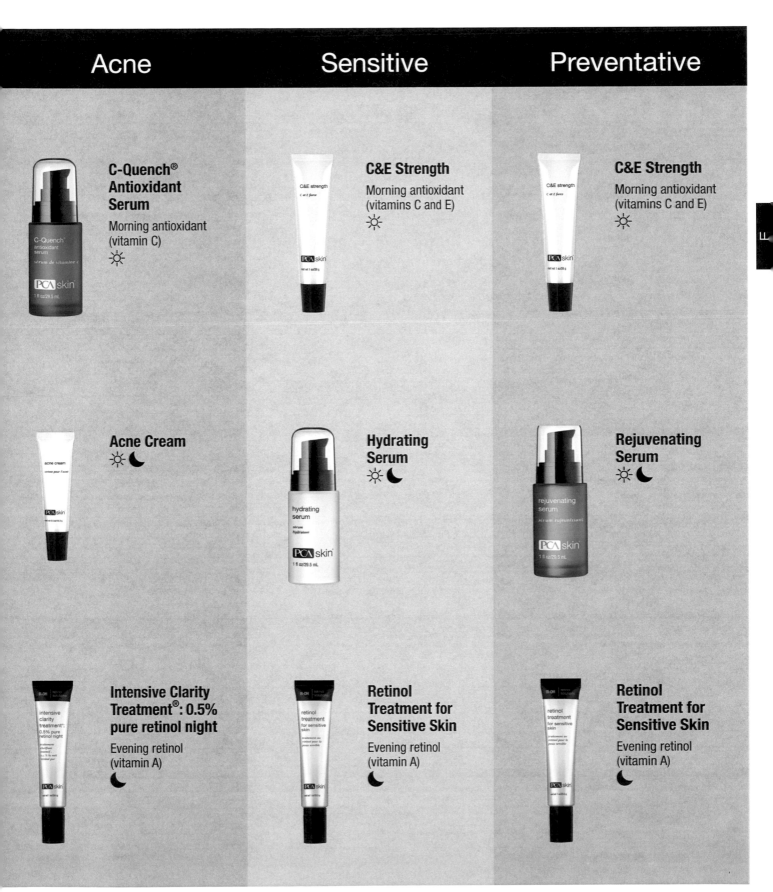

Acne

C-Quench® Antioxidant Serum

Morning antioxidant (vitamin C)

Acne Cream

Intensive Clarity Treatment®: 0.5% pure retinol night

Evening retinol (vitamin A)

Sensitive

C&E Strength

Morning antioxidant (vitamins C and E)

Hydrating Serum

Retinol Treatment for Sensitive Skin

Evening retinol (vitamin A)

Preventative

C&E Strength

Morning antioxidant (vitamins C and E)

Rejuvenating Serum

Retinol Treatment for Sensitive Skin

Evening retinol (vitamin A)

Gently remove impurities and makeup while leaving the skin hydrated, soothed and pH balanced with this cleanser including lactic acid, aloe and willow bark.

facial wash

Key ingredients:

Lactic Acid – an alpha hydroxy acid (AHA) naturally found in milk and sugars. It is part of the skin's natural moisturizing factor (NMF) and moisturizes the skin.

Aloe Vera Leaf Juice – a purifying ingredient best known for its softening and soothing benefits.

Allantoin – an antioxidant that soothes the skin.

Salix Nigra (Willow) Bark Extract – calms and soothes the skin.

Directions for use: Apply to damp skin and massage into a light foaming lather. Rinse with warm water and pat dry. Follow with the appropriate PCA SKIN® toner, treatment serums and broad spectrum SPF product in the daytime and moisturizer in the evening.

Remove excess oil, environmental impurities and makeup with this cleanser for oily and breakout-prone skin containing gluconolactone, lactic acid and aloe.

facial wash oily/problem

Key ingredients:

Gluconolactone – a gentle antioxidant polyhydroxy acid (PHA) that is calming, provides moisture and promotes a clear complexion.

Lactic Acid – an alpha hydroxy acid (AHA) naturally found in milk and sugars. It is part of the skin's natural moisturizing factor (NMF) and moisturizes the skin.

Aloe Vera Leaf Juice – a purifying ingredient best known for its softening and soothing benefits.

Directions for use: Apply to damp skin and massage into a light foaming lather. Rinse with warm water and pat dry. Follow with the appropriate PCA SKIN® toner, treatment serums and broad spectrum SPF product in the daytime and moisturizer in the evening.

total wash
face & body
cleanser

nettoyant pour
le visage et le corps

PCA skin

7 fl oz/206.5 mL

Keep skin smooth, clear and free from irritation caused by shaving with this foaming face and body cleanser containing antioxidants and purifying ingredients.

total wash face & body cleanser

Before
Condition: pseudofolliculitis barbae (ingrown hairs).*

After two months
Solution: , Blemish Control Bar, Total Wash Face & Body Cleanser, Total Strength Serum and a broad spectrum SPF.*

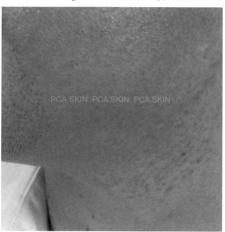

*Photos not retouched.

Key ingredients:

Aloe Vera Leaf Juice – a purifying ingredient best known for its softening and soothing benefits.

Menthyl Lactate – a combination of menthol and lactic acid that has a cooling and soothing effect on the skin.

Lactic Acid – an alpha hydroxy acid (AHA) naturally found in milk and sugars. It is part of the skin's natural moisturizing factor (NMF) and moisturizes the skin.

Tea Tree Leaf Oil – promotes a clear complexion.

Allantoin – an antioxidant that soothes the skin.

Bisabolol – a component of chamomile that provides potent calming and MMPi properties to improve and maintain skin.

Directions for use: Apply to damp skin and massage into a light foaming lather. Rinse with warm water and pat dry. Follow with the appropriate PCA SKIN® toner, treatment serums and broad spectrum SPF product in the daytime and moisturizer in the evening.

creamy cleanser

Gently remove dirt and makeup without stripping dry, sensitive skin of moisture with this hydrating cleanser containing aloe and essential fatty acids.

Key ingredients:

Rose Hip Seed Oil – strengthens skin, leaving it smoother and firmer.

Yucca Schidigera Extract – a gentle and calming foaming agent that will not strip or over dry skin.

Sunflower Seed Oil – high in omega-6 essential fatty acids (EFA) and provides antioxidants to the skin.

Aloe Vera Leaf Juice – a calming agent best known for its softening and soothing benefits.

Directions for use: Apply to damp skin and massage into a light lather. Rinse with warm water and pat dry. Follow with the appropriate PCA SKIN® toner, treatment serums and broad spectrum SPF product in the daytime and moisturizer in the evening.

Eliminate existing and future breakouts, ridding your skin of impurities with this benzoyl peroxide and gluconolactone cleanser that penetrates pores instantly.

bpo 5% cleanser

Before
Condition: acne.*

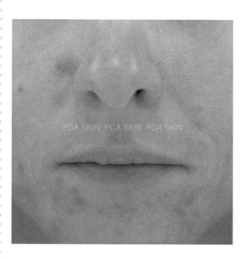

After three months
Solution: BPO 5% Cleanser, Purifying Mask, Intensive Clarity Treatment*: 0.5% pure retinol night, Acne Cream, Weightless protection Broad Spectrum SPF 45 and Clearskin.*

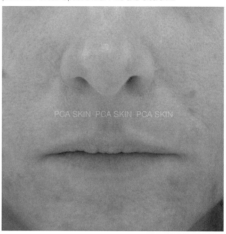

*Photos not retouched.

Active ingredient:

Benzoyl Peroxide (BPO) 5% – penetrates pores to eliminate existing acne lesions and prevent future breakouts.

Key ingredients:

Gluconolactone – a gentle polyhydroxy acid (PHA) that is calming, moisturizing and promotes a clear complexion.

Phytic Acid – a gentle exfoliating agent.

Grape Seed Extract – rich in polyphenols and proanthocyanidins, which are antioxidants. Grape seed extract contains the antioxidant resveratrol.

Directions for use: Apply to damp skin and massage into a light foaming lather. Rinse with warm water and pat dry. Follow with the appropriate PCA SKIN® toner, treatment serums and broad spectrum SPF product in the daytime and moisturizer in the evening.

Clear breakouts over large areas on the face and body with this cleansing bar formulated with 2% salicylic acid and eucalyptus to purify the skin.

blemish control bar

Active Ingredient:

Salicylic Acid (2%) – for the treatment of acne. Helps keep skin clear of new acne pimples, blackheads and/or whiteheads.

Key Ingredients:

Eucalyptus Leaf Oil – offers antiseptic and antimicrobial benefits.

Tocopherol (Vitamin E) – a fat-soluble antioxidant and emollient.

Azelaic Acid – helps promote a clear complexion and even skin tone.

Aloe Vera Leaf Juice – a purifying ingredient best known for its softening and soothing benefits.

Glycerin – a humectant and emollient that helps hydrate the skin.

Directions for use: Moisten the enclosed sponge and create a creamy lather. Cleanse the affected area, allowing the lather to remain on the skin for approximately two minutes. Rinse with warm water and pat dry. Follow with the appropriate PCA SKIN® broad spectrum SPF product in the daytime and moisturizer in the evening.
Note: store sponge outside of container.

Soothe and improve dry skin concerns including psoriasis and seborrheic dermatitis with this cleansing bar formulated with 3% salicylic acid and antioxidants.

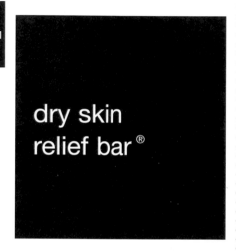

Active ingredient:

Salicylic Acid (3%) – controls and fights the recurrence of the itching, redness, flaking and irritation associated with psoriasis and seborrheic dermatitis.

Key ingredients:

Glycerin – a humectant and emollient that helps to hydrate the skin.

Aloe Vera Leaf Juice – a purifying ingredient best known for its softening and soothing benefits.

Green Tea Extract – a polyphenolic antioxidant containing beneficial vitamins, minerals and oils.

Tocopherol (Vitamin E) – a fat-soluble antioxidant vitamin and emollient ingredient.

Directions for use: Moisten the enclosed sponge and create a creamy lather. Cleanse the affected area, allowing the lather to remain on the skin for approximately two minutes. Rinse with warm water and pat dry. Follow with the appropriate PCA SKIN® broad spectrum SPF product in the daytime and moisturizer in the evening.
Note: store sponge outside of container.

Treat discolorations over large areas on the face and body for a bright, even skin tone with this cleansing bar formulated with azelaic and kojic acids.

Before
Condition: sun damage on chest.*

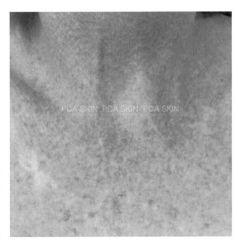

After three months
Solution: received two Smoothing Body Peel® Treatments and Pigment Bar®, Pigment Gel® HQ Free and a broad spectrum SPF.*

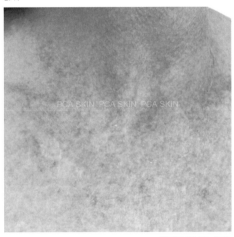

*Photos not retouched.

Key ingredients:

Azelaic Acid – helps promote a clear complexion and even skin tone.

Kojic Acid – helps promote an even skin tone.

Niacinamide – a potent, yet calming antioxidant that delivers multiple important benefits to the skin. It helps to reduce transepidermal water loss (TEWL) and improve barrier function.

Directions for use: Moisten the enclosed sponge and create a creamy lather. Cleanse the affected area, allowing the lather to remain on the skin for approximately two minutes. Rinse with warm water and pat dry. Follow with the appropriate PCA SKIN® broad spectrum SPF product in the daytime and moisturizer in the evening. Note: store sponge outside of container.

smoothing toner

Purify pores and remove dead skin cells with this astringent lactic and citric acid toner. Botanical extracts reduce surface oil and calm breakout-prone skin.

Key ingredients:

Lactic Acid – an alpha hydroxy acid (AHA) naturally found in milk and sugars. It is part of the skin's natural moisturizing factor (NMF) and moisturizes the skin.

Citric Acid – an alpha hydroxy acid (AHA) naturally found in citrus fruits.

Aloe Vera Leaf Juice – a purifying ingredient best known for its softening and soothing benefits.

Marigold, Goldenseal, Cucumber, Sage, Guarana and Ivy Extracts – provide astringent qualities to reduce the appearance of pores, as well as calm the skin.

Directions for use: After cleansing, moisten a cotton pad with a small amount of toner and apply over the face and neck. Follow with the appropriate PCA SKIN® treatment serums and broad spectrum SPF product in the daytime and moisturizer in the evening.

Refine pores and nourish the skin with this pumpkin wine-based toner filled with vitamins, amino acids and enzymes that leave the skin healthy and glowing.

nutrient toner

Key ingredients:

Pumpkin Wine – produced by fermenting enzymatically predigested whole pumpkin, releasing the many nutritional benefits of pumpkin.

Aminoguanidine – supports aging skin and keeps it soft and supple.

Glutathione – a potent antioxidant that is produced naturally by the body.

Lactic Acid – an alpha hydroxy acid (AHA) naturally found in milk and sugars. It is part of the skin's natural moisturizing factor (NMF) and moisturizes the skin.

Directions for use: After cleansing, moisten a cotton pad with a small amount of toner and apply over the face and neck. Follow with the appropriate PCA SKIN® treatment serums and broad spectrum SPF product in the daytime and moisturizer in the evening.

gentle
exfoliant

Exfoliate and polish your skin without irritation with this light, creamy scrub containing aloe vera and jojoba oil to keep skin soft and hydrated.

Key ingredients:

Aloe Vera Leaf Juice – a purifying ingredient best known for its softening and soothing benefits.

Glycolic Acid – an alpha hydroxy acid (AHA) that is excellent for oily skin types.

Jojoba Seed Oil – a stable, natural emollient that has effective moisturizing properties.

Directions for use: After cleansing, apply and work in gentle circular motions over the face. Rinse, pat dry and follow with the appropriate PCA SKIN® toner, treatment serums and broad spectrum SPF product in the daytime and moisturizer in the evening. Use morning or evening one to three times per week, based on skin type and condition.

pore refining treatment

Exfoliate and purify the skin with this advanced blend of clay, mandelic acid, enzymes, pumice and rice powder for a comprehensive skin-smoothing treatment.

Key ingredients:

Mandelic Acid – an alpha hydroxy acid (AHA) that provides chemical exfoliation and leaves skin bright.

Papain – the proteolytic fruit enzyme from papaya, which is widely used for its gentle exfoliating properties.

Rice Powder and **Pumice –** mechanical exfoliating particles with a range of sizes for a gentle yet effective exfoliating experience.

Kaolin and Bentonite – absorbent clays that help to draw impurities from the skin and clear pores.

Bisabolol – a component of chamomile that provides potent calming and MMPi properties to improve and maintain skin.

Saccharide Isomerate – a marine exopolysaccharide that increases skin renewal and exfoliation while reducing skin sensitivity and the appearance of pores.

Directions for use: After cleansing, apply and work in gentle circular motions over the face. Rinse, pat dry and follow with the appropriate PCA SKIN toner, treatment serums and broad spectrum SPF product in the daytime and moisturizer in the evening. Use morning or evening one to three times per week, based on skin type and condition.

purifying mask

Detoxify and remove impurities with this at-home clay, algae and tea tree oil mask. Microfine pumice gently exfoliates to leave your skin smooth and clear.

Key ingredients:

Algae – detoxifies and hydrates skin.

Clay – detoxifies and absorbs oil and impurities.

Pumice (microfine) – helps to gently exfoliate skin's built-up surface debris and impurities.

Grape Seed Oil – contains a high content of polyphenols, as well as the essential fatty acid (EFA) linoleic acid.

Lavender Oil, Tea Tree Leaf Oil, Spearmint Leaf Oil, Thyme Oil, Grapefruit Peel Oil – this well-balanced botanical blend helps promote a clear complexion.

Directions for use: Apply a thin, even layer over entire face (neck and chest also recommended). Leave on three to five minutes. Remove mask with warm water and gentle circular motions to activate pumice for increased exfoliation. Pat dry and follow with the appropriate PCA SKIN® moisturizer in the evening. Use in the evening, once a week or as needed.

Absorb oil and impurities with this balancing mask using Japanese white charcoal. This weekly mask keeps skin clear while minimizing the appearance of pores. For use in the morning or evening. This mask is safe for all skin types, but ideal for oily and breakout-prone skin.

Key ingredients:

Japanese White Charcoal – contains a variety of minerals and works to absorb oil and impurities from the skin. Its structure of very small pores allows it to be highly efficient at skin detoxification.

Kaolin – a type of clay that absorbs oil and impurities helping to clear pores.

Magnesium Aluminum Silicate – a naturally occurring clay-derived mineral that supports skin clearing.

Glycerin – a humectant and emollient that helps to hydrate and soothe skin.

Directions for use: Apply a thin, even layer over entire face (neck and chest also recommended). Leave on until dry. Remove mask with warm water and gentle circular motions. Pat dry and follow with the appropriate PCA SKIN® moisturizer in the morning or evening. Use once a week or as needed.

*Photos not retouched.

Invigorate your skin with this active papaya enzyme mask to exfoliate and refresh for an instant glow. Vitamin E and antioxidants soothe and protect the skin.

revitalizing mask

Key ingredients:

Papaya Fruit Enzyme – contains the proteolytic fruit enzyme papain, which is widely used for its gentle exfoliating properties. Papaya fruit is also known to be an effective skin-purifying ingredient.

Green Tea Extract – a polyphenolic antioxidant containing beneficial vitamins, minerals and oils.

Lemon Fruit, Sugarcane, Orange Fruit and **Apple Fruit Extracts** – are sources of naturally occurring alpha hydroxy acids (AHA).

Vitamin E – an antioxidant and emollient.

Honey – a humectant that helps moisturize skin.

Directions for use: Apply a thin, even layer over entire face. Leave on two to five minutes depending on sensitivity. If uncomfortable, remove immediately. Remove mask with warm water and gentle circular motions. Pat dry and follow with the appropriate PCA SKIN® moisturizer in the evening. Use no more than once a week.

Dramatically reduce crow's feet, laugh lines, forehead wrinkles and frown lines from repeated muscle movements with this targeted neuropeptide spot treatment.

Before
Condition: sun-induced hyperpigmentation and wrinkling.*

After three months
Solution: received three Protocols for Increasing Oxygenation, Hydration and Smoothing (Ultra Peel Forte®, and Oxygenating Trio®) and used Facial Wash Oily/Problem, ExLinea® Peptide Smoothing Serum, C&E Strength Max, Retinol Renewal with RestorAtive Complex, EyeXcellence, Protecting Hydrator Broad Spectrum SPF 30, Peptide Lip Therapy, Après Peel® Hydrating Balm.*

ExLinea®
peptide
smoothing
serum

*Photos not retouched.

Key ingredients:

Acetyl Hexapeptide-8 (Argireline) – works to minimize the appearance of fine lines and wrinkling.

Sodium Hyaluronate – has the ability to hold 1,000 times its weight in water; plays an important role in skin hydration.

Squalene – a naturally occurring oil found in such foods as olives and wheat germ. It helps to keep the skin moist.

Oryza Sativa (Rice) Bran Wax – helps to moisturize and smooth the skin.

Directions for use: After cleansing and toning, smooth onto areas of wrinkling and laxity, concentrating on the lines around the eyes, forehead and mouth. Use twice daily for maximum benefits. Follow with the appropriate PCA SKIN® broad spectrum SPF product in the daytime and moisturizer in the evening.

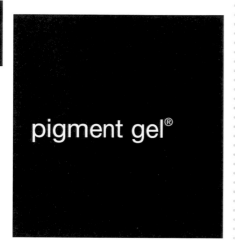

Lighten all forms of hyperpigmentation and discoloration with this spot-treatment serum with hydroquinone that delivers brilliant results.

Before
Condition: post-inflammatory hyperpigmentation.*

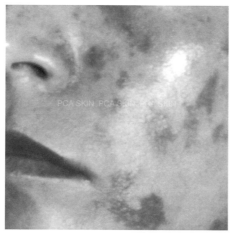

After four months
Solution: Pigment Gel® twice daily.

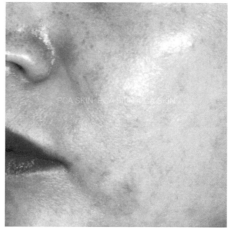

*Photos not retouched.

pigment gel®

Active ingredient:

Hydroquinone (2%) – lightens existing and prevents future hyperpigmentation.

Key ingredients:

Lactic Acid – an alpha hydroxy acid (AHA) naturally found in milk and sugars. It is part of the skin's natural moisturizing factor (NMF) and moisturizes the skin.

Phenylethyl Resorcinol – an antioxidant derived from resorcinol that promotes an even skin tone.

Azelaic Acid – helps promote a clear complexion and even skin tone.

Kojic Acid – helps promote an even skin tone.

Glutathione and Silybin – are potent antioxidants.

Directions for use: After cleansing and toning, spot-treat affected areas and allow to penetrate. Follow with the appropriate PCA SKIN® broad spectrum SPF product in the daytime and moisturizer in the evening.

Reduce discolorations and promote an even skin tone with this spot-treatment serum with kojic and azelaic acids, perfect for those sensitive to hydroquinone.

pigment gel® hq free

Before
Condition: sun damage.*

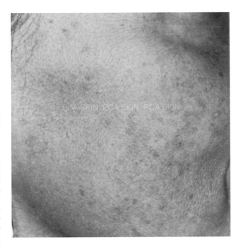

After two months
Solution: received one PCA Peel® HQ Free treatment and used Pigment Gel® HQ Free daily.*

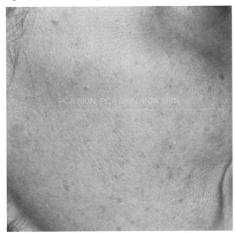

*Photos not retouched.

Key ingredients:

Lactic Acid – an alpha hydroxy acid (AHA) naturally found in milk and sugars. It is part of the skin's natural moisturizing factor (NMF) and moisturizes the skin.

Phenylethyl Resorcinol – an antioxidant derived from resorcinol that promotes an even skin tone.

Azelaic Acid – helps promote a clear complexion and even skin tone.

Kojic Acid – helps promote an even skin tone.

Glutathione and **Silybin** – potent antioxidants.

Directions for use: After cleansing and toning, spot-treat affected areas and allow to penetrate. Follow with the appropriate PCA SKIN® broad spectrum SPF product in the daytime and moisturizer in the evening.

Clear existing and prevent future acne breakouts with this fast-acting, salicylic acid treatment. A unique botanical blend controls daily oil production.

acne gel

Before
Condition: acne and post-inflammatory hyperpigmentation.*

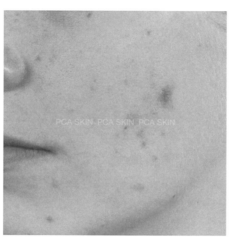

After two months
Solution: Facial Wash Oily/Problem, Purifying Mask, Acne Gel, Intensive Clarity Treatment®: 0.5% pure retinol night, Weightless Protection Broad Spectrum SPF 45 and Clearskin.

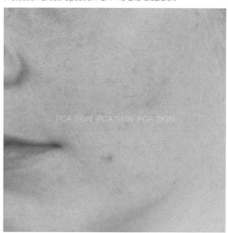

*Photos not retouched.

Active ingredient:

Salicylic Acid (2%) – For the treatment of acne. Helps keep skin clear of new acne pimples, blackheads and/or whiteheads.

Key ingredients:

Azelaic Acid – helps promote a clear complexion and even skin tone.

Cinnamon Bark, **Ginger Root**, **Green Burnet Root** and **Licorice Root Extract** – this botanical blend improves the appearance of breakout-prone skin.

Directions for use: After cleansing and toning, apply full-face or as a spot treatment. It may be used twice daily. Follow with the appropriate PCA SKIN® broad spectrum SPF product in the daytime and moisturizer in the evening.

Clear blemishes with this 5% benzoyl peroxide spot treatment including gluconolactone to prevent dryness and irritation. Essential for those with acne.

Before
Condition: acne with post-inflammatory hyperpigmentation.*

After three months
Solution: received a series of PCA Peel® with Hydroquinone treatments and used Facial Wash Oily/Problem, Purifying Mask, Acne Gel, Pigment Gel®, Intensive Clarity Treatment®: 0.5% pure retinol night, Weightless Protection Broad Spectrum SPF 45 and Clearskin.

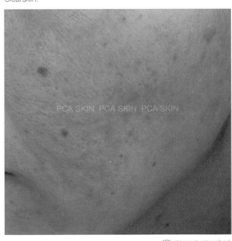

*Photos not retouched.

Active ingredient:

Benzoyl Peroxide (BPO) 5% – penetrates pores to eliminate existing acne lesions and prevent future breakouts.

Key ingredients:

Gluconolactone – a gentle antioxidant polyhydroxy acid (PHA) that is calming, moisturizing and promotes a clear complexion.

Lactic Acid – an alpha hydroxy acid (AHA) naturally found in milk and sugars. It is part of the skin's natural moisturizing factor (NMF) and moisturizes the skin.

Grape Seed Extract – a good source of the essential fatty acid (EFA) linoleic acid.

Tea Tree Leaf Oil – promotes a clear complexion.

Directions for use: After cleansing and toning, spot-treat affected areas with a smooth layer. It is not for all-over facial use. Follow with the appropriate PCA SKIN® broad spectrum SPF product in the daytime and moisturizer in the evening.

Protect your skin from free radical damage and pollutants with this gentle and strengthening antioxidant serum with lilac stem cell extract and resveratrol.

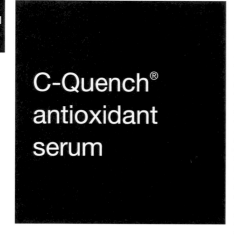

C-Quench® antioxidant serum

Before
Condition: deep wrinkling and laxity.*

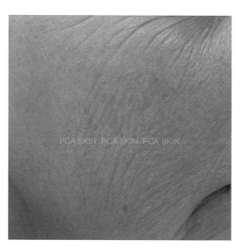

After four months
Solution: received five Ultra Peel® I and Ultra Peel® II treatments and used Facial Wash, C-Quench® Antioxidant Serum, ExLinea® Peptide Smoothing Serum, Hydrator Plus Broad Spectrum SPF 30 and ReBalance.*

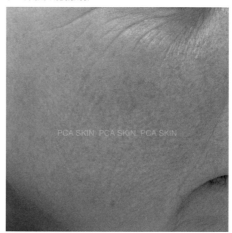

*Photos not retouched.

Key ingredients:

L-Ascorbic Acid (15%) – an antioxidant and MMPi that is the only bio-available vitamin C for the skin. It minimizes the appearance of fine lines and wrinkles while promoting an even skin tone.

Hyaluronic Acid – has the ability to hold 1,000 times its weight in water and plays an important role in skin protection, hydration, lubrication and strengthening.

Ergothioneine – an antioxidant found naturally in many plant species. It helps support the capabilities of traditional antioxidants.

Orange Oil, **Black Currant Seed Oil** and **Resveratrol** – calming polyphenolic antioxidants.

Syringa Vulgaris (Lilac) Leaf Cell Culture Extract – its major component is verbascoside, an antioxidant derived from the stem cells of the lilac plant.

Glutathione – a potent antioxidant that is produced naturally by the body.

Directions for use: Shake gently before use. After cleansing and toning, apply to the entire face and neck in the morning. Follow with the appropriate PCA SKIN® broad spectrum SPF product in the daytime.

A&C synergy
serum®

Minimize the appearance of pores, and promote a clear complexion with this astringent serum that leaves your skin with a matte finish throughout the day.

Before
Condition: acne.*

After one month
Solution: Facial Wash Oily/Problem, Purifying Mask, Acne Gel, A&C Synergy Serum®, Intensive Clarity Treatment®: 0.5% pure retinol night, Weightless Protection Broad Spectrum SPF 45 and Clearskin.*

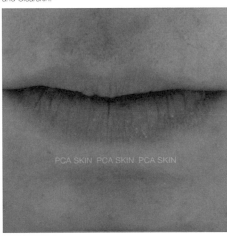

*Photos not retouched.

Key ingredients:

Retinol and **Retinyl Palmitate (Vitamin A)** – converted into retinoic acid in the skin. Vitamin A helps to promote a clear complexion and an even skin tone.

L-Ascorbic Acid (Vitamin C) – an antioxidant and MMPi that is the only bio-available vitamin C for the skin. It minimizes the appearance of fine lines and wrinkles while promoting an even skin tone.

Alpha-Arbutin, **Kojic Acid**, **Lactic Acid** and **Licorice Root Extract** – help to promote a clear, even complexion.

Resveratrol – a calming antioxidant polyphenol naturally found in red grape skins.

Directions for use: After cleansing and toning, apply to the entire face and neck twice daily for maximum results. Follow with the appropriate PCA SKIN® broad spectrum SPF product in the daytime and moisturizer in the evening.

total strength
serum
PCA skin
1 fl oz/29.5 mL

total strength serum

Lift, firm and smooth aging skin with this powerful peptide and growth factor serum that builds volume and minimizes the appearance of pores.

Before
Condition: eye area wrinkling and laxity.*

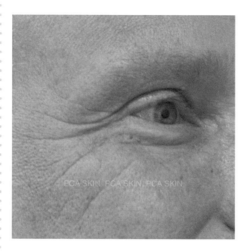

After six weeks
Solution: Total Wash Face & Body Cleanser, Total Strength Serum and broad spectrum SPF.

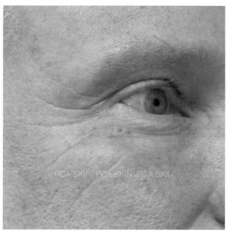

*Photos not retouched.

Key ingredients:

Palmitoyl Tripeptide-38 – the newest generation of messenger peptides that instigates the synthesis of proteins to minimize the appearance of fine lines and wrinkles.

Epidermal Growth Factor (EGF) – aids in the proliferation of healthy skin cells and improves the appearance of aging skin.

Glycosaminoglycans – important hydrating components of the extracellular matrix (ECM) that also provide MMPi action.

Cocos Nucifera (Coconut) Fruit Juice – a lipid, mineral and fatty acid-rich emollient agent.

Silybum Marianum Extract – a potent antioxidant from milk thistle.

Tocopherol and **Tocotrienols (Vitamin E)** – fat-soluble antioxidant vitamins and emollient ingredients.

Sodium Hyaluronate – a naturally occurring glycosaminoglycan with exceptional lubricating qualities. It has the ability to hold 1,000 times its weight in water and plays an important role in skin hydration.

Directions for use: After cleansing and toning, apply to the entire face and neck twice daily for maximum benefits. Follow with the appropriate PCA SKIN® broad spectrum SPF product in the daytime and moisturizer in the evening.

Nourish dry skin with this feather-light serum formulated with sodium hyaluronate and niacinamide to support skin's ability to attract and retain moisture.

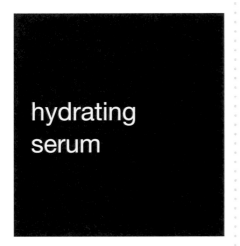

hydrating serum

Before
Condition: decreased barrier function and excessive dryness.*

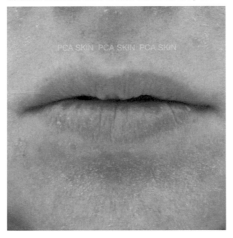

After one day
Solution: Hydrating Serum twice daily.*

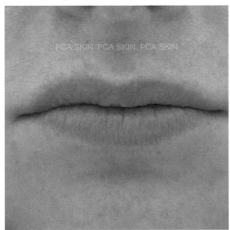

*Photos not retouched.

Key ingredients:

Aloe Vera Leaf Juice – a purifying ingredient best known for its softening and soothing benefits.

Glycerin – a humectant and emollient that helps to hydrate skin.

Sodium Hyaluronate – has the ability to hold 1,000 times its weight in water and plays an important role in skin hydration.

Panthenol (Pro-Vitamin B-5) – hydrates the skin.

Sodium PCA – hydrates the skin.

Niacinamide – a potent, yet calming antioxidant that delivers multiple important benefits to the skin. It helps to reduce transepidermal water loss (TEWL) and improve barrier function.

Urea – an essential part of the skin's natural moisturizing factor (NMF) and moisturizes the skin.

Directions: After cleansing, apply to the entire face and neck in the morning and evening for the ultimate in skin hydration. Follow with the appropriate PCA SKIN® broad spectrum SPF product in the daytime and moisturizer in the evening.

Instantly glow with this antioxidant serum that fights and prevents signs of aging, protecting skin cells using plant stem cell extract and growth factor.

rejuvenating serum

Before
Condition: fine lines, wrinkling and dehydrated skin around the eyes.*

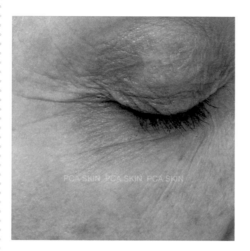

After three months
Solution: received three Ultra Peel® I and Ultra Peel® II treatments and used Facial Wash, ExLinea® Peptide Smoothing Serum, Rejuvenating Serum, A&C Synergy Serum™, Hydrator Plus Broad Spectrum SPF 30 and Collagen Hydrator.*

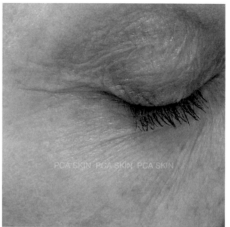

*Photos not retouched.

Key ingredients:

Epidermal Growth Factor (EGF) – helps minimize the appearance of fine lines and wrinkles.

Tocotrienols and Tocopherol (Vitamin E) – an excellent antioxidant that prevents free radical damage.

Bisabolol – a component of chamomile that provides potent calming and MMPi properties to improve and maintain skin.

Epigallocatechin Gallate (EGCG) – a polyphenol that is naturally found in green tea. It is an extremely effective antioxidant and calming ingredient.

Glutathione – an antioxidant that is produced naturally by the body.

Grape Fruit Cell Extract – an antioxidant from the stem cells of grapes.

Directions for use: After cleansing and toning, apply to the entire face and neck twice daily for maximum results. Follow with the appropriate PCA SKIN® broad spectrum SPF product in the daytime and moisturizer in the evening.

Improve redness associated with sensitive skin conditions with this calming serum containing a blend of red and brown algae, and a derivative of chamomile.

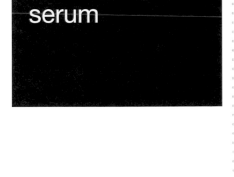

anti-redness serum

Before
Condition: diffuse redness.*

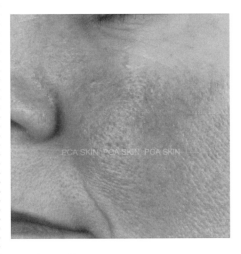

After two months
Solution: Facial Wash, Hydrating Serum, Anti-Redness Serum, Acne Gel, Protecting Hydrator Broad Spectrum SPF 30 and Clearskin.*

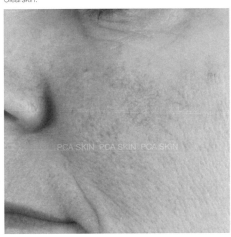

*Photos not retouched.

Key ingredients:

Aldavine – an advanced blend of brown and red algae that calms and soothes skin.

Capparenols – found in caper buds and calm and soothe the skin.

Bisabolol – a component of chamomile that provides potent calming and MMPi properties to improve and maintain skin.

Directions for use: After cleansing, apply to the entire face, focusing on areas of persistent redness. Follow with the appropriate PCA SKIN® broad spectrum SPF product in the daytime and moisturizer in the evening.

Prevent and improve early signs of aging, including wrinkles and uneven skin tone, with this gentle, yet effective blend of retinol and botanicals.

retinol renewal
with
restorAtive complex

Before
Condition: laxity and wrinkling.*

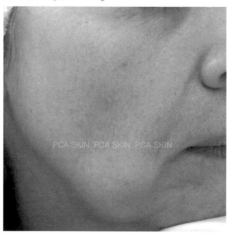

After two months
Solution: Retinol Renewal with RestorAtive Complex.*

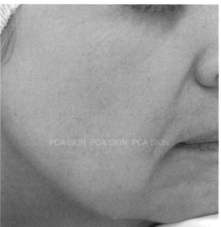

*Photos not retouched.

Key ingredients:

Retinol (Vitamin A) – converted to retinoic acid in the skin. Vitamin A helps to promote a clear complexion and an even skin tone.

Vigna Aconitifolia Seed Extract – a botanical that promotes a clear complexion and an even skin tone.

Sodium Hyaluronate – has the ability to hold 1,000 times its weight in water and plays an important role in skin hydration.

Squalene – a naturally occurring oil found in such foods as olives and wheat germ. It helps to keep the skin moist.

Superoxide Dismutase (SOD) – an enzyme that supports antioxidant defense.

Tocotrienols and **Tocopherol (Vitamin E)** – fat-soluble antioxidant vitamins and emollient ingredients.

Directions for use: After cleansing and toning, apply to the entire face and neck. Follow with the appropriate moisturizer in the evening.

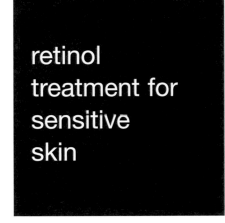

retinol treatment for sensitive skin

Reduce signs of aging without irritation with this gentle retinol solution specifically formulated for sensitive skin. Retinol is paired with niacinamide, Inflacin® and the patented OmniSome delivery system for less irritation without sacrificing efficacy.

Before
Condition: Uneven surface texture and early signs of aging

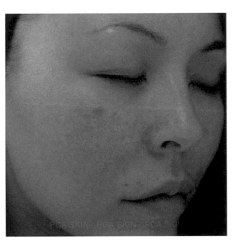

After ten weeks
Solution: Facial Wash, Hydrating Serum, Retinol Treatment for Sensitive Skin, ReBalance, Weightless Protection Broad Spectrum SPF 45

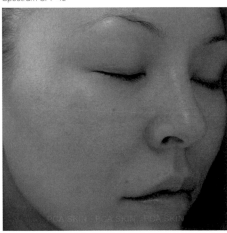

*Photos not retouched.

Key ingredients:

Retinol (vitamin A) – converted to retinoic acid in the skin. Vitamin A helps to improve skin texture, and promote a clear complexion and an even skin tone.

Niacinamide – a potent and calming antioxidant that delivers multiple important benefits to the skin. It helps to reduce transepidermal water loss (TEWI) and improve barrier function. This is critical for bright, even skin. Additionally, niacinamide helps to reduce age-related skin yellowing and redness, and create an overall youthful appearance.

Hexylresorcinol – helps to promote an even skin tone and calm skin.

Inflacin® – a patented cosmetic ingredient shown to reduce the sub-clinical inflammation that contributes to aging.

Ceramide NP – supports the renewal of the skin's natural protective layer and forms an effective barrier against moisture loss; improves long-term moisturization and protects skin from external offenders.

Avena Sative (Oat) Kernal Extract – provides the powerful polyphenols avenanthramides that function to calm and soothe skin while reducing sensitivity.

Bisabolol – helps reduce inflammation and irritation while soothing skin and restoring suppleness; it also protects the skin against daily environmental stress.

Directions for use: In the evening, apply a pea-sized amount after cleansing. Begin by limiting use to twice a week, gradually increasing application frequency to every other night, and then advancing to each evening or as tolerated. Follow with the appropriate PCA SKIN® moisturizer. Mild irritation may initially be experienced and is not a sign of a negative complication. This product is indicated for use in the evening only. Daily broad spectrum sun protection is critical while using this product.

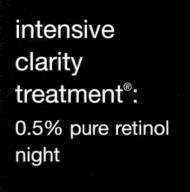

intensive clarity treatment®:

0.5% pure retinol night

Dramatically reduce and prevent acne breakouts, oil production and inflammation with this salicylic acid formula featuring retinol and niacinamide.

Before
Condition: acne.*

After four weeks
Solution: Facial Wash, Hydrating Serum, Intensive Clarity Treatment*: 0.5% pure retinol night, Weightless Protection Broad Spectrum SPF 45 and Clearskin.*

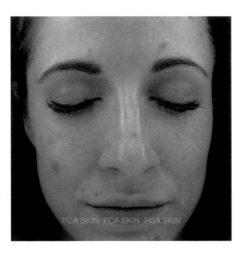

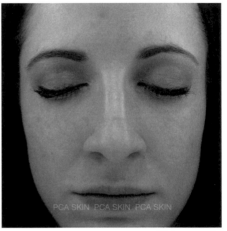

*Photos not retouched.

Active ingredients:

Salicylic Acid (2%) – for the treatment of acne. Helps keep skin clear of new acne pimples, blackheads and/or whiteheads.

Key ingredients:

0.5% Retinol (Vitamin A) – converted to retinoic acid in the skin. Vitamin A helps to promote a clear complexion and an even skin tone.

Niacinamide (4%) – a potent and calming antioxidant that delivers multiple important benefits to the skin. It helps to reduce transepidermal water loss (TEWL) and improve barrier function. This is critical for clear, even skin. Additionally, niacinamide helps to reduce redness and improve the overall appearance of an uneven skin tone.

Hexylresorcinol – helps to promote an even skin tone and calm breakout-prone skin.

Ethyl Linoleate – has been shown to calm skin, and reduce keratinization and other common causes of breakouts.

Myristoyl Nonapeptide-3 – this retinopeptide mimics retinoid activity to support breakout-fighting and collagen-building.

Bakuchiol – an effective complement to retinoids for fighting breakouts.

Syringa Vulgaris (Lilac) Leaf Cell Culture Extract – helps reduce sebum and soothe breakout-prone skin.

Directions for use: After cleansing and toning, apply to the face, avoiding the eye area and the neck. Begin by limiting use to twice a week, gradually increasing application frequency to every other night, and then advancing to each evening or as tolerated. Follow with the appropriate PCA SKIN® moisturizer in the evening. Mild irritation may initially be experienced and is not a sign of a negative complication. This product is indicated for use in the evening only. Daily broad spectrum sun protection is critical while using this product.

Visibly reduce wrinkles and strengthen skin with this retinol formula including niacinamide, retinopeptides, stem cell extract and vital hydrators.

intensive age refining treatment®: 0.5% pure retinol night

Before
Condition: fine lines, sagging and age-related yellowing.*

After six weeks
Solution:Facial Wash, Hydrating Serum, Intensive Age Refining Treatment®: 0.5% pure retinol night, Hydrator Plus Broad Spectrum SPF 30 and ReBalance.*

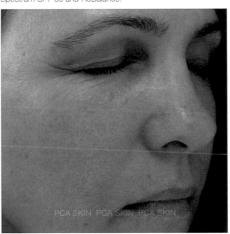

*Photos not retouched.

Key ingredients:

0.5% Retinol (Vitamin A) – converted to retinoic acid in the skin. Vitamin A helps to promote a clear complexion and an even skin tone.

Niacinamide (4%) – a potent and calming antioxidant that delivers multiple important benefits to the skin. It helps to reduce transepidermal water loss (TEWL) and improve barrier function. This is critical for bright, even skin. Additionally, niacinamide helps to reduce age-related skin yellowing and redness, and create an overall youthful appearance.

Myristoyl Nonapeptide-3 – this retinopeptide mimics retinoid activity to support skin strengthening and collagen building.

Panthenol (Pro-Vitamin B5), **Avena Sativa (Oat) Kernel Extract** and **Isosorbide Dicaprylate** – provide long-lasting hydration, barrier support and antioxidant protection.

Citrus Aurantium Dulcis Callus Culture Extract (Orange Stem Cell Extract) – increases the production of collagen and elastin, and organizes and redensifies the dermal structure to reduce fine lines and wrinkles, and increase elasticity and firmness.

Inflacin® – a patented cosmetic ingredient shown to reduce the sub-clinical inflammation that contributes to aging.

Terminalia Chebula Fruit Extract – has been shown to inhibit a variety of MMP to protect skin from oxidative damage. It also rejuvenates the extracellular matrix by stimulating collagen production and works to break collagen cross-links caused by age-related glycation.

Sodium Hylauronate – plays an important role in skin moisture retention and hydration.

Tocopherol and **Tocotrienols (Vitamin E)** – fat-soluble antioxidant and emollient ingredients.

Directions for use: After cleansing and toning, apply to the face, avoiding the eye area and the neck. Begin by limiting use to twice a week, gradually increasing application frequency to every other night, and then advancing to each evening or as tolerated. Follow with the appropriate PCA SKIN® moisturizer in the evening. Mild irritation may initially be experienced and is not a sign of a negative complication. This product is indicated for use in the evening only. Daily broad spectrum sun protection is critical while using this product.

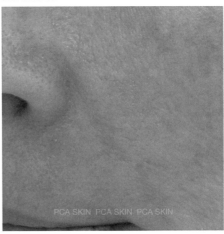

intensive
brightening
treatment:

0.5% pure retinol
night

Dramatically reduce discoloration and age-related skin yellowing with this innovative retinol formula powered with resveratrol, hexylresorcinol and niacinamide.

Before
Condition: discoloration.*

After seven weeks
Solution: received one Ultra Peel® I treatment and used Creamy Cleanser, Hydrating Serum, Intensive Brightening Treatment: 0.5% pure retinol night, Hydrator Plus Broad Spectrum SPF 30 and ReBalance.

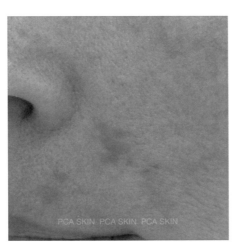

*Photos not retouched.

Key ingredients:

0.5% Retinol (Vitamin A) – converted to retinoic acid in the skin. Vitamin A helps to promote a clear complexion and an even skin tone.

Niacinamide (4.4%) – a potent, yet calming antioxidants that delivers multiple important benefits to the skin. It helps to reduce transepidermal warer loss (TEWL) and improve barrier function. This is critical for healthy, bright skin. Additionally, it helps reduce redness, skin yellowing and promotes an even skin tone.

Hexylresorcinol (1.1%) – helps to promote an even skin tone and reduce the inflammation that can lead to discoloration.

Resveratrol (1%) – a potent antioxidant. Recent studies have indicated a strong ability to promote a bright, even skin tone.

Hydroxyphenoxy Propionic Acid (2%) – helps to promote an even skin tone and leave the skin radiant.

Directions for use: After cleansing and toning, apply to the face, avoiding the eye area and the neck. Begin by limiting use to twice a week, gradually increasing application frequency to every other night, and then advancing to each evening or as tolerated. Follow with the appropriate PCA SKIN® moisturizer in the evening. Mild irritation may initially be experienced and is not a sign of a negative complication. This product is indicated for use in the evening only. Daily broad spectrum sun protection is critical while using this product.

intensive pigment eraser

Treat hyperpigmentation with this powerful, triple-action hydroquinone spot treatment. Retinol and key soothing agents leave skin even, smooth and more radiant. Note: Exclusively sold through physicians.

Before
Condition: hyperpigmentation.

After ten weeks
Solution: Creamy Cleanser, Hydrating Serum, Protecting Hydrator Broad Spectrum SPF 30, Intensive Pigment Eraser, ReBalance

*Photos not retouched.

Active ingredient:

Hydroquinone (2%) – lightens existing and prevents future hyperpigmentation.

Key ingredients:

Retinol (1%) – converted to retinoic acid in the skin. Vitamin A helps to promote a clear complexion and an even skin tone.

Inflacin® – a patented cosmetic ingredient shown to dramatically calm skin.

Niacinamide – a potent, yet calming antioxidant that delivers multiple important benefits to the skin. It helps to reduce transepidermal water loss (TEWL) and improve barrier function. This is critical for healthy, bright skin. Additionally, it helps reduce redness, skin yellowing and promotes an even skin tone.

Hexylresorcinol – helps to promote an even skin tone and calm skin to reduce the development of discoloration.

Bisabolol – a component of chamomile that provides potent calming and MMPi properties to improve and maintain skin.

Ceramide NP – supports the renewal of the skin's natural protective layer and forms an effective barrier against moisture loss; improves long-term moisturization and protects skin from external offenders.

Palmaria Palmata Extract – promotes an even skin tone.

Hydrolyzed Ceratonia Siliqua Seed Extract – accelerates the recovery of stressed skin and improves barrier function.

Mentha Piperita (Peppermint) Extract – calms skin and reduces the sensations of discomfort.

Avena Sativa (Oat) Kernel Extract – oat milk extract high in essential fatty acids (EFA). Oat milk soothes and calms the skin with natural calming action, and helps retain vital moisture, while providing the skin with powerful antioxidant protection.

Directions for use: After cleansing, apply to affected areas. Begin by limiting use to twice a week, gradually increasing application frequency to every other night, and then advancing to each evening or as tolerated. Follow with the appropriate PCA SKIN® moisturizer. Mild irritation may initially be experienced and is not a sign of a negative complication. This product is indicated for use in the evening only. Daily broad spectrum sun protection is critical while using this product. Note: Not for all over facial use.

For those new to vitamin C, strengthen, smooth and brighten skin with this antioxidant corrective loaded with 15% vitamin C and 5% vitamin E.

C&E strength

Before
Condition: fine lines, wrinkles, dullness and laxity*.

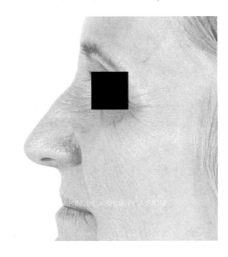

After five weeks
Solution: Facial Wash, C&E Strength, Hydrator Plus Broad Spectrum SPF 30 and Collagen Hydrator.*

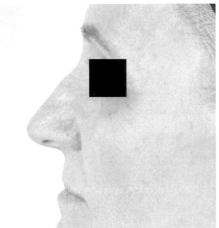

*Photos not retouched.

Key ingredients:

L-Ascorbic Acid (Vitamin C) (15%) – an antioxidant and MMPi that is the only bio-available form of vitamin C for the skin; it minimizes the appearance of fine lines and wrinkles while promoting an even skin tone.

Tocopherol (Vitamin E) (5%) – a fat-soluble antioxidant vitamin and emollient ingredient.

Bisabolol – one of the principal active compounds found in chamomile; it calms and soothes the skin.

Directions for use: After cleansing, toning and applying any PCA SKIN® treatment serums, apply to the face and neck in the morning. Patients might experience a slight tingling sensation upon application. Follow with the appropriate PCA SKIN broad spectrum SPF product.

Strengthen, smooth and brighten skin with this antioxidant corrective that has maximum vitamin concentrations: 20% vitamin C and 5% vitamin E.

C&E strength max

Before
Condition: hyperpigmentation*.

After five weeks
Solution: Facial Wash, C&E Strength Max, Perfecting Protection Broad Spectrum SPF 30 and ReBalance.*

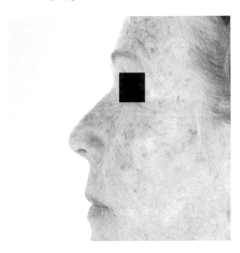

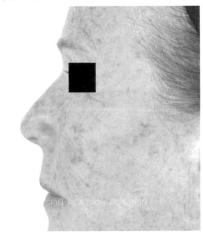

*Photos not retouched.

Key ingredients:

L-Ascorbic Acid (Vitamin C) (20%) – an antioxidant and MMPi that is the only bio-available form of vitamin C for the skin; it minimizes the appearance of fine lines and wrinkles while promoting an even skin tone

Tocopherol (Vitamin E) (5%) – a fat-soluble antioxidant vitamin and emollient ingredient.

Bisabolol – one of the principal active compounds found in chamomile; it calms and soothes the skin.

Directions for use: After cleansing, toning and applying any PCA SKIN® treatment serums, apply to the face and neck in the morning. Patients might experience a slight tingling sensation upon application. Follow with the appropriate PCA SKIN broad spectrum SPF product.

hyaluronic
acid boosting
serum

Plump and firm skin through increased hydration with this advanced hyaluronic acid formulation. This smoothing blend provides deep, long-lasting hydration on three levels: on the surface, deeper in the skin and by increasing the skin's own hyaluronic acid production.

The result of Hyaluronic Acid Boosting Serum and HA-Pro Complex™

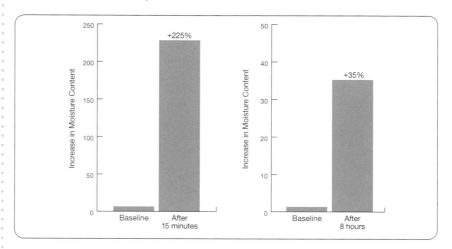

Key ingredients:

Hyaluronic Acid and **Sodium Hyaluronate (Hyaluronic Acid Sodium Salt)** – high molecular weight hyaluronic acid occludes the skin, attracting and holding 1,000 times its weight in moisture within the skin. It provides smoothing and softening of the skin while reducing transepidermal water loss (TEWL) and increasing moisture content in the upper skin layers.

Hydrolyzed Hyaluronic Acid – due to its small molecular size, it is able to penetrate through the skin to deliver deeper moisturization and significantly reduce deep wrinkles.

HA-Pro Complex™ – PCA SKIN's proprietary blend works to stimulate the production of the skin's own native hyaluronic acid. HA-Pro Complex™ delivers 24-hour moisturization through all levels of the skin, smoothing fine lines and wrinkles, and plumping and firming the skin. For long term improvement.

Ceramides – supports the renewal of the skin's natural protective layer and forms an effective barrier against moisture loss; improves long-term moisturization and protects skin from external offenders.

Niacinamide – a potent, yet calming antioxidant that delivers multiple important benefits to the skin. It helps to reduce TEWL and improve barrier function. This is critical for healthy, bright skin. Additionally, it helps reduce redness, skin yellowing and promotes an even skin tone.

Directions for use: After cleansing, apply to the entire face and neck in the morning and evening for maximum skin hydration and plumping. Follow with the appropriate PCA SKIN broad spectrum SPF product in the daytime and moisturizer in the evening.

Improve skin's barrier function while reducing sensitivity and redness with this restorative treatment including niacinamide, ceramide and protective agents.

Before
Condition: diffuse redness and impaired barrier.

After four weeks
Solution: Creamy Cleanser, Hydrating Serum, Dual Action Redness Relief, Hydrator Plus Broad Spectrum SPF 30, Collagen Hydrator.

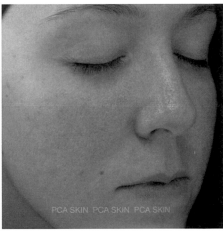

*Photos not retouched.

dual action redness relief

Key ingredients:

Niacinamide – a potent, yet calming antioxidant that delivers multiple important benefits to the skin. It helps to reduce transepidermal water loss (TEWL) and improve barrier function. This is critical for healthy, bright skin. Additionally, it helps reduce redness, skin yellowing and promotes an even skin tone.

Inflacin® – a patented cosmetic ingredient shown to reduce the sub-clinical inflammation that contributes to aging.

Dimethyl Sulfone and **Silybum Marianum Fruit Extract** – work synergistically to reduce redness, increase hydration and soothe reddened skin.

Panthenol – hydrates the skin.

Bisabolol – a component of chamomile that provides potent calming and MMPi properties to improve and maintain skin.

Ceramide NP – supports the renewal of the skin's natural protective layer and forms an effective barrier against moisture loss; improves long-term moisturization and protects skin from external offenders.

Directions for use: After cleansing, apply to the entire face and neck in the morning and evening for barrier repair and redness reduction. Follow with the appropriate PCA SKIN® broad spectrum SPF product in the daytime and moisturizer in the evening.

ideal complex®
revitalizing eye gel

Treat dark circles, puffiness, wrinkles, and sagging eyelids, with this impressive blend of peptides, growth factor and stem cell extract in a lightweight gel.

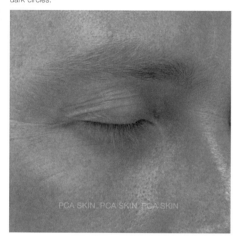

Before
Condition: fine lines, wrinkles, dullness, laxity and sagging, dark circles.*

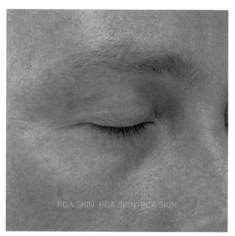

After two weeks
Solution: Ideal Complex® Revitalizing Eye Gel twice daily.*

*Photos not retouched.

Key ingredients:

Myristoyl Nonapeptide-3 – a novel peptide that mimics retinoic acid (vitamin A) to increase cell turnover and collagen synthesis without causing negative side effects, such as irritation and stinging.

Acetyl Tetrapeptide-5 – a peptide with anti-edema effects that increases skin elasticity and skin moisturization while improving the appearance of dark circles around the eyes.

Citrus Aurantium Dulcis Callus Culture Extract (Orange Stem Cell Extract) – increases the production of collagen and elastin; and organizes and redensifies the dermal structure to reduce fine lines and wrinkles, and increase elasticity and firmness.

Albizia Julibrissin Bark Extract and Darutoside – reduces upper eyelid sagging, strengthens the dermis and reduces crow's feet wrinkles, while addressing dark circles and puffiness.

Niacinamide, Fraxinus Excelsior Bark Extract and **Silanetriol** – this combination of ingredients reduces eye puffiness, dark circles and eye bags while infusing antioxidants into the skin.

Myristoyl Pentapeptide-8 and **Myristoyl Hexapeptide-4** – peptides that stimulate collagen synthesis and tissue repair, and provide an effective alternative to human growth factor.

Palmitoyl Tripeptide-38 – the newest generation of messenger peptide that insigates the synthesis of important proteins to minimize the appearance of fine lines and wrinkles.

Crocus Chrysanthus Bulb Extract and **Acacia Senegal Gum** – an effective growth factor alternative, these ingredients improve skin firmness and elasticity while reducing wrinkles in the crow's feet area.

Dipeptide Diaminobutyroyl Benzylamide Diacetate – a next generation peptide that has a fast acting wrinkle smoothing effect around the eyes, diminishing wrinkles and expression lines.

Directions for use: After cleansing, toning and applying any PCA SKIN® treatment serums, pat a small amount gently around the eye area twice daily. Follow with the appropriate PCA SKIN broad spectrum SPF product in the daytime and moisturizer in the evening.

Treat dark circles, puffiness, wrinkling and sagging eyelids with this impressive blend of peptides, growth factor and stem cell extract in a rich cream.

ideal complex®
restorative eye cream

Before
Condition: fine lines, wrinkles, dullness, laxity and sagging, dark circles.*

After one week
Solution: Ideal Complex® Restorative Eye Cream twice daily.*

*Photos not retouched.

Key ingredients:

Boron Nitride – a naturally occurring mineral that reflects light away from the eye area, leaving dark circles and under eye bags immediately brighter.

Myristoyl Nonapeptide-3 – a novel peptide that mimics retinoic acid (vitamin A) to increase cell turnover and collagen synthesis without causing negative side effects, such as irritation and stinging.

Acetyl Tetrapeptide-5 – a peptide with anti-edema effects that increases skin elasticity and skin moisturization while improving the appearance of dark circles around the eyes.

Citrus Aurantium Dulcis Callus Culture Extract (Orange Stem Cell Extract) – increases the production of collagen and elastin; and organizes and redensifies the dermal structure to reduce fine lines and wrinkles, and increase elasticity and firmness.

Albizia Julibrissin Bark Extract and Darutoside – reduces upper eyelid sagging, strengthens the dermis and reduces crow's feet wrinkles, while addressing dark circles and puffiness.

Niacinamide, Fraxinus Excelsior Bark Extract and Silanetriol – this combination of ingredients reduces eye puffiness, dark circles and eye bags while infusing antioxidants into the skin.

Myristoyl Pentapeptide-8 and Myristoyl Hexapeptide-4 – peptides that stimulate collagen synthesis and tissue repair, and provide an effective alternative to human growth factor.

Palmitoyl Tripeptide-38 – the newest generation of messenger peptide that insigates the synthesis of important proteins to minimize the appearance of fine lines and wrinkles.

Crocus Chrysanthus Bulb Extract and Acacia Senegal Gum – an effective growth factor alternative, these ingredients improve skin firmness and elasticity while reducing wrinkles in the crow's feet area.

Dipeptide Diaminobutyroyl Benzylamide Diacetate – a next generation peptide that has a fast acting wrinkle smoothing effect around the eyes, diminishing wrinkles and expression lines.

Directions for use: After cleansing, toning and applying any PCA SKIN® treatment serums, pat a small amount gently around the eye area twice daily. Follow with the appropriate PCA SKIN broad spectrum SPF product in the daytime and moisturizer in the evening.

Improve the appearance of dark circles and puffiness while preventing fine lines around the eyes with this hydrating triple-peptide cream.

eyeXcellence

Before
Condition: laxity and wrinkling in the eye area, under-eye circles and edema.*

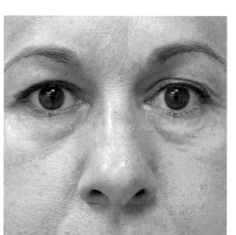

After three months
Solution: received two Ultra Peel Forte® with Esthetique Peel treatments and used Facial Wash, ExLinea® Peptide Smoothing Serum, EyeXcellence, A&C Synergy Serum,™ ReBalance and Protecting Hydrator SPF 25.*

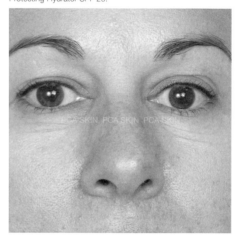

*Photos not retouched.

Key ingredients:

Dipeptide-2 – helps improve the appearance of eye area puffiness.

Palmitoyl Tetrapeptide-7 – this calming peptide helps improve the appearance of fine lines and wrinkles.

Palmitoyl Pentapeptide-4 (Matrixyl®) – improves the appearance of fine lines and wrinkles.

Licorice Root Extract – calms skin and helps promote an even skin tone.

Directions for use: After cleansing, toning and applying any PCA SKIN® treatment serums, pat a small amount gently around the eye area twice daily. Follow with the appropriate PCA SKIN broad spectrum SPF product in the daytime and moisturizer in the evening.

Firm sagging, loose skin while reducing lines and redness on the neck and chest with this luxe peptide, stem cell extract and niacinamide cream.

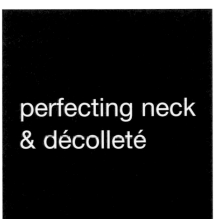

perfecting neck & décolleté

Before
Condition: photodamage and laxity.

After five weeks
Solution: Facial Wash, Pigment Bar®, Perfecting Neck & Décolleté, Hydrator Plus Broad Spectrum SPF 30

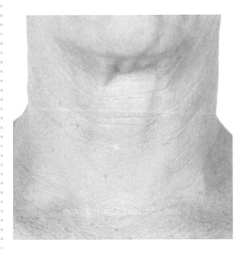

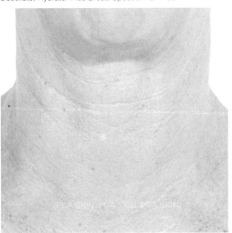

*Photos not retouched.

Key ingredients:

Palmitoyl Tripeptide-38 – the newest generation of messenger peptides that instigates the synthesis of proteins to minimize the appearance of fine lines and wrinkles.

Palmitoyl Tripeptide-5 – stimulates collagen production to strengthen skin and minimize wrinkling.

Vitis Vinifera (Grape) Fruit Cell Extract – an important antioxidant from the stem cells of grapes that works to protect epidermal stem cells from damage.

Calcium Hydroxymethionine – tested specifically on neck tissue, this ingredient fortifies and restructures thin, fragile skin.

Niacinamide – a potent, yet calming antioxidants that delivers multiple important benefits to the skin. It helps to reduce transepidermal warer loss (TEWL) and improve barrier function. This is critical for healthy, bright skin. Additionally, it helps reduce redness, skin yellowing and promotes an even skin tone.

Secale Cereale (Rye) Seed Extract – stimulates the synthesis of stress fibers to reduce laxity in the skin.

Retinol (Vitamin A) – converted to retinoic acid in the skin, vitamin A helps to promote a clear complexion and an even skin tone.

Directions for use: After cleansing and applying any PCA SKIN® treatment serums, apply to the neck and chest twice daily. Follow with the appropriate PCA SKIN broad spectrum SPF product in the daytime and moisturizer in the evening.

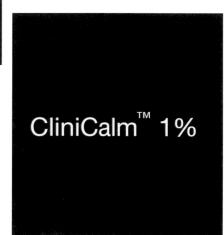

CliniCalm™ 1%

Relieve redness, itching, inflammation and irritation due to topical allergens, dermatitis, professional treatments or waxing with this 1% hydrocortisone cream.

Active ingredients:

Hydrocortisone (1%) – a corticosteroid hormone used to relieve topical itching, irritation and discomfort.

Key ingredients:

Bisabolol – a component of chamomile that provides potent calming and MMPi properties to improve and maintain skin.

Ceramide III – supports the renewal of the skin's natural protective layer and forms an effective barrier against moisture loss; improves long-term moisturization and protects skin from external offenders.

Asiaticoside – a novel ingredient that helps inhibit MMP1 to reduce collagen degradation while supporting dermal regeneration.

Hyaluronic acid, honey, phospholipids and **sphingolipids** – this blend normalizes water absorption and repairs the lipid barrier of dry and irritated skin; it forms a hydrating film and provides a long-lasting moisturizing effect.

Beta-glucan – derived from oat, this ingredient reduces irritation while also stimulating the strengthening of damaged skin.

Directions for use: After gentle cleansing, apply to the area of treatment, not to exceed three to four times daily. Follow with the appropriate PCA SKIN® broad spectrum SPF product in the daytime, moisturizer in the evening, or use as directed by your physician or skincare professional. **This product is indicated for no more than seven days of consistent use.**

Soften and hydrate the lips with a treatment including shea butter and a proprietary blend of hydrating extracts. Peptides minimize the appearance of lip lines.

peptide lip therapy

Before
Condition: dehydrated skin and flakiness of the lips.*

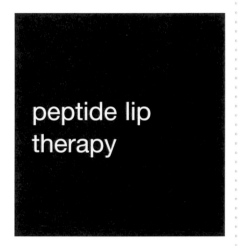

After two days
Solution: received one lip renewal treatment and used Peptide Lip Therapy twice daily.*

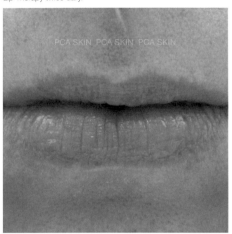

*Photos not retouched.

Key ingredients:

BMX Complex – a proprietary blend of tomato and barley that hydrates the lips.

Safflower Seed Oil, Castor Oil and **Sunflower Seed Oil** – rich in omega-3 and omega-6 essential fatty acids (EFA) to prevent water loss.

Shea Butter – softens and helps maintain moisture in the skin without greasiness. It is high in triglycerides, and vitamins A, E and the omega-6 essential fatty acid gamma linolenic acid (GLA).

Aloe Vera Leaf Extract – a purifying ingredient best known for its softening and soothing benefits.

Palmitoyl Tripeptide-38 – the newest generation of messenger peptides that instigates the synthesis of proteins to minimize the appearance of fine lines and wrinkles.

Portulaca Pilosa Extract – helps minimize the appearance of fine lines and wrinkles in the lip area.

Bisabolol – a component of chamomile that provides potent calming and MMPi properties to improve and maintain skin.

Directions for use: Apply to lips twice daily to protect against environmental damage, improve hydration and dramatically minimize lip lines. With daily use, this product will reduce peeling and promote smoother, fuller lips.

weightless protection broad spectrum spf 45

Experience UVA/UVB protection that feels like it disappears in this fast-absorbing SPF product with caffeine and milk thistle for extra environmental protection.

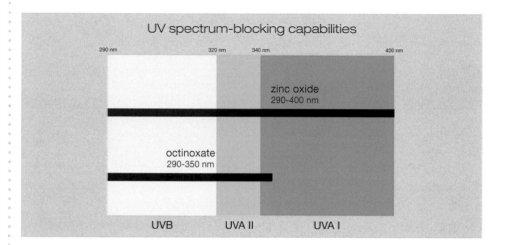

Active ingredients:

Zinc Oxide (9.0%) – provides broad spectrum UV protection by reflecting, scattering and absorbing UV rays.

Octinoxate (7.5%) – absorbs and filters UV rays.

Key ingredients:

Caffeine – supports antioxidant activity.

Silybin – an antioxidant.

Tocopheryl Acetate (Vitamin E) – a fat-soluble antioxidant vitamin and emollient ingredient.

Directions for use: After cleansing, toning and applying any PCA SKIN® treatment serums, smooth onto the skin. Allow to absorb 15 minutes prior to daytime exposure. Reapply after two hours of sun exposure and repeat every two hours as needed. It is recommended for daily use.

Defend from UVA/UVB rays with this sheer SPF that has five discoloration-fighting ingredients. Added antioxidants increase protection from free-radical damage.

perfecting protection broad spectrum spf 30

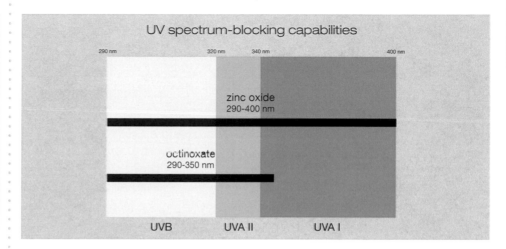

Active ingredients:

Zinc Oxide (9.8%) – provides broad spectrum UV protection by reflecting, scattering and absorbing UV rays.

Octinoxate (7.5%) – absorbs and filters UV rays.

Key ingredients:

Caffeine – supports antioxidant activity.

Silybin – an antioxidant.

Bearberry – an antioxidant and skin conditioning agent that helps promote an even skin tone.

Licorice Root Extract – a calming ingredient that helps promote an even skin tone.

Kojic Acid – helps promote an even skin tone.

Mulberry Root Extract – an effective melanogenesis inhibitor that assists in evening skin discoloration.

Lactic Acid – an alpha hydroxy acid (AHA) naturally found in milk and sugars. It is part of the skin's natural moisturizing factor (NMF) and moisturizes the skin.

Directions for use: After cleansing, toning and applying any PCA SKIN® treatment serums, smooth onto the skin. Allow to absorb 15 minutes prior to daytime exposure. Reapply after two hours of sun exposure and repeat every two hours as needed. It is recommended for daily use.

Protect your skin against UVA and UVB rays with this non-oily daily hydrator with SPF. Added antioxidants increase protection from free-radical damage.

protecting hydrator broad spectrum spf 30

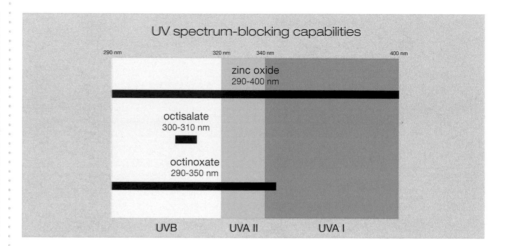

Active ingredients:

Octinoxate (7.5%) – absorbs and filters UV rays.

Zinc Oxide (4.3%) – provides broad spectrum UV protection by reflecting, scattering and absorbing UV rays.

Octisalate (3.6%) – absorbs and filters UV rays.

Key ingredients:

Caffeine – supports antioxidant activity.

Silybin – an antioxidant.

Panthenol (Pro-Vitamin B-5) – hydrates the skin.

Directions for use: After cleansing, toning and applying any PCA SKIN® treatment serums, smooth onto the skin. Allow to absorb 15 minutes prior to daytime exposure. Reapply after two hours of sun exposure and repeat every two hours as needed. It is recommended for daily use.

Protect aging skin against UVA and UVB rays with our most hydrating sunscreen. Added antioxidants increase protection from free-radical damage.

hydrator plus broad spectrum spf 30

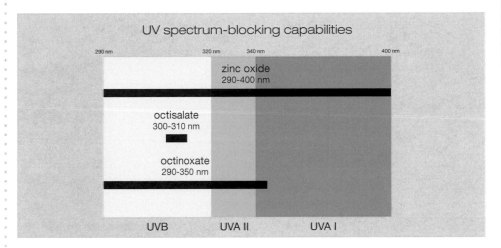

Active ingredients:

Octinoxate (7.5%) – absorbs and filters UV rays.

Zinc Oxide (4.3%) – provides broad spectrum UV protection by reflecting, scattering and absorbing UV rays.

Octisalate (3.6%) – absorbs and filters UV rays.

Key ingredients:

Caffeine – supports antioxidant activity.

Silybin – an antioxidant.

Sodium Hyaluronate – has the ability to hold 1,000 times its weight in water and plays an important role in skin hydration.

Glycerin – a humectant and emollient that helps to hydrate skin.

Tocopheryl Acetate (Vitamin E) – a fat-soluble antioxidant vitamin and emollient ingredient.

Panthenol (Pro-Vitamin B-5) – hydrates the skin.

Directions for use: After cleansing, toning and applying any PCA SKIN® treatment serums, smooth onto the skin. Allow to absorb 15 minutes prior to daytime exposure. Reapply after two hours of sun exposure and repeat every two hours as needed. It is recommended for daily use.

Providing water-resistant, UVA/UVB protection, this light SPF is perfect for outdoor activity. Added antioxidants increase protection from free-radical damage.

active broad spectrum spf 45: water resistant

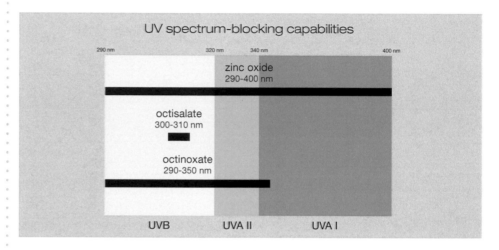

UV spectrum-blocking capabilities

zinc oxide
290-400 nm

octisalate
300-310 nm

octinoxate
290-350 nm

UVB — UVA II — UVA I

Active ingredients:

Zinc Oxide (8.0%) – provides broad spectrum UV protection by reflecting, scattering and absorbing UV rays.

Octinoxate (7.5%) – absorbs and filters UV rays.

Octisalate (3.0%) – absorbs and filters UV rays.

Key ingredients:

Caffeine – supports antioxidant activity.

Silybin – an antioxidant.

Directions for use: After cleansing, toning and applying any PCA SKIN® treatment serums, smooth onto the skin. Allow to absorb 15 minutes prior to daytime exposure. Reapply after two hours of sun exposure and repeat every two hours as needed. It is recommended for daily use.

Protect your skin from UVA/UVB rays with this luxurious physical SPF tinted to blend with most skin tones. Ubiquinone adds extra antioxidant protection.

sheer tint
broad
spectrum
spf 45

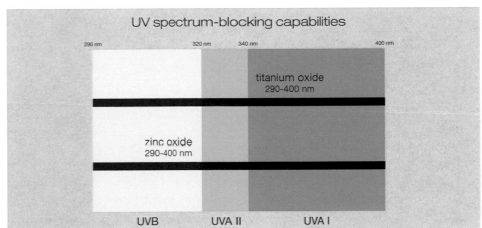

Active ingredients:

Titanium dioxide (6.0%) – provides broad spectrum UV protection by reflecting, scattering and absorbing UV rays.

Zinc oxide (8.0%) – provides broad spectrum UV protection by reflecting, scattering and absorbing UV rays.

Key ingredients:

Ubiquinone (CoEnzyme Q10) – a potent antioxidant that fights free-radical damage. This is especially useful, as UV exposure generates free radicals in the skin.

Iron Oxides – can be naturally occurring or synthesized and are commonly used to impart natural color into topical products.

Dimethicone – a silicone that contributes to the luxurious slip and finish of this tinted SPF.

Directions for use: Smooth onto skin after cleansing. Allow to absorb 30 minutes prior to daytime exposure. Reapply after two hours of sun exposure and repeat every two hours as needed. It is recommended for daily use.

healthy hydration

Reduce breakouts and control oil production

Reduce redness and breakouts, balance the skin's natural oil production and provide antioxidant protection with 4% niacinamide in this light hydrator.

clearskin

Key ingredients:

Niacinamide (4%) – a potent, yet calming antioxidants that delivers multiple important benefits to the skin. It helps to reduce transepidermal water loss (TEWL) and improve barrier function. This is critical for healthy, bright skin. Additionally, it helps reduce redness, skin yellowing and promotes an even skin tone.

Butcher's Broom Root Extract – an ingredient used for its calming and MMPi activity.

Borage Seed Oil – an excellent source of the omega-6 essential fatty acid (EFA) gamma linolenic acid (GLA). GLA is synthesized from linoleic acid, the most important essential fatty acid with potent calming action.

Wheat Amino Acids – natural growth factors for the skin, used for their softening properties. This is an excellent source of plant-derived protein, which is highly moisturizing.

Bisabolol – a component of chamomile that provides potent calming and MMPi properties to improve and maintain skin.

Retinyl Palmitate (Vitamin A) – converted to retinoic acid in the skin. Vitamin A helps to promote a clear complexion and an even skin tone.

Marigold Flower Oil and Cucumber Fruit Extract – provide purifying, calming and astringent benefits.

Directions for use: After cleansing, toning and applying any PCA SKIN® treatment serums, smooth onto the skin day or night. Follow with the appropriate PCA SKIN broad spectrum SPF product in the daytime.

Calm and soothe even the most sensitive skin with this light and quick-absorbing moisturizer formulated with vitamin E for powerful antioxidant protection.

Key ingredients:

Borage Seed Oil – a calming ingredient that is an excellent source of the omega-6 essential fatty acid (EFA) gamma linolenic acid (GLA).

Evening Primrose Seed Oil – a calming ingredient that is an excellent source of GLA.

Tocopherol (Vitamin E) – a fat-soluble antioxidant and emollient ingredient.

Directions for use: After cleansing, toning and applying any PCA SKIN® treatment serums, smooth onto the skin day or night. Follow with the appropriate PCA SKIN broad spectrum SPF product in the daytime.

Improve the overall appearance of aging skin with this light-textured moisturizer containing chasteberry, soy isoflavones, and olive and wheat germ oils.

après peel® hydrating balm

Key ingredients:

Chasteberry Fruit Extract – hydrates the skin.

Soy Isoflavones – are a rich source of the antioxidant genistein that help to improve the overall appearance of aging skin.

Olive Fruit Oil – a gentle emollient and a high source of antioxidant polyphenols.

Wheat Germ Oil – an effective emollient with a high percentage of the omega-6 essential fatty acid (EFA) gamma linolenic acid (GLA) and vitamin E.

Hydrolyzed Milk Protein – an emollient and moisturizer.

Directions for use: After cleansing, toning and applying any PCA SKIN® treatment serums, smooth onto the skin day or night. Follow with the appropriate PCA SKIN broad spectrum SPF product in the daytime.

Deliver intense hydration with this rich, antioxidant nightly moisturizer containing shea butter, olive fruit oil and sweet almond fruit extract.

collagen hydrator

Key ingredients:

Shea Butter – softens and helps maintain moisture in the skin without greasiness. It is high in triglycerides, and vitamins A, E and the omega-6 essential fatty acid (EFA) gamma linolenic acid (GLA).

Hydrolyzed Wheat Protein – an emollient and moisturizer.

Olive Fruit Oil – a gentle emollient and a high source of powerful antioxidant polyphenols.

Sweet Almond Fruit Extract – adds a smoothing film to the skin that is firming and nutritive.

Directions for use: After cleansing, toning and applying any PCA SKIN® treatment serums, smooth onto the skin day or night. Follow with the appropriate PCA SKIN broad spectrum SPF product in the daytime.

Soothe, rejuvenate and protect dry, mature skin or skin in harsh climates with our heaviest moisturizer including antioxidants, botanicals and hydrolyzed silk.

silkcoat® balm

Key ingredients:

Jojoba Seed Oil – a stable, natural emollient that has effective moisturizing properties.

Hydrolyzed Silk – a light, non-greasy moisturizer and skin conditioning agent.

Tocopheryl Acetate (Vitamin E) – a fat-soluble antioxidant and emollient ingredient.

Squalane – a naturally occurring oil found in such foods as olives and wheat germ. It helps to keep the skin moist.

Thyme Leaf Extract – a calming agent.

Directions for use: After cleansing, toning and applying any PCA SKIN® treatment serums, smooth onto the skin day or night. Follow with the appropriate PCA SKIN broad spectrum SPF product in the daytime.

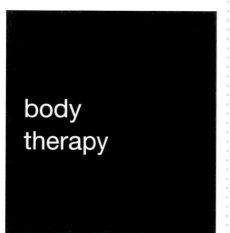

body therapy

Smooth and moisturize rough, dry skin with this rich therapeutic treatment with 12% lactic acid and advanced hydrators to maximize moisture in the skin.

Before
Condition: hyperkeratinization and severe dryness of the feet.*

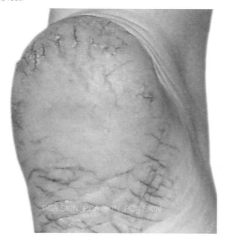

After eight weeks
Solution: received three Smoothing Body Peel® Treatments and used Body Therapy twice daily.

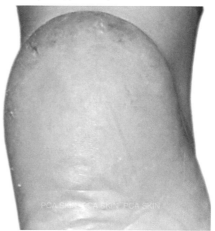

*Photos not retouched.

Key ingredients:

Lactic Acid (12%) – an alpha hydroxy acid (AHA) naturally found in milk and sugars. It is part of the skin's natural moisturizing factor (NMF) and moisturizes the skin.

Glycerin – a humectant and emollient that helps to hydrate skin.

Sodium Hyaluronate – has the ability to hold 1,000 times its weight in water and plays an important role in skin hydration.

Shea Butter – softens and helps maintain moisture in the skin without greasiness. It is high in triglycerides, and vitamins A, E and the omega-6 essential fatty acid (EFA) gamma linolenic acid (GLA).

Panthenol (Pro-Vitamin B-5) – hydrates the skin.

Directions for use: After bathing or showering, apply liberally to the entire body immediately. Follow with the appropriate PCA SKIN® broad spectrum SPF product in the daytime. Use twice daily or as needed.

daily care solutions for specific conditions

See clearer skin in as little as one week with this four-step system that contains a powerful combination of benzoyl peroxide, vitamin A and niacinamide.

the acne control regimen

Before
Condition: acne.*

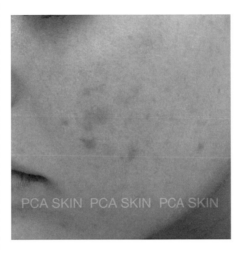

After one week
Solution: The Acne Control Regimen and Weightless Protection Broad Spectrum SPF 45.
Note: no professional treatments were applied.*

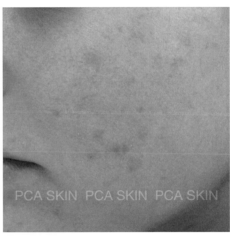

*Photos not retouched.

Products:

BPO 5% Cleanser – Eliminate existing and future breakouts, ridding your skin of impurities with this benzoyl peroxide and gluconolactone cleanser that penetrates pores instantly.

Acne Cream – Clear blemishes with this 5% benzoyl peroxide spot treatment including gluconolactone to prevent dryness and irritation. Essential for those with acne.

Intensive Clarity Treatment®: 0.5% pure retinol night – Dramatically reduce and prevent acne breakouts, oil production and inflammation with this salicylic acid formula featuring retinol and niacinamide.

Clearskin – Reduce redness and breakouts, balance the skin's natural oil production and provide antioxidant protection with 4% niacinamide in this light hydrator.

the trial kits

Each PCA SKIN® daily care product offers a unique solution to a variety of skin conditions. When used together in the appropriate combinations, these products can be even more effective in creating healthy, beautiful skin. We have designed a series of five trial-sized kits, geared towards challenging skin conditions: aging, acne, discoloration, sensitive skin and preventative skin concerns.

Each kit features the foundational products necessary for each condition. The trial-sizes offer an excellent option for introducing patients to PCA SKIN daily care and are a great tool for preparing a patient's skin for in-office treatments. All of our solutions come with easy-to-follow regimens and complement PCA SKIN professional treatments to achieve the healthy, glowing complexion your patients desire.

Diminish dark spots with key ingredients, including hydroquinone, retinol and skin brighteners for a more even overall skin tone.

the
discoloration
kit

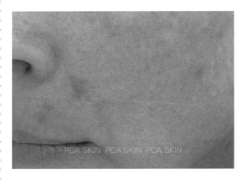

Before
Condition: discoloration and uneven skin tone.*

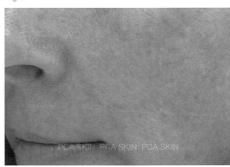

After seven weeks
Solution: Intensive Brightening Treatment: 0.5% pure retinol night.*

*Photos not retouched.

Products:

Pigment Gel® – lighten all forms of hyperpigmentation and discoloration with this spot-treatment serum with hydroquinone that delivers brilliant results.

C&E Strength Max – strengthen, smooth and brighten skin with this antioxidant corrective that has maximum vitamin concentrations: 20% vitamin C and 5% vitamin E.

Intensive Brightening Treatment: 0.5% pure retinol night – dramatically reduce discoloration and skin yellowing with this innovative retinol formula powered with resveratrol, hexylresorcinol and niacinamide.

Perfecting Protection Broad Spectrum SPF 30 – defend from UVA/UVB rays with this sheer SPF that has five discoloration-fighting ingredients. Added antioxidants increase protection from free-radical damage.

ReBalance – calm and soothe even the most sensitive skin with this light and quick-absorbing moisturizer formulated with vitamin E for powerful antioxidant protection.

Calm and soothe sensitive or reddened skin with a mix of products that ease irritation and strengthen the skin while preventing redness.

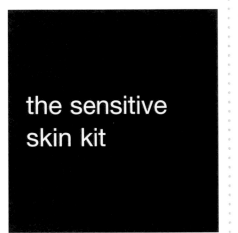

Before
Condition: Rosacea.*

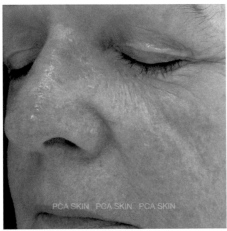

After one month
Solution: Hydrating Serum.*

the sensitive skin kit

*Photos not retouched.

Products:

Hydrating Serum – nourish dry skin with this feather-light serum formulated with hyaluronic acid and niacinamide to support skin's ability to attract and retain moisture.

Anti-Redness Serum – improve redness associated with sensitive skin conditions with this calming serum containing a blend of red and brown algae, and caper bud extract.

Retinol Treatment for Sensitive Skin – specifically formulated for sensitive skin, reduce signs of aging and redness without irritation using retinol, niacinamide and additional calming ingredients.

Protecting Hydrator Broad Spectrum SPF 30 – protect your skin against UVA/UVB rays with this hydrating, non-oily SPF. Added antioxidants increase protection from free-radical damage.

ReBalance – calm and soothe even the most sensitive skin with this light and quick-absorbing moisturizer formulated with vitamin E for powerful antioxidant protection.

Reduce signs of aging, brighten the skin, smooth, hydrate and protect from damage with this collection of advanced products specifically curated for aging skin.

the anti-aging kit

Before
Condition: fine lines, sagging and age-related skin yellowing.*

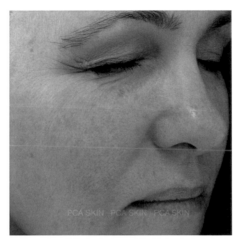

After six weeks
Solution: Intensive Age Refining Treatment®: 0.5% pure retinol night.*

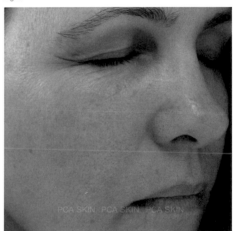

*Photos not retouched.

Products:

ExLinea® Peptide Smoothing Serum – dramatically reduce crow's feet, laugh lines, forehead wrinkles and frown lines from repeated muscle movements with this targeted neuropoptide spot treatment.

C&E Strength Max – strengthen, smooth and brighten skin with this antioxidant corrective that has maximum vitamin concentrations: 20% vitamin C and 5% vitamin E.

Intensive Age Refining Treatment®: 0.5% pure retinol night – crucial to reduce signs of aging, improve texture and boost collagen production, this retinol has hydrating ingredients sodium hyaluronate and panthenol.

Hydrator Plus Broad Spectrum SPF 30 – protect aging skin against UVA and UVB rays with our most hydrating sunscreen. Added antioxidants increase protection from free-radical damage.

Collagen Hydrator – deliver intense hydration with this rich, antioxidant nightly moisturizer containing shea butter, olive fruit oil and sweet almond fruit extract.

As the most common skin condition, acne severity can vary from person to person, so there's no one-size-fits-all solution. Using a balance of products and maintaining consistency in your regimen will give you the best results.

the acne kit

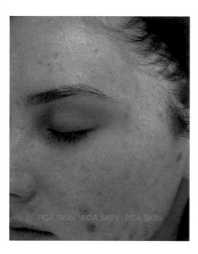

Before
Condition: acne.*

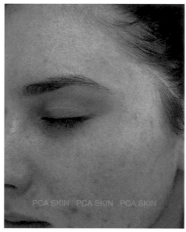

After three weeks
Solution: BPO 5% Cleanser, Acne Cream, Intensive Clarity Treatment®: 0.5% pure retinol night, Clearskin, Weightless Protection Broad Spectrum SPF 45.*

*Photos not retouched.

Products:

BPO 5% Cleanser – Eliminate existing and future breakouts, ridding your skin of impurities with this benzoyl peroxide and gluconolactone cleanser that penetrates pores instantly.

Acne Cream – Clear blemishes with this 5% benzoyl peroxide spot treatment including gluconolactone to prevent dryness and irritation. Essential for those with acne.

Intensive Clarity Treatment®: 0.5% pure retinol night – Dramatically reduce and prevent acne breakouts, oil production and inflammation with this salicylic acid formula featuring retinol and niacinamide.

Weightless Protection Broad Spectrum SPF 45 – Experience UVA/UVB protection that feels like it disappears in this fast-absorbing SPF product with caffeine and milk thistle for extra environmental protection.

Clearskin – Reduce redness and breakouts, balance the skin's natural oil production and provide antioxidant protection with 4% niacinamide in this light hydrator.

Prevent skin damage and premature signs of aging with this mix of growth factor, antioxidants, a gentle cleanser and a broad spectrum SPF

the preventative kit

Before
Condition: fine lines, wrinkles, dullness, laxity and uneven texture.*

After one week
Solution: C&E Strength.*

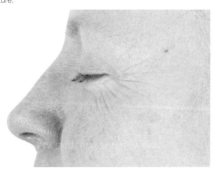
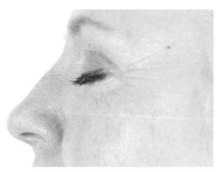

*Photos not retouched.

Products:

Rejuvenating Serum – using epidermal growth factor and plant stem cell extract, this antioxidant serum fights and prevents signs of aging.

C&E Strength – for those new to vitamin C, strengthen, smooth and brighten skin with this antioxidant corrective loaded with 15% vitamin C and 5% vitamin E.

Retinol Treatment for Sensitive Skin – specifically formulated for sensitive skin, reduce signs of aging and redness without irritation using retinol, niacinamide and additional calming ingredients.

Protecting Hydrator Broad Spectrum SPF 30 – protect your skin against UVA/UVB rays with this hydrating, non-oily SPF. Added antioxidants increase protection from free-radical damage.

ReBalance – calm and soothe even the most sensitive skin with this light and quick-absorbing moisturizer formulated with vitamin E for powerful antioxidant protection.

Help calm, soothe and support skin under stress during chemotherapy and radiation with products that address the skin's unique needs during treatment.

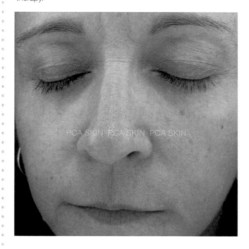

Before chemotherapy
Condition: dermal effects of chemotherapy or radiation therapy.

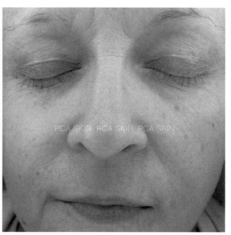

After 4 months of chemotherapy
Solution: The Solution for Chemotherapy and Radiation Therapy Support.*

*Photos not retouched.

the solution for chemotherapy and radiation therapy support

Products:

Creamy Cleanser – gently remove impurities and makeup while leaving the skin hydrated, soothed and pH balanced with this cleanser including lactic acid, aloe and willow bark.

Hydrating Serum – nourish dry skin with this feather-light serum formulated with hyaluronic acid and niacinamide to support skin's ability to attract and retain moisture.

Anti-Redness Serum – improve redness associated with sensitive skin conditions with this calming serum containing a blend of red and brown algae, and caper bud extract.

Perfecting Protection Broad Spectrum SPF 30 – defend from UVA/UVB rays with this sheer SPF that has five discoloration-fighting ingredients. Added antioxidants increase protection from free-radical damage.

CliniCalm™ 1% – relieve redness, itching, inflammation and irritation due to topical allergens, dermatitis, professional treatments or waxing with this 1% hydrocortisone cream.

ReBalance – calm and soothe even the most sensitive skin with this light and quick-absorbing moisturizer formulated with vitamin E for powerful antioxidant protection.

Silkcoat® Balm – soothe, rejuvenate and protect dry, mature skin or skin in harsh climates with our heaviest moisturizer including antioxidants, botanicals and hydrolyzed silk.

Peptide Lip Therapy – soften and hydrate the lips with a treatment including shea butter and a proprietary blend of hydrating extracts. Peptides minimize the appearance of lip lines.

Soothe, hydrate and protect skin in the days after a professional treatment. Improve treatment results with this strategically selected collection of products

the post-procedure solution

Products:

Facial Wash – gently remove impurities and makeup while leaving the skin hydrated, soothed and pH balanced with this cleanser including lactic acid, aloe and willow bark.

CliniCalm™ 1% – relieve redness, itching, inflammation and irritation due to topical allergens, dermatitis, professional treatments or waxing with this 1% hydrocortisone cream.

Perfecting Protection Broad Spectrum SPF 30 – defend from UVA/UVB rays with this sheer SPF that has five discoloration-fighting ingredients. Added antioxidants increase protection from free-radical damage.

ReBalance – calm and soothe even the most sensitive skin with this light and quick-absorbing moisturizer formulated with vitamin E for powerful antioxidant protection.

Silkcoat® Balm – soothe, rejuvenate and protect dry, mature skin or skin in harsh climates with our heaviest moisturizer including antioxidants, botanicals and hydrolyzed silk.

daily care regimens

G

hyperpigmentation

Pigment control with HQ

When used as directed, the OTC ingredient hydroquinone delivered in this protocol will help correct uneven pigmentation, while additional products included minimize the appearance of fine lines and wrinkles.

Note: Mild irritation may initially be experienced with use of the retinol product in this protocol and is not a sign of a negative complication. Introduce slowly, starting at once or twice a week and building up to every other night or nightly, depending on tolerance.

Morning:

1. Cleanse with a small amount of **Facial Wash**. Rinse with warm water and pat dry.

2. Spot-treat areas of hyperpigmentation with one to two pumps of **Pigment Gel**®.

3. Apply a pea-sized amount of **C&E Strength Max** to the entire face and neck to minimize the appearance of fine lines and wrinkles.

4. Apply the appropriate PCA SKIN® broad spectrum SPF product for daytime moisture and broad spectrum UV protection.

Evening:

1. Cleanse with a small amount of **Facial Wash**. Rinse with warm water and pat dry.

2. Spot-treat areas of hyperpigmentation with one to two pumps of **Pigment Gel**®.

3. Apply a pea-sized amount of **Intensive Brightening Treatment: 0.5% pure retinol night** to the entire face to encourage cell turnover and promote an even skin tone.

4. Apply a small amount of **ReBalance** to soothe and hydrate the skin.

Tip: Patients attending physician's offices can opt for **Pigment Gel**® in the morning and **Intensive Pigment Eraser** in the evening instead of using both **Pigment Gel**® and **Intensive Brightening Treatment: 0.5% pure retinol night** in the evening.

Pigment control

This regimen is designed to help promote an even skin tone in darker and more sensitive skin types, while minimizing the appearance of fine lines and wrinkles.

Note: Mild irritation may initially be experienced with use of the retinol product in this protocol and is not a sign of a negative complication. Introduce slowly, starting at once or twice a week and building up to every other night or nightly, depending on tolerance.

Morning:

1. Cleanse with a small amount of **Facial Wash**. Rinse with warm water and pat dry.

2. Spot-treat areas of discoloration with one to two pumps of **Pigment Gel® HQ Free**.

3. Apply a pea-sized amount of **C&E Strength Max** to the entire face and neck to minimize the appearance of fine lines and wrinkles.

4. Apply the appropriate PCA SKIN® broad spectrum SPF product for daytime moisture and broad spectrum UV protection.

Evening:

1. Cleanse with a small amount of **Facial Wash**. Rinse with warm water and pat dry.

2. Spot-treat areas of uneven skin tone with one to two pumps of **Pigment Gel® HQ Free**.

3. Apply a pea-sized amount of **Intensive Brightening Treatment: 0.5% pure retinol night** to the entire face to encourage cell turnover and promote an even skin tone.

4. Apply a small amount of **ReBalance** to soothe and hydrate the skin.

Acneic hyperpigmented skin

This regimen is designed for skin that may have hyperpigmentation due to repeated acne breakouts.

Note: Mild irritation may initially be experienced with use of the retinol product in this protocol and is not a sign of a negative complication. Introduce slowly, starting at once or twice a week and building up to every other night or nightly, depending on tolerance.

Morning:

1. Cleanse with **Blemish Control Bar**. Rinse with warm water and pat dry.

2. Spot-treat with one to two pumps of **Acne Gel** to penetrate follicles to clear existing and prevent future acne lesions.

3. Gently pat **Pigment Gel**® onto the hyperpigmented areas. Allow to penetrate and dry.

4. Hydrate, protect from UV exposure and encourage a clear complexion with a combination of the appropriate PCA SKIN® broad spectrum SPF product and **Clearskin**.

5. For the lips, apply **Peptide Lip Therapy** to improve hydration and reduce the appearance of lip lines.

   Note: Apply the appropriate PCA SKIN broad spectrum SPF product prior to applying **Peptide Lip Therapy** to protect the lips from UV exposure.

Evening:

1. Cleanse with a small amount of **Facial Wash Oily/Problem** and warm water. **Blemish Control Bar** may also be used in the evening. Rinse with warm water and pat dry.

2. Tone with **Smoothing Toner** (a.m. or p.m., not to exceed once daily).

3. Spot-treat with one to two pumps of **Acne Gel**.

4. Gently pat **Pigment Gel**® onto the hyperpigmented areas. Allow to penetrate and dry.

5. Apply a pea-sized amount of **Intensive Clarity Treatment**®: **0.5% pure retinol night** to the entire face to encourage cell turnover and reduce breakouts.

6. Hydrate and encourage a clear complexion with a small amount of **Clearskin**.

7. For the lips, apply **Peptide Lip Therapy**.

Weekly:

1. Cleanse with a small amount of **Facial Wash Oily/Problem** or **Blemish Control Bar**. Rinse with warm water and pat dry.

2. Tone with **Smoothing Toner**. Let dry.

3. Apply an even layer of **Purifying Mask** and leave on for approximately five minutes.

4. Remove mask with warm water using gentle, circular motions to activate the microfine pumice for the ultimate in skin smoothing and detoxification.

5. Gently pat **Pigment Gel**® onto the hyperpigmented areas. Allow to penetrate and dry.

6. Apply a pea-sized amount of **Intensive Clarity Treatment**®: **0.5% pure retinol night** to the entire face to encourage cell turnover and reduce breakouts.

7. Apply the appropriate PCA SKIN broad spectrum SPF product for daytime moisture and broad spectrum UV protection.

Pigment changes during pregnancy and lactation

Hormonal changes during pregnancy and lactation cause many types of skin challenges. Melasma, or the "mask of pregnancy", is one. You must select the products you use during pregnancy and lactation carefully. The following suggestions will help to keep skin healthy-looking, with the use of gentle and appropriate products. For questions about the safety of any of the suggested products during pregnancy and lactation, please ask your obstetrician.

Morning:

1. Cleanse with **Pigment Bar**®. Rinse with warm water and pat dry.

2. Gently pat **Pigment Gel**® **HQ Free** onto the uneven areas to promote an even skin tone. Allow to penetrate and dry.

3. Apply a mixture of **C-Quench**® **Antioxidant Serum** and **C&E Strength** to the entire face and neck to minimize the appearance of fine lines and wrinkles.

4. Apply the appropriate PCA SKIN® broad spectrum SPF product for broad spectrum UV protection and a hydrated, even skin tone.

5. For the lips, apply **Peptide Lip Therapy** to improve hydration and reduce the appearance of lip lines.

   Note: Apply the appropriate PCA SKIN broad spectrum SPF product prior to applying **Peptide Lip Therapy** to protect the lips from UV exposure.

Evening:

1. Cleanse with a small amount of **Facial Wash Oily/Problem**. Rinse with warm water and pat dry.

2. Tone with **Nutrient Toner** as needed (a.m. or p.m., not to exceed once daily).

3. Gently pat **Pigment Gel**® **HQ Free** onto the uneven areas. Allow to penetrate and dry.

4. Apply a mixture of **C-Quench**® **Antioxidant Serum** and **C&E Strength** to the entire face and neck to minimize the appearance of fine lines and wrinkles.

5. Depending on level of dryness, moisturize with a small amount of **Silkcoat**® **Balm** for extremely dry skin, **Collagen Hydrator** for dry skin, **ReBalance** for normal to oily skin, or **Clearskin** for breakout-prone, oily skin.

6. For the lips, apply **Peptide Lip Therapy**.

Weekly:

1. Cleanse with a small amount of **Facial Wash Oily/Problem**. Rinse with warm water and pat dry.

2. Tone with **Nutrient Toner**.

3. Apply **Gentle Exfoliant** with wet fingertips and massage gently, using circular motions. Rinse with warm water and pat dry.

4. Gently pat **Pigment Gel**® **HQ Free** onto the uneven areas. Allow to penetrate and dry.

5. Apply a mixture of **C-Quench**® **Antioxidant Serum** and **C&E Strength** to the entire face and neck to minimize the appearance of fine lines and wrinkles.

6. Apply the appropriate PCA SKIN broad spectrum SPF product for broad spectrum UV protection and a hydrated, even skin tone (daytime) and **ReBalance** or **Collagen Hydrator** (nighttime).

acne control

Acne control with BPO

This regimen is designed for more resilient acneic skin types. The products included are formulated with the OTC acne drug ingredient benzoyl peroxide, proven to penetrate follicles to clear existing and prevent future acne lesions. This protocol fights breakouts while keeping the skin healthy and hydrated.

Note: Mild irritation may initially be experienced with use of the retinol product in this protocol and is not a sign of a negative complication. Introduce slowly, starting at once or twice a week and building up to every other night or nightly, depending on tolerance.

Morning:

1. Cleanse the skin with a small amount of **BPO 5% Cleanser**. Rinse with warm water and pat dry.

2. Apply a smooth layer of **Acne Cream** to reduce breakouts.

3. **Optional:** Apply a small amount of **Clearskin** for light hydration and to promote a clear complexion.

4. Apply the appropriate PCA SKIN® broad spectrum SPF product for daytime moisture and broad spectrum UV protection.

Evening:

1. Cleanse the skin with a small amount of **BPO 5% Cleanser**. Rinse with warm water and pat dry.

2. Apply a smooth layer of **Acne Cream**.

3. Apply a pea-sized amount of **Intensive Clarity Treatment®: 0.5% pure retinol night** to increase cell turnover and promote a clear complexion.

4. Apply a small amount of **Clearskin**.

Weekly:

1. Cleanse the skin with a small amount of **BPO 5% Cleanser**. Rinse with warm water and pat dry.

2. Apply an even layer of **Purifying Mask** and leave on for approximately five minutes.

3. Remove mask with warm water using gentle circular motions to activate the microfine pumice for the ultimate in skin smoothing and detoxification.

4. Apply the appropriate PCA SKIN broad spectrum SPF product in the morning, or **Clearskin** in the evening.

Tips: Add **Smoothing Toner** once daily to oily skin. **A&C Synergy Serum®** may also be used to encourage an even skin tone. Apply one to two pumps of **Hydrating Serum** to obtain optimal moisture levels. Apply one to two pumps of **Rejuvenating Serum** for soothing benefits. Apply one to two pumps of **Anti-Redness Serum** to calm skin and reduce the appearance of redness.

Acne control with salicylic acid

This regimen is designed for blemish-prone and oily skin types. The products included are formulated to penetrate follicles to help clear existing acne blemishes and prevent future breakouts, while keeping the skin healthy-looking and hydrated.

Note: Mild irritation may initially be experienced with use of the retinol product in this protocol and is not a sign of a negative complication. Introduce slowly, starting at once or twice a week and building up to every other night or nightly, depending on tolerance.

Morning:

1. Cleanse the skin with a small amount of **Facial Wash Oily/Problem**. Rinse with warm water and pat dry.

2. Apply a pea-sized amount of **Acne Gel** to eliminate existing acne lesions and prevent future breakouts.

3. **Optional:** Apply a small amount of **Clearskin** for hydration and to promote a clear complexion.

4. Apply the appropriate PCA SKIN® broad spectrum SPF product for daytime moisture and broad spectrum UV protection.

Evening:

1. Cleanse the skin with the **Blemish Control Bar**. Rinse with warm water and pat dry.

2. Apply a pea-sized amount of **Acne Gel** to lesions.

3. Apply a pea-sized amount of **Intensive Clarity Treatment®: 0.5% pure retinol night** to increase cell turnover and to promote a clear complexion.

4. Apply a small amount of **Clearskin** for soothing, non-oily hydration.

Weekly:

1. Cleanse the skin with a small amount of **Facial Wash Oily/Problem**. Rinse with warm water and pat dry.

2. Apply an even layer of **Purifying Mask**, and leave on for approximately five minutes.

3. Remove mask with warm water using gentle circular motions to activate the microfine pumice for the ultimate in skin smoothing and detoxification.

4. Apply the appropriate PCA SKIN broad spectrum SPF product in the morning, or **Clearskin** in the evening.

Tips: Add **Smoothing Toner** once daily to oily skin. **A&C Synergy Serum®** may also be used to improve skin tone. Apply one to two pumps of **Hydrating Serum** to obtain optimal moisture levels. **Rejuvenating Serum** may also be used for calming, soothing, and to minimize the appearance of fine lines and wrinkles. Apply one to two pumps of **Anti-Redness Serum** to reduce the appearance of redness. **ReBalance** helps reduce the look of redness.

Acne control during pregnancy

Acne during pregnancy and lactation is particularly frustrating as many of the most effective acne-fighting drug ingredients are considered off-limits during this time. The following suggestions will help to keep skin clear and healthy-looking. Because you must select the products you use during pregnancy and lactation carefully, we recommend asking your obstetrician prior to beginning any new skin care regimen.

Morning:

1. Cleanse with a small amount of **Facial Wash Oily/Problem**. Rinse with warm water and pat dry.
2. Apply one to two pumps of **Hydrating Serum** to increase hydration and balance moisture levels in the skin.
3. Apply a ne to two pumps of **C-Quench® Antioxidant Serum** to calm skin, and minimize the appearance of fine lines and wrinkles.
4. Apply the appropriate PCA SKIN® broad spectrum SPF product for daytime moisture and broad spectrum UV protection.

Evening:

1. Cleanse with **Pigment Bar®**. Rinse with warm water and pat dry.
2. Tone with **Smoothing Toner** (a.m. or p.m., not to exceed once daily).
3. Apply one to two pumps of **Rejuvenating Serum** to the face and neck for calming and soothing that leads to healthier-looking, clearer skin.
4. Apply a small amount of **Clearskin** for breakout-prone, oily skin.

Weekly:

1. Cleanse with a small amount of **Facial Wash Oily/Problem**. Rinse with warm water and pat dry.
2. Tone with **Smoothing Toner**.
3. Apply an even layer of **Detoxifying Mask** and leave on until dry.
4. Remove mask with warm water using gentle circular motions to activate the microfine pumice for the ultimate in skin smoothing and detoxification.
5. Apply a mixture of **Rejuvenating Serum** and **Hydrating Serum** for calming, strengthening and hydrating action.
6. Apply the appropriate PCA SKIN broad spectrum SPF product in the morning, or **Clearskin** in the evening.

Daily care regimen for patients on isotretinoin therapy (Accutane®)

This regimen is designed to dramatically increase moisture levels and calm the skin of patients undergoing isotretinoin therapy (Accutane®). The products included are deeply moisturizing and calming to provide maximum hydration and soothe. Isotretinoin therapy instigates a major change in the skin, so patients may need to try several product combinations during their course of treatment to determine the optimum combination for their skin.

Morning:

1. Cleanse the skin with a small amount of **Creamy Cleanser**. Rinse with warm water and pat dry.

2. Apply one to two pumps of **Rejuvenating Serum** to hydrate, soothe, and reduce the appearance of fine lines and wrinkles.

3. Apply one to two pumps of **Hyaluronic Acid Boosting Serum** to increase moisture.

4. Apply the appropriate PCA SKIN® broad spectrum SPF product for daytime moisture and broad spectrum UV protection.

5. For the lips, apply **Peptide Lip Therapy** to improve hydration and reduce the appearance of lip lines.

   Note: Apply the appropriate PCA SKIN broad spectrum SPF product prior to applying **Peptide Lip Therapy** to protect the lips from UV exposure.

Evening:

1. Cleanse the skin with a small amount of **Creamy Cleanser**. Rinse with warm water and pat dry.

2. Apply a mixture of **Hyaluronic Acid Boosting Serum** and **Dual Action Redness Relief** to improve hydration and barrier function.

3. Apply a small amount of **Silkcoat® Balm** for hydration with additional calming benefits, or **Clearskin** for light hydration and to promote a clear complexion.

4. For the lips, apply **Peptide Lip Therapy**.

Tip: When first starting isotretinoin therapy (Accutane®), a variety of dosage levels may be tried before finding the correct level for a patient. During this time, and at any time of increased inflammation and irritation, apply **CliniCalm™ 1%**. Due to the maximum strength of hydrocortisone contained in **CliniCalm™ 1%**, it should only be used for seven-day intervals or as directed by a physician. For increased hydration, apply **Hyaluronic Acid Boosting** to lips prior to the application of **Peptide Lip Therapy**. For times of intense dryness, apply **Hyaluronic Acid Boosting** throughout the day.

Dry, dehydrated or mature acne

This regimen is designed for acne sufferers with surface dryness. The products included will reduce and prevent acne lesions without over-drying.

Note: Mild irritation may initially be experienced with use of the retinol product in this protocol and is not a sign of a negative complication. Introduce slowly, starting at once or twice a week and building up to every other night or nightly, depending on tolerance.

Morning:

1. Cleanse the skin with a small amount of **Facial Wash**. Rinse with warm water and pat dry.

2. Apply a pea-sized amount of **Acne Gel** to eliminate existing lesions and prevent future breakouts.

3. Apply one to two pumps of **Hyaluronic Acid Boosting Serum** to increase hydration instantly and long-term.

4. **Optional:** Apply a small amount of **ReBalance** for soothing hydration.

5. Apply the appropriate PCA SKIN® broad spectrum SPF product for non-oily, broad spectrum UV protection.

6. For the lips, apply **Peptide Lip Therapy** to improve hydration and reduce the appearance of lip lines.

   Note: Apply the appropriate PCA SKIN broad spectrum SPF product prior to applying **Peptide Lip Therapy** to protect the lips from UV exposure.

Evening:

1. Cleanse the skin with a small amount of **Facial Wash**. Rinse with warm water and pat dry.

2. Apply a pea-sized amount of **Acne Gel** to breakouts.

3. Apply one to two pumps of **Hyaluronic Acid Boosting Serum**.

4. Apply a pea-sized amount of **Intensive Age Refining Treatment®: 0.5% pure retinol night** to increase moisture, and minimize the appearance of fine lines and wrinkles.

5. Apply a small amount of **ReBalance**.

6. For the lips, apply **Peptide Lip Therapy**.

Weekly:

1. Cleanse the skin with a small amount of **Facial Wash**. Rinse with warm water and pat dry.

2. Apply an even layer of **Purifying Mask** and leave on for approximately five minutes.

3. Remove mask with warm water using gentle circular motions to activate the microfine pumice for the ultimate in skin smoothing and detoxification.

4. Apply the appropriate PCA SKIN broad spectrum SPF product in the morning, or a small amount of **ReBalance** in the evening.

Inflamed acne

This regimen is designed for sensitized acne patients prone to redness. This is appropriate for those with a tendency toward redness, or those in the habit of excoriating (picking) blemishes.

Morning:

1. Cleanse the skin with the **Blemish Control Bar**. Rinse with warm water and pat dry.

2. Apply a pea-sized amount of **Acne Gel** to eliminate existing lesions and prevent future breakouts.

3. Apply one to two pumps of **Hydrating Serum** for soothing and hydrating benefits.

4. **Optional:** Apply a small amount of **ReBalance** for soothing hydration.

5. Apply the appropriate PCA SKIN® broad spectrum SPF product for daytime moisture and broad spectrum UV protection.

6. For the lips, apply **Peptide Lip Therapy** to improve hydration and reduce the appearance of lip lines.

   Note: Apply the appropriate PCA SKIN broad spectrum SPF product prior to applying **Peptide Lip Therapy** to protect the lips from UV exposure.

Evening:

1. Cleanse the skin with a small amount of **Facial Wash**. Rinse with warm water and pat dry.

2. Apply a pea-sized amount of **Acne Gel** to breakouts.

3. Apply one to two pumps of **Anti-Redness Serum** to calm, soothe and improve sensitive or sensitized breakout-prone skin.

4. Apply a small amount of **ReBalance** for calming hydration.

5. For the lips, apply **Peptide Lip Therapy**.

Tip: Once the skin begins to improve, add a once-daily application of **Nutrient Toner**, morning or night.

sensitive skin

Sensitive [dry]

This regimen contains products with ingredients to improve the appearance of sensitive or sensitized, normal to dry skin prone to redness. When used as directed, this regimen will leave skin calm and even.

Morning:

1. Cleanse the skin with a small amount of **Creamy Cleanser**. Rinse with warm water and pat dry.

2. Apply one to two pumps of **Hyaluronic Acid Boosting Serum** to increase hydration instantly and long-term.

3. Apply one to two pumps of **Dual Action Redness Relief** to improve the skin's barrier function, calm the skin and reduce inflammation that leads to redness.

4. Apply the appropriate PCA SKIN® broad spectrum SPF product for daytime moisture and broad spectrum UV protection.

Evening:

1. Cleanse the skin with a small amount of **Creamy Cleanser**. Rinse with warm water and pat dry.

2. Apply one to two pumps of **Hyaluronic Acid Boosting Serum**.

3. Apply one to two pumps of **Dual Action Redness Relief**.

4. Apply a pea-sized amount of **Retinol Treatment for Sensitive Skin** to encourage cell turnover, calm the skin and reduce redness.

5. Apply a small amount of **ReBalance** for calming, light hydration.

Sensitive [oily]

This regimen contains products with ingredients that improve the appearance of sensitive or sensitized, normal to oily skin prone to redness. When used as directed, this regimen will leave skin calm and even.

Morning:

1. Cleanse the skin with a small amount of **Facial Wash**. Rinse with warm water and pat dry.

2. Apply a pea-sized amount of **Acne Gel** to control oil production.

3. Apply one to two pumps of **Hydrating Serum** to increase hydration and balance moisture levels.

4. Apply one to two pumps of **Anti-Redness Serum** to improve the appearance of sensitive and sensitized skin prone to redness.

5. Apply the appropriate PCA SKIN® broad spectrum SPF product for daytime moisture and broad spectrum UV protection.

Evening:

1. Cleanse the skin with a small amount of **Facial Wash**. Rinse with warm water and pat dry.

2. Apply a pea-sized amount of **Acne Gel**.

3. Apply one to two pumps of **Hydrating Serum**.

4. Apply one to two pumps of **Anti-Redness Serum**.

5. Apply a pea-sized amount of **Retinol Treatment for Sensitive Skin** to encourage cell turnover, calm the skin and reduce redness.

6. Apply a small amount of **Clearskin** for calming, light hydration.

Severely dry skin with heightened sensitivity

This regimen is designed to increase moisture levels in more sensitive skin types. The products included are rich and emollient to provide maximum hydration.

Morning:

1. Cleanse the skin with a small amount of **Creamy Cleanser**. Rinse with warm water and pat dry.

2. Apply one to two pumps of **Rejuvenating Serum** to hydrate, soothe, and improve the appearance of fine lines and wrinkles.

3. Apply a mixture of **Hyaluronic Acid Boosting Serum** and **Dual Action Redness Relief** to improve long-term hydration, calm the skin and reduce inflammation.

4. Apply the appropriate PCA SKIN® broad spectrum SPF product for daytime moisture and broad spectrum UV protection.

5. For the lips, apply **Peptide Lip Therapy** to improve hydration and reduce the appearance of lip lines.

   Note: Apply the appropriate PCA SKIN broad spectrum SPF product prior to applying **Peptide Lip Therapy** to protect the lips from UV exposure.

Evening:

1. Cleanse the skin with a small amount of **Creamy Cleanser**. Rinse with warm water and pat dry.

2. Apply a mixture of **Hyaluronic Acid Boosting Serum** and **Dual Action Redness Relief**.

3. Apply a small of **Silkcoat® Balm** for deep hydration.

4. For the lips, apply **Peptide Lip Therapy**.

Sensitive skin types with papulopustular breakouts

This regimen is designed to promote a clear complexion without exacerbating sensitive skin.

Morning:

1. Cleanse the skin with a small amount of **Facial Wash Oily/Problem**. Rinse with warm water and pat dry.

2. Apply a pea-sized amount of **Acne Gel** as needed to areas of breakouts.

3. Apply one to two pumps of **Anti-Redness Serum** to calm and soothe skin.

4. Apply the appropriate PCA SKIN® broad spectrum SPF product for daytime moisture and broad spectrum UV protection.

5. For the lips, apply **Peptide Lip Therapy** to improve hydration and reduce the appearance of lip lines.

   Note: Apply the appropriate PCA SKIN broad spectrum SPF product prior to applying **Peptide Lip Therapy** to protect the lips from UV exposure.

Evening:

1. Cleanse the skin with a small amount of **Facial Wash**. Rinse with warm water and pat dry.

2. Apply **Nutrient Toner** to the face and neck with a cotton pad.

3. Apply a thin layer of **Acne Gel** as needed to areas of breakouts.

4. Apply one to two pumps of **Anti-Redness Serum**.

5. Apply a pea-sized amount of **Retinol Treatment for Sensitive Skin** to encourage cell turnover, calm the skin and reduce redness.

6. Mix equal amounts of **Clearskin** and **ReBalance** for calming, light hydration and to gently promote a clear complexion.

7. For the lips, apply **Peptide Lip Therapy**.

Tip: Consider using maximum strength **CliniCalm™ 1%** in seven-day intervals or as directed by a physician to reduce inflammation and irritation.

Non-inflamed psoriasis or eczema

This regimen is designed for those with non-inflamed psoriasis, eczema and other dry skin conditions associated with cellular buildup.

Morning:

1. Cleanse with **Dry Skin Relief Bar**® and warm water. Allow the lather to sit on the area of treatment for one to two minutes. Rinse and pat dry.

2. To minimize the appearance of fine lines and wrinkles, and soothe the skin, apply one to two pumps of **Rejuvenating Serum**.

3. Apply one to two pumps of **Hyaluronic Acid Boosting Serum** to improve instant and long-term hydration.

4. Apply one to two pumps of **Dual Action Redness Relief** to improve the skin's barrier function, calm, reduce redness and inflammation.

5. Apply a small amount of **ReBalance** for calming hydration.

6. Apply the appropriate PCA SKIN® broad spectrum SPF product for daytime moisture and broad spectrum UV protection.

7. For the lips, apply **Peptide Lip Therapy** to improve hydration and reduce the appearance of lip lines.

   Note: Apply the appropriate PCA SKIN broad spectrum SPF product prior to applying **Peptide Lip Therapy** to protect the lips from UVA and UVB exposure.

Evening:

1. Cleanse with a small amount of **Creamy Cleanser**. Rinse with warm water and pat dry.

2. Tone with **Nutrient Toner** as needed (a.m. or p.m., not to exceed once daily).

3. Apply one to two pumps of **Rejuvenating Serum**.

4. Apply one to two pumps of **Hyaluronic Acid Boosting Serum**.

5. Apply one to two pumps of **Dual Action Redness Relief**.

6. Apply a pea-sized amount of **Retinol Treatment for Sensitive Skin** to encourage cell turnover, calm the skin and reduce redness.

7. Apply a small amount of **ReBalance** for normal to dry skin, or **Silkcoat**® **Balm** for extremely dry skin.

8. For the lips, apply **Peptide Lip Therapy**.

Tip: Apply a pea-sized amount of **CliniCalm™ 1%** when skin is irritated or itchy. Due to the maximum strength of hydrocortisone contained in **CliniCalm™ 1%**, it should only be used for seven-day intervals or as directed by a physician.

Weekly:

1. Cleanse skin with a small amount of **Creamy Cleanser**, mixed with a small amount of **Gentle Exfoliant** with warm water on fingertips and gently massage in circular motions. Rinse and pat dry.

2. Tone with **Nutrient Toner**.

3. Apply a small amount of **ReBalance** mixed with the appropriate PCA SKIN® broad spectrum SPF product for broad spectrum UV protection.

Aggravated psoriasis or eczema

This regimen is designed for sensitive, dry skin conditions associated with cellular buildup. Consult your dermatologist if the condition persists or worsens.

Morning:

1. Cleanse with a small amount of **Creamy Cleanser**. Rinse with warm water and pat dry.

2. To help soothe the skin, apply one to two pumps of **Rejuvenating Serum**.

3. Apply one to two pumps of **Hyaluronic Acid Boosting Serum** to improve instant and long-term hydration.

4. Apply one to two pumps of **Dual Action Redness Relief** to improve the skin's barrier function, calm the skin, and reduce redness and inflammation.

5. Apply **CliniCalm™ 1%** when skin is irritated or itchy. Due to the maximum strength of hydrocortisone contained in **CliniCalm™ 1%**, it should only be used for seven-day intervals or as directed by a physician.

6. Apply a small amount of **ReBalance** for calming hydration.

7. Apply the appropriate PCA SKIN® broad spectrum SPF product for daytime moisture and broad spectrum UV protection.

8. Apply a semi-occlusive lubricant to open areas as a protective barrier.

9. For the lips, apply **Peptide Lip Therapy** to improve hydration and reduce the appearance of lip lines.

   Note: Apply the appropriate PCA SKIN broad spectrum SPF product prior to applying **Peptide Lip Therapy** to protect the lips from UVA and UVB exposure.

Evening:

1. Cleanse the affected area with **Dry Skin Relief Bar®**. Allow the lather to sit on the area of treatment for one to two minutes. Rinse with warm water and pat dry.

2. Apply one to two pumps of **Rejuvenating Serum**.

3. Apply one to two pumps of **Hyaluronic Acid Boosting Serum**.

4. Apply one to two pumps of **Dual Action Redness Relief**.

5. Apply a pea-sized amount of **CliniCalm™ 1%** when skin is irritated or itchy.

6. Apply a small amount of **Silkcoat® Balm** to deeply moisturize skin. Once the skin has normalized, have the patient use a small amount of **ReBalance** to calm and soothe skin.

7. Apply a semi-occlusive lubricant to open areas as a protective barrier.

8. For the lips, apply **Peptide Lip Therapy**.

aging skin

Age control [dry]

This regimen is designed to help minimize the appearance of fine lines, wrinkles and dark circles, while strengthening and firming normal to dry skin. The products included were selected by studying the intrinsic and extrinsic factors responsible for the visible signs of aging skin and by combining best-in-class ingredients.

Note: Mild irritation may initially be experienced with use of the retinol product in this protocol and is not a sign of a negative complication. Introduce slowly, starting at once or twice a week and building up to every other night or nightly, depending on tolerance.

Morning:

1. Cleanse with a small amount of **Creamy Cleanser**. Rinse with warm water and pat dry.

2. Apply one to two pumps of **ExLinea® Peptide Smoothing Serum** to areas of apparent facial wrinkling and laxity.

3. Apply a mixture of **Total Strength Serum** and **Hyaluronic Acid Boosting Serum** to minimize the appearance of fine lines and wrinkles, and improve skin hydration.

4. Apply a pea-sized amount of **C&E Strength Max** to the face and neck to minimize the appearance of fine lines and wrinkles.

5. Pat a pea-sized amount of **Ideal Complex® Restorative Eye Cream** around the delicate eye area and directly to the eyelid to reduce the appearance of dark circles, puffiness, fine lines and wrinkles.

6. Apply the appropriate PCA SKIN® broad spectrum SPF product for daytime moisture and broad spectrum UV protection.

Evening:

1. Cleanse with a small amount of **Creamy Cleanser**. Rinse with warm water and pat dry.

2. Apply one to two pumps of **ExLinea® Peptide Smoothing Serum** to areas of apparent facial wrinkling and laxity.

3. Apply mixture of **Total Strength Serum** and **Hyaluronic Acid Boosting Serum** to the face and neck.

4. Apply a pea-sized amount of **Intensive Age Refining Treatment®: 0.5% pure retinol night** to hydrate and soothe, while minimizing the appearance of fine lines and wrinkles.

5. Pat a pea-sized amount of **Ideal Complex® Restorative Eye Cream** around the delicate eye area and directly to the eyelid.

6. Apply a small amount of **Collagen Hydrator** for nourishing evening moisture.

Tips: You may substitute **Après Peel® Hydrating Balm** or **Silkcoat® Balm** in the evening for increased occlusion and hydration. One to two pumps of **Pigment Gel® HQ Free** may be applied to promote an even skin tone. Apply a pea-sized amount of **Perfecting Neck & Décolleté** to the neck and chest for smoother, younger-looking skin.

Age control [oily]

This regimen is designed to help minimize the appearance of fine lines, wrinkles and dark circles, while strengthening and firming normal to oily skin. The products included were selected by studying the intrinsic and extrinsic factors responsible for the visible signs of aging skin, and by combining best-in-class ingredients.

Note: Mild irritation may initially be experienced with use of the retinol product in this protocol and is not a sign of a negative complication. Introduce slowly, starting at once or twice a week and building up to every other night or nightly, depending on tolerance.

Morning:

1. Cleanse with a small amount of **Facial Wash**. Rinse with warm water and pat dry.

2. Apply one to two pumps of **ExLinea® Peptide Smoothing Serum** to areas of apparent facial wrinkling and laxity.

3. Apply one to two pumps of **Total Strength Serum** to minimize the appearance of fine lines and wrinkles.

4. Apply a pea-sized amount of **C&E Strength Max** to the face and neck to minimize the appearance of fine lines and wrinkles.

5. Pat a pea-sized amount of **Ideal Complex® Revitalizing Eye Gel** around the delicate eye area and directly to the eyelid to reduce the appearance of dark circles, puffiness, fine lines and wrinkles.

6. Apply the appropriate PCA SKIN® broad spectrum SPF product for daytime moisture and broad spectrum UV protection.

Evening:

1. Cleanse with a small amount of **Facial Wash**. Rinse with warm water and pat dry.

2. Apply one to two pumps of **ExLinea® Peptide Smoothing Serum** to areas of apparent facial wrinkling and laxity.

3. Apply one to two pumps of **Total Strength Serum** to the face and neck.

4. Apply a pea-sized amount of **Intensive Age Refining Treatment®: 0.5% pure retinol night** to hydrate and soothe, while minimizing the appearance of fine lines and wrinkles.

5. Pat a pea-sized amount of **Ideal Complex® Revitalizing Eye Gel** around the delicate eye area and directly to the eyelid.

6. Apply a small amount of **Après Peel® Hydrating Balm** for nourishing evening moisture.

Tip: Nutrient Toner may be added daily to nourish skin, and help refine the appearance of pores.

Photoaging with significant hyperpigmentation

This regimen is designed to help minimize the appearance of fine lines and wrinkles, and promote an even skin tone. The products used focus on the appearance of both concerns simultaneously for optimal results.

Note: Mild irritation may initially be experienced with use of the retinol product in this protocol and is not a sign of a negative complication. Introduce slowly, starting at once or twice a week and building up to every other night or nightly, depending on tolerance.

Morning:

1. Cleanse with **Pigment Bar**®. Rinse with warm water and pat dry.

2. Apply one to two pumps of **ExLinea**® **Peptide Smoothing Serum** to areas of apparent facial wrinkling and laxity.

3. Spot-treat areas of hyperpigmentation with **Pigment Gel**®.

4. Apply a pea-sized amount of **C&E Strength Max** to the face and neck to minimize the appearance of fine lines and wrinkles.

5. Pat a pea-sized amount of **Ideal Complex**® **Revitalizing Eye Gel** or **Ideal Complex**® **Restorative Eye Cream** around the delicate eye area and directly to the eyelid to reduce the appearance of dark circles, puffiness, fine lines and wrinkles.

6. Apply the appropriate PCA SKIN® broad spectrum SPF product for daytime moisture and broad spectrum UV protection.

7. For the lips, apply **Peptide Lip Therapy** to improve hydration and reduce the appearance of lip lines.

   Note: Apply the appropriate PCA SKIN broad spectrum SPF product prior to applying **Peptide Lip Therapy** to protect the lips from UV exposure.

Evening:

1. Cleanse with a small amount of **Creamy Cleanser**. Rinse with warm water and pat dry.

2. Apply one to two pumps of **ExLinea**® **Peptide Smoothing Serum** to areas of apparent facial wrinkling and laxity.

3. Spot-treat areas of hyperpigmentation with **Pigment Gel**®.

4. Apply one to two pumps of **Total Strength Serum** to the face and neck to minimize the appearance of fine lines and wrinkles.

5. Apply a pea-sized amount of **Intensive Brightening Treatment: 0.5% pure retinol night** to the entire face to encourage cell turnover and promote an even skin tone.

6. Pat a pea-sized amount of **Ideal Complex**® **Revitalizing Eye Gel** or **Ideal Complex**® **Restorative Eye Cream** around the delicate eye area and directly to the eyelid.

7. Apply a small amount of **Après Peel**® **Hydrating Balm** for nourishing evening moisture.

8. For the lips, apply **Peptide Lip Therapy**.

Tip: Patients attending physician's offices can opt for **Pigment Gel**® in the morning and **Intensive Pigment Eraser** in the evening instead of using both **Pigment Gel**® and **Intensive Brightening Treatment: 0.5% pure retinol night** in the evening.

Intensive vitamin C

This regimen is designed to help strengthen skin, and improve the appearance of UV-induced fine lines and wrinkles.

Note: Mild irritation may initially be experienced with use of the retinol product in this protocol and is not a sign of a negative complication. Introduce slowly, starting at once or twice a week and building up to every other night or nightly, depending on tolerance.

Morning:

1. Cleanse with a small amount of **Creamy Cleanser**. Rinse with warm water and pat dry.

2. Spot-treat with one to two pumps of **ExLinea® Peptide Smoothing Serum** on areas of apparent facial wrinkling and laxity.

3. Apply a mixture of **C-Quench® Antioxidant Serum** and **C&E Strength Max** to entire face and neck to minimize the appearance of fine lines and wrinkles, and infuse the skin with antioxidants.

4. Moisturize with the appropriate PCA SKIN® broad spectrum SPF product for broad spectrum UV protection.

5. For the lips, apply **Peptide Lip Therapy** to improve hydration and reduce the appearance of lip lines.

   Note: Apply the appropriate PCA SKIN broad spectrum SPF product prior to applying **Peptide Lip Therapy** to protect the lips from UVA and UVB exposure.

Evening:

1. Cleanse with a small amount of **Creamy Cleanser**. Rinse with warm water and pat dry.

2. Tone with **Nutrient Toner** as needed (a.m. or p.m., not to exceed once daily).

3. Spot-treat with one to two pumps of **ExLinea® Peptide Smoothing Serum** on areas of apparent fine lines, wrinkling and laxity.

4. Apply a pea-sized amount of **Intensive Age Refining Treatment®: 0.5% pure retinol night** to minimize the appearance of fine lines and wrinkles, and promote an even skin tone.

5. Apply a mixture of **C-Quench® Antioxidant Serum** and **C&E Strength Max** to entire face and neck.

6. Moisturize with a small amount of **Silkcoat® Balm** for very dry skin, **Collagen Hydrator** for dry skin, **Après Peel® Hydrating Balm** for normal to dry skin, **ReBalance** or normal to oily skin and **Clearskin** for oily skin.

7. For the lips, apply **Peptide Lip Therapy**.

Weekly:

1. Cleanse with a small amount of **Creamy Cleanser**. Rinse with warm water and pat dry.

2. Tone with **Nutrient Toner**.

3. Apply **Gentle Exfoliant** with wet fingertips and massage gently, using circular motions. Rinse with warm water and pat dry.

4. Spot-treat with one to two pumps **ExLinea® Peptide Smoothing Serum** to areas of apparent facial wrinkling and laxity.

5. Moisturize with a smal amount of **Silkcoat® Balm** for very dry skin, **Collagen Hydrator** for dry skin, **Après Peel® Hydrating Balm** for normal to dry skin, **ReBalance** for normal to oily skin and **Clearskin** for oily skin.

for men

Daily care

This regimen provides a simple three-step system scientifically formulated to soothe, clear and firm men's skin.

Morning and Evening:

1. Wet face and hands with warm water. Squeeze small amount of **Total Wash Face & Body Cleanser** into hands and work into a creamy lather. Wash face and body using circular motions, and rinse with warm water.

2. After cleansing and shaving, apply one to two pumps of **Total Strength Serum** to entire face and neck twice daily for maximum benefits.

3. In the morning, apply a pea-sized amount of **Weightless Protection Broad Spectrum SPF 45** and spread evenly over face and neck until completely absorbed for broad spectrum UV protection, and to calm skin after shaving. In the evening, apply a small amount of **ReBalance** to soothe and hydrate the skin.

Pseudofolliculitis barbae (ingrown hairs)

This regimen is appropriate for all skin types that have a tendency toward ingrown hairs. It will effectively smooth rough surface texture, allowing the hair to release from the impacted follicle. This protocol will also help calm skin, leaving it smooth and clear.

Morning:

1. Cleanse the skin thoroughly with **Blemish Control Bar**. Allow the lather to remain on the area of treatment for one to two minutes. Rinse with warm water and pat dry.

2. Continue with an application of one to two pumps of **A&C Synergy Serum**® to promote an even skin tone.

3. To strengthen the skin, apply one to two pumps of **Rejuvenating Serum**.

4. For additional soothing and anti-inflammatory benefits, apply a pea-sized amount of **CliniCalm™ 1%**. Due to the maximum strength of hydrocortisone contained in **CliniCalm™ 1%**, it should only be used for seven-day intervals or as directed by a physician.

5. Finish with a mixture of **ReBalance** and the appropriate PCA SKIN® broad spectrum SPF product to calm, hydrate and provide broad spectrum UV protection.

Evening:

1. Cleanse the skin thoroughly with **Blemish Control Bar**. Allow the lather to remain on the area of treatment for one to two minutes. Rinse with warm water and pat dry.

2. Apply one to two pumps of **Rejuvenating Serum**.

3. Apply a pea-sized amount of **Retinol Treatment for Sensitive Skin** to minimize the appearance of fine lines and wrinkles, and promote an even skin tone.

4. Finish with a mixture of **CliniCalm™ 1%** and **ReBalance**.

chemotherapy support

Daily care

This regimen will help to support skin during chemotherapy. The products included will help to minimize the appearance of some of the common skin concerns brought on by these cancer treatments. Patients undergoing cancer treatments should consult their oncologist before starting any new skincare regimens.

Morning:

1. Cleanse the skin with a small amount of **Creamy Cleanser**. Rinse with warm water and pat dry.

2. Apply one to two pumps of **Anti-Redness Serum** (as needed) to reduce the appearance of redness and calm skin.

3. Apply one to two pumps of **Hydrating Serum** to maintain important moisture levels in the skin to minimize excessive dryness and discomfort.

4. Apply the appropriate PCA SKIN® broad spectrum SPF product for broad spectrum UV protection and a hydrated, even skin tone.

5. For the lips, apply **Peptide Lip Therapy** to improve hydration and reduce the appearance of lip lines.

   Note: Apply the appropriate PCA SKIN broad spectrum SPF product prior to applying **Peptide Lip Therapy** to protect the lips from UV exposure.

Evening:

1. Cleanse the skin with a small amount of **Creamy Cleanser**. Rinse with warm water and pat dry.

2. Apply one to two pumps of **Anti-Redness Serum**.

3. Apply one to two pumps of **Hydrating Serum**.

4. Apply a small amount of **ReBalance** for light hydration, and additional skin calming. **Silkcoat® Balm** may be used in addition to or in place of **ReBalance** to support extremely dry skin.

5. For the lips, apply **Peptide Lip Therapy**.

Tips: Apply **Hydrating Serum** throughout the day to maintain hydration. Consider using maximum strength **CliniCalm™ 1%** in seven-day intervals or as directed by a physician to reduce inflammation and irritation.

Chemotherapy patients with folliculitis

This protocol is designed for chemotherapy patients who are experiencing folliculitis. Patients undergoing cancer treatments should consult their oncologist before starting any new skincare regimens.

Morning:

1. Cleanse the skin with **Blemish Control Bar**. Rinse with warm water and pat dry. (Consider using a cleansing tool like the Clarisonic® Skin Brush to lather and apply the cleansing bar, and to gently decrease impactions.)

2. Apply one to two pumps of **Anti-Redness Serum** to calm skin.

3. Apply one to two pumps of **Hydrating Serum** to maintain important moisture levels in the skin to minimize excessive dryness and discomfort.

4. Apply the appropriate PCA SKIN® broad spectrum SPF product for daytime moisture and broad spectrum UV protection.

5. For the lips, apply **Peptide Lip Therapy** to improve hydration and reduce the appearance of lip lines.

   Note: Apply the appropriate PCA SKIN broad spectrum SPF product prior to applying **Peptide Lip Therapy** to protect the lips from UV exposure.

Evening:

1. Cleanse the skin with **Blemish Control Bar**. Rinse with warm water and pat dry.

2. Apply a thin layer of **Acne Gel** (as needed) to areas of breakouts.

3. Apply one to two pumps of **Hydrating Serum**.

4. Apply a small amount of **ReBalance** for light hydration, and additional skin calming. **Silkcoat® Balm** may be used in addition to or in place of **ReBalance** to support extremely dry skin.

5. For the lips, apply **Peptide Lip Therapy**.

Tips: Apply **Hydrating Serum** throughout the day to maintain hydration. Consider using maximum strength **CliniCalm™ 1%** in seven-day intervals or as directed by a physician to reduce inflammation and irritation.

Chemotherapy patients with hyperpigmentation

This protocol is designed for chemotherapy patients who are experiencing an uneven skin tone as a result of cancer treatments. The ingredients will gently promote an even skin tone in all skin types and ethnicities. Patients undergoing cancer treatments should consult their oncologist before starting any new skincare regimens.

Morning:

1. Cleanse the skin with **Pigment Bar**®. Rinse with warm water and pat dry.

2. Apply one to two pumps of **C-Quench**® **Antioxidant Serum** to increase hydration and encourage an even skin tone.

3. Apply the appropriate PCA SKIN® broad spectrum SPF product for daytime moisture and broad spectrum UV protection.

4. For the lips, apply **Peptide Lip Therapy** to improve hydration and reduce the appearance of lip lines.

   Note: Apply the appropriate PCA SKIN broad spectrum SPF product prior to applying **Peptide Lip Therapy** to protect the lips from UV exposure.

Evening:

1. Cleanse the skin with a small amount of **Facial Wash**. Rinse with warm water and pat dry.

2. Apply one to two pumps of **Hydrating Serum** to maintain important moisture levels in the skin to minimize excessive dryness and calm skin.

3. Apply a small amount of **ReBalance** for light hydration, and additional skin calming. **Silkcoat**® **Balm** may be used in addition to or in place of **ReBalance** to support extremely dry skin.

4. For the lips, apply **Peptide Lip Therapy**.

Tips: Apply **Hydrating Serum** throughout the day to maintain hydration. Consider using maximum strength **CliniCalm**™ **1%** in seven-day intervals or as directed by a physician to reduce inflammation and irritation.

post-procedure care

This regimen is designed to soothe and hydrate skin after any PCA SKIN® chemical peel or professional treatment, microdermabrasion, non-ablative laser or IPL treatment.

Use until peeling has resolved, typically three to five days. For those with more sensitive skin or after more intense treatments, consider using the post-procedure regimen for 10 days.

Morning:

1. Cleanse with a small amount of **Facial Wash**. Rinse with warm water and pat dry.

2. Apply a mixture of **CliniCalm™ 1%** and **ReBalance**. Due to the maximum strength of hydrocortisone contained in **CliniCalm™ 1%**, it should only be used for seven-day intervals or as directed by a physician.

3. Apply the appropriate PCA SKIN® broad spectrum SPF product for daytime moisture and broad spectrum UV protection.

4. Repeat steps 2 and 3 as necessary to keep the skin lubricated, protected and comfortable throughout the day.

Evening:

1. Cleanse with a small amount of **Facial Wash**. Rinse with warm water and pat dry.

2. Apply a mixture of **CliniCalm™ 1%** and **ReBalance**.

3. Apply a small amount of **Silkcoat® Balm** as a nighttime moisturizing treatment for your skin.

   Note: If your physician or PCA SKIN Certified Professional has made recommendations different from those stated above, please follow the recommendations of your physician or skincare professional.

Once skin has returned to normal: Return to your regular PCA SKIN daily care regimen as recommended by your physician or skincare professional.

Tip: Apply **Hydrating Serum**, **ReBalance** or **Silkcoat® Balm** throughout the day to maintain hydration and decrease the appearance of flaking.

pre-surgery daily care regimen

It is recommended that the patient begin this regimen three to four weeks pre-procedure to obtain the best possible result from a facelift, brow lift or blepharoplasty. This regimen will encourage a more satisfactory long-term result.

Note: Mild irritation may initially be experienced with use of the retinol product in this protocol and is not a sign of a negative complication. Introduce slowly, starting at once or twice a week and building up to every other night or nightly, depending on tolerance.

Pre-Procedure:

Morning:

1. Cleanse with a small amount of **Creamy Cleanser**. Rinse with warm water and pat dry.

2. Apply one to two pumps of **Rejuvenating Serum** to the face and neck to help minimize the appearance of fine lines and wrinkles, and leave skin glowing.

3. Apply the appropriate PCA SKIN® broad spectrum SPF product for daytime moisture and broad spectrum UV protection.

4. For the lips, apply **Peptide Lip Therapy** to improve hydration and reduce the appearance of lip lines.

   Note: Apply the appropriate PCA SKIN broad spectrum SPF product prior to applying **Peptide Lip Therapy** to protect the lips from UVA and UVB exposure.

Evening:

1. Cleanse with a small amount of **Creamy Cleanser**. Rinse with warm water and pat dry.

2. Tone with **Nutrient Toner** as needed (a.m. or p.m., not to exceed once daily).

3. Apply one to two pumps of **Rejuvenating Serum**.

4. Apply a pea-sized amount of **Intensive Age Refining Treatment®: 0.5% pure retinol night** to hydrate and soothe, while minimizing the appearance of fine lines and wrinkles.

5. Moisturize and soothe with a small amount of **ReBalance**. If additional hydration is desired, apply **Silkcoat® Balm**.

6. For the lips, apply **Peptide Lip Therapy**.

Tips: Apply one to two pumps of **ExLinea® Peptide Smoothing Serum** morning and evening to help strengthen the skin, reduce the appearance of existing lines and increase skin moisture. Apply **Hydrating Serum** to increase hydration and maintain optimal moisture levels.

post-surgery (after incisions have healed)

Morning:

1. Cleanse with a small amount of **Creamy Cleanser** and rinse gently with lukewarm water.

2. Apply one to two pumps of **Anti-Redness Serum** to calm skin.

3. Apply a mixture of **Rejuvenating Serum** and **C&E Strength** .

4. Apply the appropriate PCA SKIN® broad spectrum SPF product for daytime moisture and broad spectrum UV protection.

5. For the lips, apply **Peptide Lip Therapy** to improve hydration and reduce the appearance of lip lines.

   Note: Apply the appropriate PCA SKIN broad spectrum SPF product prior to applying **Peptide Lip Therapy** to protect the lips from UVA and UVB exposure.

Evening:

1. Cleanse with a small amount of **Creamy Cleanser** and rinse gently with lukewarm water.

2. Tone with **Nutrient Toner** as needed (a.m. or p.m., not to exceed once daily).

3. Apply one to two pumps of **Anti-Redness Serum**.

4. Apply a mixture of **Rejuvenating Serum** and **C&E Strength**.

5. Moisturize with a small amount of **Silkcoat® Balm**.

6. For the lips, apply **Peptide Lip Therapy**.

7. **Optional:** To soothe skin, a small amount of **ReBalance** may also be applied.

Tip: Apply one to two pumps of **ExLinea® Peptide Smoothing Serum** morning and evening to help strengthen the skin, reduce the appearance of existing lines and increase skin moisture. Apply **Hydrating Serum** to increase hydration and maintain optimal moisture levels.

G

lip renewal

This regimen is designed to improve lip hydration and minimize the appearance of lip lines. When used twice weekly, this solution will leave your lips smooth and hydrated. Recommended for use in the evening when skin is most receptive to nourishment.

Morning and evening:

1. Massage a small amount of **Gentle Exfoliant** in a circular motion over the lip area. Remove with warm water.

2. Apply one to two pumps of **Hyaluronic Acid Boosting Serum** to increase hydration and maintain optimal moisture levels, leading to smoother lips.

3. Apply a small amount of **Silkcoat® Balm** for soothing and maximum hydration.

4. Finish with a liberal application of **Peptide Lip Therapy**.

   Note: If performed in the morning, apply a small amount of the appropriate PCA SKIN® broad spectrum SPF product prior to applying **Peptide Lip Therapy** for broad spectrum UV protection.

Purifying Mask (weekly)

Purifying Mask is appropriate for all skin types and conditions, excluding hypersensitive skin. The combination of algae and clay supplies the skin with a rich blend of minerals, amino acids and enzymes, while simultaneously drawing impurities from the skin. The addition of vitamins A and E helps hydrate and strengthen the skin. Note: Due to retinol use, follow this protocol in the evening.

1. Cleanse with a small amount of **Facial Wash**. Rinse with warm water and pat dry.

2. Tone with **Nutrient Toner**.

3. Apply an even layer of **Purifying Mask** over entire face (neck and chest also recommended). Leave on for approximately three to five minutes. Remove mask with warm water, using gentle circular motions, allowing the pumice to remove dead skin cells and buildup. Rinse with warm water and pat dry.

4. Apply one to two pumps of **Rejuvenating Serum** to minimize the appearance of fine lines and wrinkles, and leave skin glowing.

5. Apply one to two pumps of **Hyaluronic Acid Boosting Serum** to hydrate and plump the skin, and encourage the skin's natural hyaluronic acid production.

6. Apply a pea-sized amount of **Retinol Treatment for Sensitive Skin** to encourage cell turnover, calm the skin and reduce redness.

7. Apply a small of the appropriate PCA SKIN® moisturizer for nighttime:

   - For normal to dry skin use **Silkcoat® Balm**, **Collagen Hydrator** or **Après Peel® Hydrating Balm**.

   - For normal to oily skin use **ReBalance** or **Clearskin**.

8. For the lips, apply **Peptide Lip Therapy** to improve hydration and reduce the appearance of lip lines.

Dextoxifying Mask (weekly)

Dextoxifying Mask is appropriate for all skin types and conditions, and is particularly beneficial for those who are oily or breakout-prone. The addition of Japanese white charcoal and clay absorb impurities, including excess oil, dirt and debris. Pores are cleared and appear smaller.

1. Cleanse with a small amount of **Facial Wash**. Rinse with warm water and pat dry.

2. Tone with **Nutrient Toner**.

3. Apply a thin, even layer of **Dextoxifying Mask** over entire face. Leave on until dry. The mask will turn light gray when completely dry. Remove with warm water.

4. Apply one to two pumps of **Hydrating Serum** to increase hydration and maintain optimal moisture levels.

5. Apply one to two pumps of **Rejuvenating Serum** to minimize the appearance of fine lines and wrinkles, and leave skin glowing.

6. Apply the appropriate PCA SKIN® moisturizer for nighttime:

   - For normal to dry skin, use **Silkcoat® Balm**, **Collagen Hydrator** or **Après Peel® Hydrating Balm**.

   - For normal to oily skin, use **ReBalance** or **Clearskin**.

7. For the lips, apply **Peptide Lip Therapy** to improve hydration and reduce the appearance of lip lines.

Revitalizing Mask (weekly)

Revitalizing Mask is appropriate for all skin types and conditions, except for hypersensitive or reactive skin. This enzyme mask combines papaya puree and fruit extracts from lemon, orange and apple to brighten dull complexions and gently exfoliate the skin, leaving a healthy glow. With the addition of green tea, vitamin E and honey, skin will be soft and hydrated immediately following treatment.

1. Cleanse with a small amount of **Facial Wash**. Rinse with warm water and pat dry.

2. Tone with **Nutrient Toner**.

3. Apply a thin, even layer of **Revitalizing Mask** over entire face. Leave on for approximately two to five minutes, depending on sensitivity. If uncomfortable, remove immediately. Remove mask with warm water using gentle, circular motions. Pat dry.

4. Apply one to two pumps of **Rejuvenating Serum** to minimize the appearance of fine lines and wrinkles, and leave skin glowing.

5. Apply one to two pumps of **Hyaluronic Acid Boosting Serum** to increase instant and long-term hydration, and smooth the skin.

6. Apply a small amount of the appropriate PCA SKIN® moisturizer for nighttime:

   - For normal to dry skin, use **Silkcoat® Balm**, **Collagen Hydrator** or **Après Peel® Hydrating Balm**.

   - For normal to oily skin, use **ReBalance** or **Clearskin**.

7. For the lips, apply **Peptide Lip Therapy** to improve hydration and reduce the appearance of lip lines.

PCA SKIN® peel fundamentals

PCA SKIN® peel fundamentals

Achieving success with PCA SKIN peels

We have dedicated decades to perfecting the art of achieving healthy skin with PCA SKIN peels. As a healthcare company, PCA SKIN values products and procedures that are not only highly effective, but also safe and easy to use. We strive to share the deep understandings we have gained about chemical peels; which to choose, how they function and what to expect. Armed with this education, success as a PCA SKIN Certified Professional comes easily.

Becoming a PCA SKIN Certified Professional is the first step toward success with PCA SKIN peels. We require all clinicians and medical professionals to attend **the PCA SKIN® certification seminar** prior to being able to administer any PCA SKIN professional treatments. For those who need additional practical experience, PCA SKIN offers continuing advanced education courses. The knowledge gained makes the physician, medical professional and licensed skincare clinician well-suited to make peel selections for each patient. Patients sometimes come to the clinic asking for a specific type of peel. Remember that everyone's skin is unique and the trained professional should always make the decision of which solution to apply.

PCA SKIN treatment philosophy

Layer and leave on

When performing PCA SKIN peels, clinicians use varying blends of peel solutions in a layering technique to determine the depth of penetration to either the stratum corneum or to the deeper, underlying tissue. (Only physicians should perform peels that are considered medium-depth.) This technique is possible due to the fact that PCA SKIN liquid peel formulations are self-neutralizing. Unlike straight acid alpha hydroxy acid peels that can potentially collect in the upper portions of the skin and cause surface irritation or burns, PCA SKIN liquid peel solutions are naturally neutralized by constituents of the skin and its water content. The strength and depth of the treatment is controlled by the trained professional based on the number of layers applied during treatment. After peel application, nutritive topicals and calming broad spectrum SPF products are applied, and the patient leaves with a glowing, healthy complexion. This technique is less stressful for both the clinician and the patient compared to peels that require timing, neutralizing and removal. This unique PCA SKIN technique makes the treatment process more relaxing and easier to perform.

Progressive approach

Consumers are often mistaken that if a little of something is good, more is better. This is especially untrue when it comes to treating the skin. Inflammation is the underlying cause of many skin conditions we work to treat, and triggering irritation and inflammation in the skin with overly aggressive treatments and products will only worsen, not correct, the situation. By treating the skin gently and infusing it with beneficial nourishing and strengthening ingredients during professional treatments, you will consistently see faster, more dramatic treatment outcomes. This supports the PCA SKIN progressive, not aggressive, treatment philosophy. Clinicians often think they need high percentages and aggressive solutions to get quick results. This strategy typically leads to post-inflammatory hyperpigmentation, acne breakouts and other complications. If the goal is healthy, beautiful skin, then a progressive approach is usually the best choice.

Healthy skin is beautiful skin

To achieve this goal, one needs to supplement professional treatments with a customized skin maintenance program. PCA SKIN® daily care products containing alpha hydroxy acids (AHA), peptides, MMPi and other advanced actives are targeted for particular skin conditions. Natural skin cell turnover usually follows our four-week biological calendar like many other body cycles; however, the speed of the cell-turnover cycle slows as we age. PCA SKIN professional treatments increase the natural skin cell turnover. Collagen, elastin and glycosaminoglycans (GAG), which comprise a large part of our skin's extracellular matrix (ECM) or support structure, also decrease with time. PCA SKIN's treatments can be used to combat the visible changes that come with aging skin and can also maintain the results. For treating specific conditions, such as hyperpigmentation, acne, sensitive and aging skin, and to maximize effectiveness, it is best to follow the schedule listed in the **Frequency of Treatment** chart.

most commonly used skin classifications

Glogau classification

Mild - type I "no wrinkles"	Moderate - type II "wrinkles in motion"	Advanced - type III "wrinkles at rest"	Severe - type IV "only wrinkles"
Early mild photoaging: • mild pigmentary changes • no keratoses (small rough spots on chronically sun damaged skin; precancerous) • minimal wrinkles Patient age - 20s or 30s Minimal or no makeup	Moderate photoaging: • early visible solar lentigines (sun-induced hyperpigmentation) • keratoses palpable but not visible • parallel smile lines beginning to appear Patient age - late 30s or 40s Usually wears some foundation	advanced photoaging: • obvious dyschromia (discoloration) and telangiectasia • visible keratoses • wrinkles even when not moving Patient age - 50s Always wears heavy foundation	Severe photoaging: • yellow-gray color of skin • keratosis and skin malignancies (cancers) • wrinkled throughout, little normal skin Patient age - 60s or 70s Can't wear makeup - "cakes and cracks"

Fitzpatrick scale

Skin	Skin color	Reaction to sun	
I	Very white or freckled	Always burns	
II	White	Usually burns	
III	White to olive	Sometimes burns	
IV	Brown	Rarely burns	
V	Dark brown	Very rarely burns	
VI	Black	Never burns*	

*Although it was once thought that Fitzpatrick VI skin types do not burn because they may not show visible redness, this is not the case.

Global heritage model

What is your ancestry?

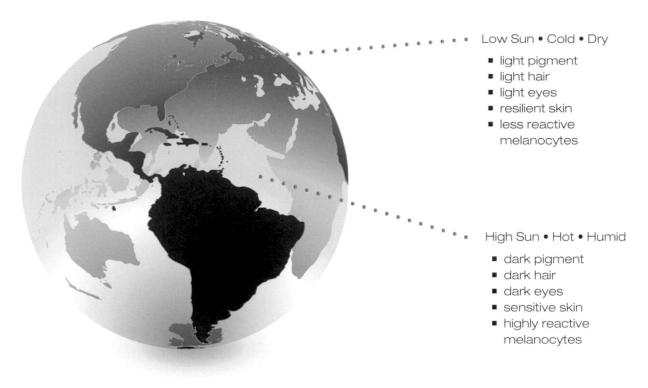

Low Sun • Cold • Dry

- light pigment
- light hair
- light eyes
- resilient skin
- less reactive melanocytes

High Sun • Hot • Humid

- dark pigment
- dark hair
- dark eyes
- sensitive skin
- highly reactive melanocytes

Treatment guidelines:

Polar region ancestry

- typically tolerate more inflammation
- less prone to hyperpigmentation
- mild to moderate edema and erythema may be present

Equator region ancestry

- cannot typically tolerate inflammation
- more prone to hyperpigmentation

Fitzpatrick's classification of skin type & correlating sensitivity

Fitzpatrick skin type	Skin color	Common hereditary backgrounds	Visual reaction to sun	Typical sensitivity to chemical peels	Common adverse responses to UV rays
I	Pale white	Nordic, Scandinavian (Swedish, Danish)	Always burns, never tans	Very resilient	Skin cancer & hypopigmentation
II	White	Irish, English, Welsh	Usually burns	Resilient	Skin cancer & telangiectasias
III	Light brown (naturally tan)	Asian, Mediterranean (Italian, Greek)	Mildly burns, tans relatively well	Moderately responsive	Skin cancer, telangiectasias & hyperpigmentation
IV	Moderate brown	Hispanic, Middle Eastern, African American, Native American	Rarely burns, tans well	Sensitive	Hyperpigmentation
V	Dark brown	Hispanic, Middle Eastern, African American, Native American, Southeast Asian	Very rarely burns, tans easily	Moderately sensitive	Hyperpigmentation
VI	Black	African American, Southeast Asian	Least likely to burn, tans very darkly	Very sensitive	Hyperpigmentation

depth of peel penetration

There are many physical factors that will affect the depth of peel penetration: pre-treatment with retinoids, glycolic or other strong AHA products; previous peels; variances in skin density; and thickness of the stratum corneum, to name a few. Completing a thorough **Patient Profile** is crucial in determining these factors for each individual patient. Unless you adequately interview your peel patient, your treatment may penetrate much deeper than you might have anticipated.

Medium-depth and deeper peels have long been used by physicians and can cause **blanching** (white protein coagulation) that will stimulate a healing response in the skin, which will reveal new skin. Blanching can be the expected and desired end point of straight trichloroacetic acid (TCA) and phenol peels that are performed by physicians. Do not confuse blanching with superficial **frosting**, which is a crystal residue of salicylic acid that accumulates on the surface of the skin and can be wiped away. Although very fine in texture, these crystals can be seen when using Jessner's solution, the **PCA Peel®** formulas and solutions containing salicylic acid.

Peel depth is typically characterized by the type and percentage of acid. The following illustration identifies the general depth of different straight acid solutions. We must keep in mind, however, that the additional ingredients in our blended formulations will have an affect on the depth of penetration. The addition of lactic acid may enhance penetration, while some melanogenesis inhibitors and polysaccharides may slightly reduce penetration, but they will enhance outcomes through their non-exfoliative mechanisms. If full blanching is achieved with the **Ultra Peel Forte®**, it is likely penetrating to the deeper epidermis and maybe the upper papillary dermis, depending on the patient. The more prominent the white appearance is, the deeper the solution has penetrated (e.g. light grayish appearance is not as deep as a solid white appearance). The deeper the peel, the more critical post-procedure care becomes. Using **The Post-Procedure Solution**, **Hyaluronic Acid Boosting Serum** and **Dual Action Redness Relief** for the first three to five days or until flaking has resolved (longer with a medium-depth peel), will ensure optimal outcomes.

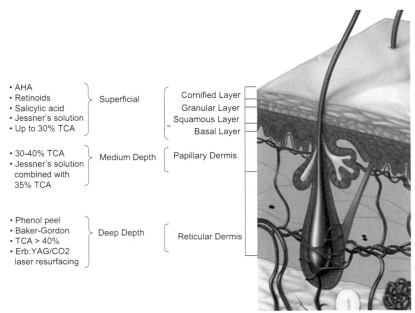

• AHA • Retinoids • Salicylic acid • Jessner's solution • Up to 30% TCA	Superficial	Cornified Layer Granular Layer Squamous Layer Basal Layer
• 30-40% TCA • Jessner's solution combined with 35% TCA	Medium Depth	Papillary Dermis
• Phenol peel • Baker-Gordon • TCA > 40% • Erb:YAG/CO2 laser resurfacing	Deep Depth	Reticular Dermis

© Physicians Care Alliance, LLC

important peeling ingredients

Alpha hydroxy acids (AHA)

Alpha hydroxy acids are a group of water-soluble carboxylic acids that work to release the desmosomes that hold skin cells together. This action allows for easier exfoliation and increased cell turnover. AHA are also thought to stimulate fibroblasts to produce collagen and elastin, to strengthen the matrix and firm the skin.

Types of AHA:

- **Glycolic acid** is naturally found in sugars and has a very low molecular weight. This small size makes its penetration into the skin very quick, which leads to potential irritation and inflammation. It also has strong degreasing properties, making it appropriate for oily acneic skin, but not the best choice for aging skin, sensitive skin or hyperpigmentation. Because inflammation is one of the four main causes of acne, glycolic acid must still be used carefully in inflammatory acne conditions.

- **Malic acid** is naturally found in apples, and provides humectant and antioxidant benefits.

- **Tartaric acid** is naturally found in grapes and, in addition to its desmosome-releasing action, it also acts as an antioxidant.

- **Mandelic acid** is naturally found in bitter almonds and has shown some initial promise for treating hyperpigmentation.

- **Citric acid** is naturally found in citrus fruits and works to thicken the epidermis, and increase the hyaluronic acid content in the skin, allowing the skin to more effectively attract and hold moisture. It is an excellent ingredient for anti-aging, as well as skin brightening.

- **Lactic acid** is naturally found in milk and sugars. Its larger molecular size compared to glycolic acid allows it to penetrate into the skin slowly, reducing the chances of irritation and inflammation. It also acts as an antimicrobial and hydrating ingredient, and suppresses the formation of tyrosinase.

Beta hydroxy acids (BHA)

The only BHA typically used in skincare is salicylic acid. Salicylic acid is lipophilic and has the ability to penetrate into oil-filled follicles and breakdown impaction. It also functions to normalize the excess inter-follicular cell shedding that contributes to the formation of microcomedones. Salicylic acid has a keratolytic action that works to break down surface impaction, leaving the skin smooth. Because of this, salicylic acid produces little to no post-treatment exfoliation.

Trichloroacetic acid (TCA)

TCA typically causes protein denaturation (blanching) when applied topically. It is a safe peeling agent that has been used for over 50 years. It does not absorb into the bloodstream. This acid is typically used at higher percentages by physicians for traditional chemical resurfacing procedures. When used as a single acid at high percentages, it is best for textural concerns, such as scarring and moderate to deeper wrinkling, because of its action as a cauterant (breaking down living tissue). It is typically more aggressive when used as a single acid, but can be safely applied as a superficial peel, even on higher Fitzpatricks and sensitive skin, when used in a blended formulation.

Retinoids

Retinoids, which are vitamin A derivatives, have many benefits for the skin. They are ingredients that have many normalizing benefits. They work to increase cell turnover and, at high percentages, act to increase post-treatment exfoliation. This is particularly important for lifting pigmentation, reducing impaction in acne patients and when treating aging skin that has a naturally slowed cell turnover cycle.

Additionally, retinoids act as melanogenesis inhibitors by preventing melanosome transfer from the melanocyte to the keratinocyte.

Proteolytic enzymes

Many enzymes are native to the human body and are critical to myriad biological functions. They are catalyst-proteins that either start or accelerate an action. There are thousands of types of enzymes, but fruit-derived enzymes are most frequently used in skincare. They are considered proteolytic because they digest the keratin protein on the surface of the skin to reveal the healthy skin below. Fruit enzymes are gentle and safe, and are an excellent treatment option for all Fitzpatrick skin types and a wide variety of skin conditions.

patient peel expectations

Patient expectations for superficial chemical peel treatments can occasionally be unrealistic. Although patients sign a consent form that clearly states that several treatments may be necessary to achieve the results they desire, they may forget this detail after their treatment. Even a well-written consent form does not guarantee accurate patient expectations. The fault of the unrealistic expectation is ours if we do not properly educate the patient as to anticipated results. When patients hear the word "peel" they expect to see visible exfoliation post-treatment. PCA SKIN® peels deliver excellent visible results whether or not actual visible peeling occurs. Frequently, exfoliation is at a cellular level and not apparent to the naked eye; however, the peels will create a tighter and firmer complexion and appearance. PCA SKIN professional treatments are formulated to preserve, promote and protect healthy skin, regardless of whether the patient sees visible exfoliation following treatment. In today's busy society, this progressive, rather than aggressive, approach is advantageous, as patients will experience minimal downtime yet still have outstanding results.

The carefully selected blends of peeling ingredients work to break down surface buildup and loosen the desmosome bonds holding the keratinocytes together. Our blends incorporate additional targeted ingredients that nourish, strengthen and protect the skin. The open environment created by the peel application allows the skin to be flooded with these beneficial actives during treatment. Regular superficial peels also enhance the penetration and efficacy of the daily care products the patient uses at home.

When using superficial chemical peel solutions, we highly recommend the skin be pre-treated with a PCA SKIN daily care regimen prior to commencing in-office peel treatments to ensure optimum results and fewer chances of complications. This is not a requirement, but our results are based on the use of both daily care and peels.

the sensitivity scale of 1 to 10

Everyone's response to a peel is slightly different. Patch testing prior to peel application helps determine each patient's sensitivity level and will help guide the peel selection. We recommend using **Smoothing Toner** to prepare and degrease the skin, as well as to patch test for sensitivity.

To test sensitivity:

- Cleanse with **Facial Wash Oily/Problem.**

- Degrease with **Smoothing Toner**. This product will sting/tingle on some individuals. Ask the patient, "On a scale of one to ten, ten being extremely active, how do you rate this sensation (or feeling)?"

  Patients with **resilient skin** will answer in the range of **0 to 1**.

  Patients with **moderately resilient skin** will answer in the range of **1 to 3**.

  Patients with **sensitive skin** will answer in the range of **3 to 6**.

  Patients with **highly sensitive skin** will answer in the range of **6 to 10**.

  Note: Use of this gentle alcohol-free toner is preferable to the use of acetone as a degreasing agent. Acetone strips not only the excess sebum and debris from the skin, but also the beneficial lipids that protect the skin. As a result, the use of acetone impairs barrier function and leads to increased transepidermal water loss (TEWL) following treatment.

- Apply in layers according to the needs, goals and individual sensitivity of the patient. Use this scale of 1 to 10 to gauge sensitivity. Fan the skin to keep the patient cool between layers. If the patient responds higher than a six on any layer, do not proceed with another layer. If the patient's response is between one and five, you may proceed with another layer.

- Wait until the patient's sensitivity begins to subside before applying the next layer. This indicates that the peel solution is beginning to neutralize. The patient will begin to rate lower on the scale of 1 to 10 approximately one to five minutes after each layer is applied.

- The lower the response number, the more resilient the skin and a greater number of layers of peel solution typically may be applied. Be aware that it is expected that applying more layers will increase the patient's 1 to 10 response. Continue to ask for a response on the sensitivity scale as you apply additional layers of the peel solution.

- Know that the higher the response of the patient on the 1 to 10 scale, the more sensitive and the more likely the patient is to blanch and potentially hyperpigment.

avoid complications

Complications from PCA SKIN® professional treatments are unlikely, but they are possible. There are many variables that contribute to the outcome of a chemical peel. The clinician's level of training and experience, full disclosure on a patient profile, pre-treatment and post-procedure care with PCA SKIN daily care products all play a role. Regardless of the reason, PCA SKIN wants you to know the best ways to avoid them and how to respond to complications should they happen. Our highly trained Physician Consultants, on-site medical practice, and research and development team are all on hand to assist you with questions or concerns. Please call **877.PCA.SKIN** [722.7546] for assistance.

Performing a consultation two weeks prior to treatment is your best tool to avoid complications. Recommending PCA SKIN daily care products prior to treatment also lowers your chance of negative reactions and enhances your results. PCA SKIN professional treatments and daily care products are formulated with the same philosophy and many similar ingredients, so before the patient would have a chance to react to a peel, they likely would have already presented the allergy or sensitivity to a daily care product. Allergies or sensitivities to PCA SKIN products are rare, but it is always safer to identify them with the use of a daily care product rather than a peel. This is especially important for more reactive ingredients such as hydroquinone (HQ). We recommend performing a patch test in front of or behind the ear at least one week prior to treatment with hydroquinone as it is a common irritant for patients with more sensitive skin.

Antidote for extreme heat
Use the following protocol for extreme redness and heat. Remember, don't use water or ice with any PCA SKIN chemical peel solutions, unless a severe allergic reaction occurs.

1. Apply **Calming Balm** with a new pair of gloves and fan patient's skin for three minutes.

2. Ask patient their number on the sensitivity scale of 1 to 10:
   - If less than five, you may proceed with the treatment protocol.
   - If higher than five, conclude the treatment with **ReBalance** mixed with the appropriate PCA SKIN broad spectrum SPF product.
   - The decision to proceed with the treatment depends on each situation and patient's sensitivity level.

post-procedure care

For post-procedure care, please refer back to the **Post-Procedure Skin Treatment Tips** in the **Patient Consultation** section of this textbook.

The Post-Procedure Solution

Facial Wash

CliniCalm™ 1%

Perfecting Protection Broad Spectrum SPF 30

Silkcoat® Balm

ReBalance

addressing complications

Allergic reactions

Although allergic reactions are rare with PCA SKIN® products, asking the proper questions will help the clinician avoid the application of an ingredient to which someone is allergic. If an extreme reaction to a peel solution does occur, wash the solution off with water and call 911 if the reaction is dramatic, or the patient seems to be having trouble breathing. This is the only circumstance in which adding water is recommended as it will help dilute the solution and restore skin to its natural pH faster. A good treatment product to address histamine responses during a treatment is **Calming Balm**. This product is formulated with bisabolol, allantoin, aloe, vitamin E and mushroom extract in an antioxidant gel/cream base. It has a cooling sensation on the skin and will help the reaction subside. Send the patient home with **CliniCalm™ 1%**. This should be applied liberally. Many physicians also suggest taking an over-the-counter antihistamine, such as Claritin® or Benadryl®, as well, to help calm the response.

Unintentional blanching

Protein coagulation, which is called "blanching", usually occurs only from deeper peeling. Physicians will sometimes perform a medium-depth or deeper peel during which a full-face blanch is desired and anticipated. Skincare clinicians who are not physicians or working under the advisement of a physician should **not** perform treatments of this nature. If a patient is peeled too deeply, blanching and open oozing areas may result. Keep in mind that if a patient's peel penetrates deeper in specific areas, those areas will have a pH closer to blood (7.3-7.4) than intact skin (5.5). Products must be chosen carefully to accommodate for this change in pH. Apply physician-recommended occlusive lubricants to keep the area protected and moist. Advise the patient that they will peel more and will probably have some temporary darkening at the blanch site until it peels. With proper care the skin discoloration should dissipate. Once the area is re-epithelialized (approximately 48 hours), the patient may introduce **Hyaluronic Acid Boosting Serum** and **Silkcoat® Balm** to create an environment that can effectively produce natural moisturizing factor (NMF). Once the skin has normalized, have the patient use **Dual Action Redness Relief** and **ReBalance** to help promote healthy skin and reduce redness. This is not a common occurrence when following PCA SKIN treatment protocols. Patients who experience minor surface blanching may continue using the PCA SKIN **The Post-Procedure Solution**.

Periorbital edema (puffy eyes)

Mild to moderate edema can occur in some patients following chemical peel treatments. This is actually not considered a complication, but rather a side effect. Patients experiencing swelling around the eyes should not apply ice packs, as superficial freezing will only serve to traumatize the area more. The best course of action is to apply a cool cloth to the eye area and sleep with the head slightly elevated to aid in the reduction of the swelling.

PCA SKIN® professional treatments: facts and protocols

PCA SKIN® professional treatments

Recognized in medical textbooks as the originator of the modified and enhanced Jessner's chemical peel formulations, PCA SKIN consistently applies innovation and scientific research in the development of effective professional treatments and daily care product formulations. Our treatments have been addressing numerous skin conditions with proven formulations for over two decades.

These advanced solutions combine exfoliating acids, melanogenesis inhibitors and skin-strengthening agents to provide maximum benefits with minimal discomfort and little to no downtime. The synergistic effect of their ingredients provides corrective and nutritive benefits while exfoliating the surface of the skin to help minimize the appearance of fine lines and wrinkles, and even skin tone.

When carefully selected and combined with PCA SKIN daily care products, our professional treatment options will help your patients achieve healthy, beautiful results. In this section of the textbook, we will provide you with the standard procedure for performing the different types of professional treatments in the PCA SKIN line. You can maximize your treatment outcomes by learning the art of customizing your choice of peels and serums.

PCA SKIN's easy-to-use and skin-friendly professional treatments are separated into the following six distinct categories:

- **Modified** and **enhanced Jessner's peels** soften the appearance of surface lines around the eyes and nasolabial folds, help improve acne, smooth skin texture and even skin tone, especially in oily skin.

- **Blended TCA peels** are exceptional for the treatment of aging skin, acne, uneven skin tone, and the appearance of lines and wrinkles, especially in dry skin.

- The variety of corrective ingredients found in each of our **therapeutic masks** provide exfoliation, hydration and calming action, depending on the formulation chosen.

- The PCA SKIN **retinoid treatments** create mild occlusion to enhance absorption of the vitamins, antioxidants and rich actives into the skin for maximum benefits. The retinol content also increases cell turnover and post-treatment exfoliation.

- Use our **peel alternatives** to keep skin free of pollutants and toxins, leading to a brighter and clearer complexion, especially in dull or breakout-prone skin.

- The PCA SKIN **treatment enhancements** provide an additional corrective component to any professional treatment by infusing the skin with essential antioxidants and vitamins, facilitating circulation-enhancing massage and reducing potential post-procedure inflammation.

PCA Peel® modified and enhanced Jessner's peels

These three peel solutions soften the appearance of surface lines around the eyes and nasolabial folds, help promote a clear complexion, smooth skin texture and even skin tone. They are especially beneficial for oily skin. These blends combine AHA with kojic acid, (with or without hydroquinone) with a modified Jessner's solution to address uneven skin tone from sun damage and hormonal changes. AHA and melanogenesis inhibitors suppress the chain reaction responsible for the creation of new melanin. Resorcinol and hydroquinone are optional in these formulas.

Modified Jessner's: 14% lactic acid, 14% salicylic acid, 14% resorcinol and 50% +/- denatured alcohol

PCA SKIN added: 3% kojic acid, 2% hydroquinone and citric acid
The Jessner's Peeling Solution consists of 14% each of lactic acid, salicylic acid and resorcinol blended in an alcohol base and is considered a superficial chemical peeling agent. This combination of ingredients was first documented in the JAMA in 1941 by Joseph Eller, M.D. and Shirley Wolff.[1] Joseph C. Urkov, M.D. and F. C. Combes, M.D. utilized varying percentages of these substances throughout the 1940's and Dr. Max Jessner popularized the 14% standard available today in the early 1950's.[2,3] The first modified and enhanced Jessner's Peel was developed and made available to physicians in 1993 by Margaret Ancira (Founder, PCA SKIN).[4] Two of the modified and enhanced versions contain no resorcinol, reducing the risk of toxicity, sensitivity and allergies, as well as making it more suitable to treat darker skin types.[4] The addition of citric and kojic acids, and hydroquinone (2%) increases the benefits of the traditional exfoliating method.

The use of citric acid increases glycosaminoglycan content, hydration and epidermal thickness[5], while hydroquinone and kojic acid assist in evening skin tone. Kojic acid has been studied at varied percentages topically, and has anti-fungal and melanogenesis inhibiting properties with negligible or no risk of human toxicity.[6]

- **PCA Peel® Hydroquinone Free** is ideal for more sensitive skin types, ethnic skin or those allergic to hydroquinone. This peel will help rejuvenate and improve the appearance of breakout-prone skin.

- **PCA Peel® with Hydroquinone** is for those who have no sensitivity to hydroquinone. This peel helps promote an even skin tone and a clear complexion.

- **PCA Peel® with Hydroquinone & Resorcinol** will even skin tone and provide more exfoliation for oilier, thicker and more resilient skin types.

Footnotes:
1. Eller, Joseph J & Wolff, Shirley. Skin peeling and scarification. JAMA 1941; volume 116:pp. 934-938.
2. Urkov, Joseph C. Surface defects of skin: treatment by controlled exfoliation. Ill Med J 1946; volume 89:pp. 75-81.
3. Brody Harold J, et al. A History of Chemical Peeling. Dermatologic Surgery 2000; volume 26:pp. 405-409.
4. Dover, Jeffery S. Rubin, Mark G. Et al. Procedures in Cosmetic Dermatology: Chemical Peels. Philadelphia: Elsevier Saunders, 2006, pp. 57-71.
5. Bernstein, Eric F. et al. Citric Acid Increases Viable Epidermal Thickness and Glycosaminoglycan Content of Sun-Damaged Skin, Dermatologic Surgery 1997, volume 23: pp. 689-694.
6. Nohynek G J, et al. An assessment of the genotoxicity and human health risk of topical use of kojic acid [5-hydroxy-2-(hydroxymethyl)-4H-pyran-4-one]. Food and Chemical Toxicology 2004, volume 42: pp. 93-105.

trichloroacetic acid (TCA) peels

All four of the PCA SKIN® TCA solutions are exceptional for aging skin, breakout-prone skin, improving the appearance of fine lines and wrinkles, and promoting an even skin tone.

- **Sensi Peel®** is formulated for all Fitzpatrick skin types. It is an exceptional choice for ethnic skin or those with extremely sensitive skin types. This TCA and lactic acid solution offers skin smoothing, melanogenesis inhibition, strengthening and hydration to many who previously would not have been candidates for chemical exfoliation procedures (e.g. rosacea). It is highly effective with virtually no stimulation.

- **Ultra Peel® I** is a blend of TCA and lactic acid with the addition of phytohormones for plumping and hydration. It is an exceptional choice for darker skin types and mature skin. Kojic and azelaic acids act as antibacterial agents, as well as melanogenesis inhibitors. L-ascorbic acid is present for skin strengthening and brightening.

- **Ultra Peel Forte®** is a blend of TCA and lactic acid. This formula is available only to physicians, as it is a more active treatment product that is capable of producing a medium-depth peel. It is formulated with melanogenesis inhibitors and skin-strengthening agents, which makes it effective with little discomfort and significantly less downtime than a traditional TCA peel.

- **Smoothing Body Peel®** is a two-step treatment, specifically for the skin on the body, with an exclusive blend of TCA, salicylic and lactic acids, as well as melanogenesis inhibitors: arbutin and kojic acids. This solution provides keratolytic, smoothing, firming and brightening benefits, producing an overall improvement in skin tone, texture and appearance.

therapeutic masks

The therapeutic mask series provides options for every skin type and condition. Smoothing, calming and deep hydration are possible with these advanced clinical masks.

- **Hydrate: Therapeutic Oat Milk Mask** was strategically formulated to soothe and hydrate impaired skin conditions of all kinds. A host of actives including oat milk, honey, arnica and cucumber provide deep, soothing hydration.

- **Detoxify: Therapeutic Charcoal Mask** uses Japanese white charcoal to draw out impurities from deep within the skin, absorb excess oil and minimize the appearance of pores. The addition of kaolin and magnesium aluminum silicate supports skin clearing.

- **Revitalize: Therapeutic Papaya Mask** combines papaya puree and additional fruit extracts from lemon, orange and apple to brighten dull complexions and exfoliate, leaving the skin with a healthy glow. Green tea, vitamin E and honey are moisturizing antioxidants that help keep the skin soft and hydrated. This results-oriented therapeutic mask is appropriate for all skin types and conditions.

- **Clarify: Therapeutic Salicylic Acid Mask** is a blend of 20% salicylic acid with antioxidant and botanical ingredients to brighten dull complexions. Its exfoliating and calming action refines skin texture for a clear, smooth complexion.

- **Retexturize: Therapeutic Pumpkin Mask** is an active blend of enzymes, vitamins and nutrients that simultaneously nourishes and exfoliates while drawing impurities out of the skin. Pumpkin enzymes and salicylic acid smooth the skin by removing the dead surface cells that cause rough texture.

retinoid treatments

These treatments create mild occlusion to enhance absorption of the vitamins, antioxidants and rich actives into the skin for maximum benefits.

- **Advanced Treatment Booster** is a chemical peel treatment addition that enhances exfoliation for accelerated results. Retinoids encourage cell turnover, while an advanced blend of additional ingredients, including lentil seed, panthenol, escin, butcher's broom, gotu kola extract and marigold, restores normal keratinization and reduces sensations experienced during treatment. This formula also reduces redness from chemical peel treatment.

- **4% Pure Retinol Peel** is great for all skin types, and is an extremely calming treatment. In pre-portioned packettes, this creamy treatment uses 4% retinol to encourage cell turnover for dramatic skin revitalization.

- **6% Pure Retinol Peel** is for physicians' use only most suitable for those with resilient skin. It provides dramatic and rapid rejuvenation of the skin. Skin is visibly smoother and brighter with improved tone. This treatment option also comes in pre-portioned packettes.

peel alternatives

Use these treatments to keep skin free of pollutants and toxins, leading to a brighter and clearer complexion, especially in breakout-prone skin. Both of these treatments are options for all skin types and can be used on pregnant and lactating women, with the consent of their obstetrician.

- **Detox Gel Deep Pore Treatment** is an excellent choice for detoxifying all skin types. The active blend of antioxidants, lactic, glycolic and salicylic acids exfoliates and promotes a purified and clear complexion. This gentle, deep pore cleansing treatment provides clarifying benefits.

- **Oxygenating Trio®** is a three-step formulation that contains antioxidants and enzymes that leave skin smooth, purified and glowing.

treatment enhancements

These supplemental corrective products may be added to any professional treatment protocol for additional protective, nutritive and soothing benefits. Both may be used as needed on any skin type or condition to enhance treatment benefits.

- **Replenishing Gel** nourishes and supports skin post-treatment with a panel of antioxidants, vitamins and essential fatty acids. This treatment enhancement product also serves as an effective medium for performing circulation-enhancing massage.

- **Calming Balm** is a versatile treatment enhancement that can be used during any protocol to add nutritive and calming benefits to the skin. **Calming Balm** incorporates antioxidants and the advanced soothing botanicals bisabolol, allantoin, aloe, vitamin E and mushroom extract.

PCA SKIN® professional treatment procedure

Chart: professional treatment procedure

Step	Product	Procedure
Cleanse	**Facial Wash Oily/Problem**	Cleanse the skin to remove excess sebum and cell debris.
Prep/degrease	**Smoothing Toner**	Degrease the skin and gauge patient sensitivity.
Treat	Professional treatment	Apply appropriate peel solution or therapeutic mask.
Correct	Corrective daily care products	Apply appropriate advanced treatment serums and creams to customize protocol.
Retinoid booster (optional)	**Advanced Treatment Booster**	Apply retinoid booster to increase cell turnover and restore barrier function.
Hydrate & protect	**ReBalance** Appropriate PCA SKIN broad spectrum SPF product **Peptide Lip Therapy**	Apply to restore pH, soothe and protect the skin. Alternative PCA SKIN moisturizers can be used to increase customization.

This enhanced Jessner's solution is ideal for more sensitive skin types, ethnic skin or those allergic to or sensitive to hydroquinone. This treatment will help to rejuvenate and improve the appearance of breakout-prone skin, while also promoting an even, bright skin tone.

PCA Peel®
hydroquinone
free

Before
Condition: melasma.*

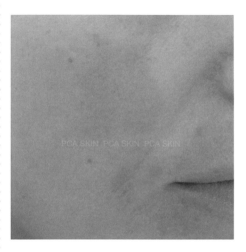

After five treatments
Solution: PCA Peel® Hydroquinone Free, Pigment Gel® HQ Free, PCA SKIN retinol product.*

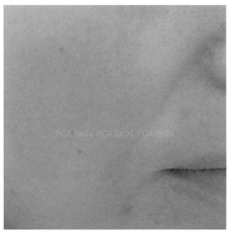

*Photos not retouched.

Key ingredients:

Lactic Acid (14%) – an alpha hydroxy acid (AHA) naturally found in milk and sugars. It is part of the skin's natural moisturizing factor (NMF) and moisturizes the skin.

Salicylic Acid (14%) – a calming lipophilic beta hydroxy acid (BHA) that helps promote a clear complexion.

Kojic Acid (3%) – helps promote and even skin tone.

Citric Acid – an alpha hydroxy acid (AHA) naturally found in citrus fruits.

This enhanced Jessner's formula is for those who want an even skin tone and have no sensitivity to hydroquinone. This peel helps promote an even skin tone and a clear complexion.

PCA Peel® with hydroquinone

Before
Condition: acne and post-inflammatory hyperpigmentation.*

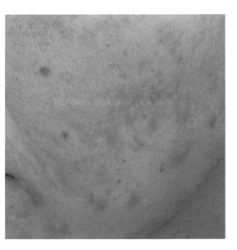

After six treatments
Solution: PCA Peel® with Hydroquinone, Purifying Mask, Acne Gel, Intensive Clarity Treatment®: 0.5% pure retinol night, Pigment Gel®.*

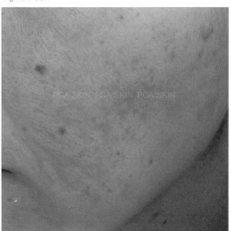

*Photos not retouched.

Key ingredients:

Lactic Acid (14%) – an alpha hydroxy acid (AHA) naturally found in milk and sugars. It is part of the skin's natural moisturizing factor (NMF) and moisturizes the skin.

Salicylic Acid (14%) – a calming lipophilic beta hydroxy acid (BHA) that helps promote a clear complexion.

Kojic Acid (3%) – helps promote an even skin tone.

Citric Acid – an alpha hydroxy acid (AHA) naturally found in citrus fruits.

Hydroquinone (2%) – helps to promote an even skin tone.

The most potent of our enhanced Jessner's formulas, this peel will even skin tone and provide more exfoliation for oilier, thicker and more resilient skin types. It is extremely effective on sun-damaged and thickened skin. It is also excellent for those with active or cystic acne and asphyxiated skin (dry on the surface, oily underneath), or those who require deeper treatment.

PCA Peel® with hydroquinone & resorcinol

Before
Condition: melasma.*

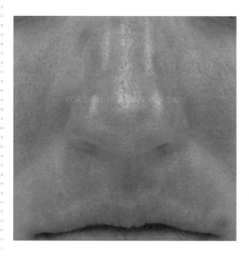

After four treatments
Solution: PCA Peel® with Hydroquinone & Resorcinol, Pigment Gel®, PCA SKIN retinol product.

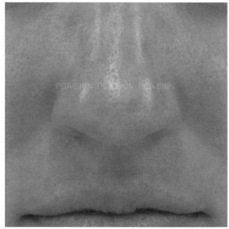

*Photos not retouched.

Key ingredients:

Lactic Acid (14%) – an alpha hydroxy acid (AHA) naturally found in milk and sugars. It is part of the skin's natural moisturizing factor (NMF) and moisturizes the skin.

Salicylic Acid (14%) – a calming lipophilic beta hydroxy acid (BHA) that helps promote a clear complexion.

Kojic Acid (3%) – helps promote an even skin tone.

Citric Acid – an alpha hydroxy acid (AHA) naturally found in citrus fruits.

Hydroquinone (2%) – helps to promote an even skin tone.

Resorcinol – a flaking agent.

PCA Peel® treatment protocol

Cleanse

1. **Facial Wash Oily/Problem** – Cleanse the area of treatment thoroughly. Rinse and pat dry.

Prep/degrease

2. **Smoothing Toner** – Apply with a cotton pad to prep (degrease) the skin. Allow the skin to dry. This product may sting or tingle on some individuals. Assess sensitivity by asking the patient, "On a scale of one to ten, ten being extremely active, how do you rate this sensation (or feeling)?"

Treat

3. **PCA Peel®** – Choose the formula appropriate for skin type and condition.

   - Before using, gently agitate the product. Apply the first layer with a cotton pad.

   - Use the scale of 1 to 10 to gauge sensitivity. Fan the skin to keep the patient cool between layers. If the patient responds higher than a 6, do not proceed with another layer. If the patient's response is between 1 and 5, proceed with another layer.

   - Wait until the patient's sensitivity begins to subside before applying the next layer. The patient will begin to rate lower on the scale of 1 to 10 approximately one to five minutes after each layer is applied.

   - The total number of layers is determined by the needs, goals and individual sensitivity of the patient.

   - The maximum number of layers is six.

Correct

4. After the peel solution has been absorbed into the skin, customize the protocol with a combination of corrective daily care products to address your patient's particular concerns and skincare goals. Refer to your customization chart on page 286 for suggestions.

Retinoid booster (optional)

5. **Advanced Treatment Booster** – Dispense two pumps into gloved hands. Gently spread the product over the area of treatment, keeping application even and thin.

   - Use the scale of 1 to 10 to gauge sensitivity. Most patients will not have any sensitivity to this product.

   - The maximum number of layers is one.

Indications:

Uneven skin tone

Photodamage

Acne

Asphyxiated skin

Oily skin

PCA Peel® Hydroquinone Free: Fitzpatrick types I-V

PCA Peel® with Hydroquinone: Fitzpatrick types I-IV

PCA Peel® with Hydroquinone & Resorcinol: Fitzpatrick types I-III

Maximum Layers:

Face: 6

Neck and chest: 2

contraindications:

Alcohol sensitivities

Pregnancy

Lactation

Allergy to aspirin (salicylates)

Rosacea

PCA Peel® Hydroquinone Free: hypersensitive skin

PCA Peel® with Hydroquinone: sensitive skin hydroquinone sensitivities

PCA Peel® with Hydroquinone & Resorcinol: sensitive skin resorcinol and hydroquinone sensitivities

Hydrate & protect

6. **ReBalance** and the appropriate PCA SKIN® broad spectrum SPF product – Complete the treatment with this combination to calm, hydrate and protect the skin from UVA and UVB exposure.

7. **Peptide Lip Therapy** – Finish with a liberal application to improve hydration and reduce the appearance of lip lines.

   Note: Apply the appropriate PCA SKIN broad spectrum SPF product prior to applying **Peptide Lip Therapy** to protect the lips from UVA and UVB exposure.

Sensi Peel® is formulated as a unique peeling option for all patients, including those with highly sensitive skin. This gentle 6% TCA solution will improve surface texture and brighten the skin while helping to promote an even skin tone. This multi-faceted and skin-brightening treatment is an excellent option for sensitive skin and higher Fitzpatrick skin types.

Before
Condition: pseudofolliculitis barbae (ingrown hairs).*

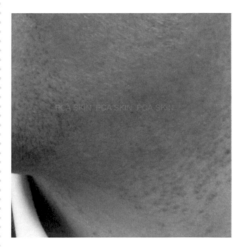

After four treatments
Solution: Sensi Peel® with microdermabrasion, Blemish Control Bar, Total Strength Serum.*

*Photos not retouched.

Key ingredients:

Lactic Acid (12%) – an alpha hydroxy acid (AHA) naturally found in milk and sugars. It is part of the skin's natural moisturizing factor (NMF) and moisturizes the skin.

Trichloroacetic Acid (TCA) (6%) – most commonly used as a superficial and medium-depth peeling agent to improve the appearance of fine lines and wrinkles.

Kojic Acid – helps promote an even skin tone.

Azelaic Acid – helps promote a clear complexion and even skin tone.

Arbutin – an antioxidant that also helps promote an even skin tone.

L-Ascorbic Acid (Vitamin C) – an antioxidant and MMPi that is the only bio-available form of vitamin C for the skin. It minimizes the appearance of fine lines and wrinkles while promoting an even skin tone.

Indications:

Fitzpatrick types I-VI

Fine lines

Uneven skin tone

Dehydrated skin

Sensitive skin

Highly inflamed acne

Sensi Peel® treatment protocol

Cleanse

1. **Facial Wash Oily/Problem** – Cleanse the area of treatment thoroughly. Rinse and pat dry.

Prep/degrease

2. **Smoothing Toner** – Apply with a cotton pad to prep (degrease) the skin. Allow the skin to dry. This product may sting or tingle on some individuals. Assess sensitivity by asking the patient, "On a scale of one to ten, ten being extremely active, how do you rate this sensation (or feeling)?"

Treat

3. **Sensi Peel®**

   - Before using, gently agitate the product. Apply the first layer with a cotton pad.

   - Use the scale of 1 to 10 to gauge sensitivity. Fan the skin to keep the patient cool between layers. If the patient responds higher than a 6, do not proceed with another layer. If the patient's response is between 1 and 5, proceed with another layer.

   - Wait until the patient's sensitivity begins to subside before applying the next layer. The patient will begin to rate lower on the scale of 1 to 10 approximately one to five minutes after each layer is applied.

   - The total number of layers is determined by the needs, goals and individual sensitivity of the patient.

   - The maximum number of layers is four.

Maximum Layers:

Face: 4

Neck and chest: 2

Correct

4. After the peel solution has been absorbed into the skin, customize the protocol with a combination of corrective daily care products to address your patient's particular concerns and skincare goals. Refer to your customization chart on page 286 for suggestions.

Retinoid booster (optional)

5. **Advanced Treatment Booster** – Dispense two pumps into gloved hands. Gently spread the product over the area of treatment, keeping application even and thin.

   - Use the scale of 1 to 10 to gauge sensitivity. Most patients will not have any sensitivity to this product.

   - The maximum number of layers is one.

Contraindications:

Pregnancy

Lactation

Hydrate & protect

6. **ReBalance** and the appropriate PCA SKIN® broad spectrum SPF product – Complete the treatment with this combination to calm, hydrate and protect the skin from UVA and UVB exposure.

7. **Peptide Lip Therapy** – Finish with a liberal application to improve hydration and reduce the appearance of lip lines.

   Note: Apply the appropriate PCA SKIN broad spectrum SPF product prior to applying **Peptide Lip Therapy** to protect the lips from UVA and UVB exposure.

Specially formulated to treat maturing skin, **Ultra Peel**® I is also appropriate for many other skin types, conditions and sensitivities. It will help improve the appearance of fine lines and wrinkles, while promoting an even skin tone and clear complexion.

Ultra Peel® I

Before
Condition: facial wrinkling, laxity and dehydration.*

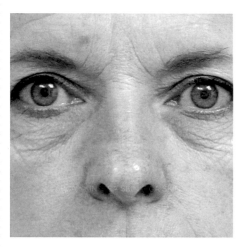

After three treatments
Solution: Ultra Peel® I, Rejuvenating Serum, ExLinea® Peptide Smoothing Serum, C&E Strength.*

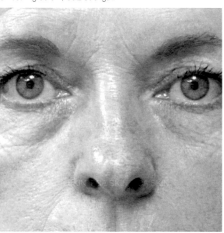

*Photos not retouched.

Key ingredients:

Lactic Acid (20%) – an alpha hydroxy acid (AHA) naturally found in milk and sugars. It is part of the skin's natural moisturizing factor (NMF) and moisturizes the skin.

Trichloroacetic Acid (TCA) (10%) – most commonly used as a superficial and medium-depth peeling agent to improve the appearance of fine lines and wrinkles.

Kojic Acid – helps promote an even skin tone.

Azelaic Acid – helps promote a clear complexion and even skin tone.

L-Ascorbic Acid (Vitamin C) – an antioxidant and MMPi that is the only bio-available form of vitamin C for the skin. It minimizes the appearance of fine lines and wrinkles while promoting an even skin tone.

Ultra Peel® I treatment protocol

Cleanse

1. **Facial Wash Oily/Problem** – Cleanse the area of treatment thoroughly. Rinse and pat dry.

Prep/degrease

2. **Smoothing Toner** – Apply with a cotton pad to prep (degrease) the skin. Allow the skin to dry. This product may sting or tingle on some individuals. Assess sensitivity by asking the patient, "On a scale of one to ten, ten being extremely active, how do you rate this sensation (or feeling)?"

Treat

3. **Ultra Peel® I**

   - Before using, gently agitate the product. Apply the first layer with a cotton pad.

   - Use the scale of 1 to 10 to gauge sensitivity. Fan the skin to keep the patient cool between layers. If the patient responds higher than a 6, do not proceed with another layer. If the patient's response is between 1 and 5, proceed with another layer.

   - Wait until the patient's sensitivity begins to subside before applying the next layer. The patient will begin to rate lower on the scale of 1 to 10 approximately one to five minutes after each layer is applied.

   - The total number of layers is determined by the needs, goals and individual sensitivity of the patient.

   - The maximum number of layers is four.

Correct

4. After the peel solution has been absorbed into the skin, customize the protocol with a combination of corrective daily care products to address your patient's particular concerns and skincare goals. Refer to your customization chart on page 286 for suggestions.

Retinoid booster (optional)

5. **Advanced Treatment Booster** – Dispense two pumps into gloved hands. Gently spread the product over the area of treatment, keeping application even and thin.

   - Use the scale of 1 to 10 to gauge sensitivity. Most patients will not have any sensitivity to this product.

   - The maximum number of layers is one.

Indications:
Fitzpatrick types I-V
Fine lines and wrinkles
Laxity
Uneven skin tone
Dry skin
Dehydrated or adult acne
Uneven surface texture

Maximum Layers:
Face: 4
Neck and chest: 2

Contraindications:
Pregnancy
Lactation
Hypersensitive skin

Hydrate & protect

6. **ReBalance** and the appropriate PCA SKIN® broad spectrum SPF product – Complete the treatment with this combination to calm, hydrate and protect the skin from UVA and UVB exposure.

7. **Peptide Lip Therapy** – Finish with a liberal application to improve hydration and reduce the appearance of lip lines.

   Note: Apply the appropriate PCA SKIN broad spectrum SPF product prior to applying **Peptide Lip Therapy** to protect the lips from UVA and UVB exposure.

The most suitable candidates for this more active treatment are those with resilient skin. **Ultra Peel Forte**® rejuvenates the skin and improves the appearance of fine lines and wrinkles while promoting an even skin tone. Note: For physicians' use only.

Before
Condition: weak capillaries, laxity and wrinkling.*

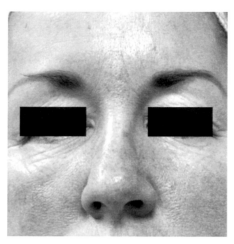

After two treatments
Solution: Ultra Peel Forte®, Pigment Gel®, ExLinea® Peptide Smoothing Serum, C&E Strength Max.*

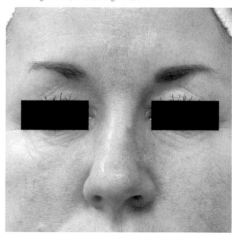

*Photos not retouched.

Key ingredients:

Trichloroacetic Acid (TCA) (20%) – most commonly used as a superficial and medium-depth peeling agent to improve the appearance of fine lines and wrinkles.

Lactic Acid (10%) – an alpha hydroxy acid (AHA) naturally found in milk and sugars. It is part of the skin's natural moisturizing factor (NMF) and moisturizes the skin.

Kojic Acid – helps promote an even skin tone.

Azelaic Acid – helps promote a clear complexion and even skin tone.

L-Ascorbic Acid (Vitamin C) – an antioxidant and MMPi that is the only bio-available form of vitamin C for the skin. It minimizes the appearance of fine lines and wrinkles while promoting an even skin tone.

Ultra Peel Forte® treatment protocol
For physicians' use only

Cleanse

1. **Facial Wash Oily/Problem** – Cleanse the area of treatment thoroughly. Rinse and pat dry.

Prep/degrease

2. **Smoothing Toner** – Apply with a cotton pad to prep (degrease) the skin. Allow the skin to dry. This product may sting or tingle on some individuals. Assess sensitivity by asking the patient, "On a scale of one to ten, ten being extremely active, how do you rate this sensation (or feeling)?"

Treat

3. **Ultra Peel Forte®**

   - Before using, gently agitate the product. Apply the first layer with a cotton pad.

   - Use the scale of 1 to 10 to gauge sensitivity. Fan the skin to keep the patient cool between layers. If the patient responds higher than a 6, do not proceed with another layer. If the patient's response is between 1 and 5, proceed with another layer.

   - Wait until the patient's sensitivity begins to subside before applying the next layer. The patient will begin to rate lower on the scale of 1 to 10 approximately one to five minutes after each layer is applied.

   - The total number of layers is determined by the needs, goals and individual sensitivity of the patient.

   - The maximum number of layers is two.

Maximum Layers:
Face: 2
Neck and chest: 1

Correct

4. After the peel solution has been absorbed into the skin, customize the protocol with a combination of corrective daily care products to address your patient's particular concerns and skincare goals. Refer to your customization chart on page 286 for suggestions.

Retinoid booster (optional)

5. **Advanced Treatment Booster** – Dispense two pumps into gloved hands. Gently spread the product over the area of treatment, keeping application even and thin.

   - Use the scale of 1 to 10 to gauge sensitivity. Most patients will not have any sensitivity to this product.

   - The maximum number of layers is one.

Hydrate & protect

6. **ReBalance** and the appropriate PCA SKIN® broad spectrum SPF product – Complete the treatment with this combination to calm, hydrate and protect the skin from UVA and UVB exposure.

7. **Peptide Lip Therapy** – Finish with a liberal application to improve hydration and reduce the appearance of lip lines.

    Note: Apply the appropriate PCA SKIN broad spectrum SPF product prior to applying **Peptide Lip Therapy** to protect the lips from UVA and UVB exposure.

Fitzpatrick types I-III
Deep wrinkling
Laxity
Photodamage
Acne scarring
Uneven surface texture

Ultra Peel Forte® medium-depth treatment protocol
For physicians' use only

Cleanse

1. **Facial Wash Oily/Problem** – Cleanse the area of treatment thoroughly. Rinse and pat dry.

Prep/degrease

2. **Smoothing Toner** – Apply with a cotton pad to prep (degrease) the skin. Allow the skin to dry. This product may sting or tingle on some individuals. Assess sensitivity by asking the patient, "On a scale of one to ten, ten being extremely active, how do you rate this sensation (or feeling)?"

Treat

3. **Ultra Peel Forte®**

   - Before using, gently agitate the product. Apply in layers as needed with a fan brush.

   - Use the scale of 1 to 10 to gauge sensitivity. Fan the skin to keep the patient cool between layers. The skin will have a slightly tacky feeling and with each additional layer, your patient will rate slightly higher on the scale of 1 to 10. Proceed with caution as patient is likely to blanch with subsequent layers.

   - The total number of layers is determined by the needs, goals and individual sensitivity of the patient.

   - The maximum number of layers is left to the discretion of the physician.

Maximum Layers:
The maximum number of layers is left to the discretion of the physician.

Correct

4. Due to this treatment's depth of penetration, the application of corrective products is typically avoided.

Retinoid booster (optional)

5. **Advanced Treatment Booster** – Dispense two pumps into gloved hands. Gently spread the product over the area of treatment, keeping application even and thin.

   - Use the scale of 1 to 10 to gauge sensitivity. Most patients will not have any sensitivity to this product.

   - The maximum number of layers is one.

Contraindications:
Pregnancy
Lactation
Sensitive skin
Higher Fitzpatrick types

Hydrate & protect

6. **ReBalance** and the appropriate PCA SKIN® broad spectrum SPF product –
   Complete the treatment with this combination to calm, hydrate and protect
   the skin from UVA and UVB exposure.

7. **Peptide Lip Therapy** – Finish with a liberal application to improve hydration
   and reduce the appearance of lip lines.

   Note: Apply the appropriate PCA SKIN broad spectrum SPF product prior to
   applying **Peptide Lip Therapy** to protect the lips from UVA and UVB exposure.

Smoothing Body Peel® Treatment

Pre-Peel Accelerator Mask (Step 1) provides nourishing ingredients that soften and hydrate the skin's surface, while **Smoothing Body Peel®** **(Step 2)** improves the appearance and texture of the skin with a combination of exfoliating, smoothing and brightening ingredients. This treatment is an excellent choice for promoting an even skin tone and clear complexion on the arms, legs, back, chest, hands and feet.

Before
Condition: hyperkeratosis and extremely dry skin on feet.

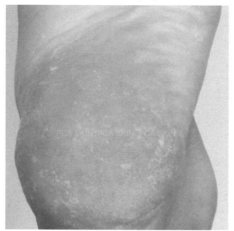

After three treatments
Solution: Smoothing Body Peel®, Acne Gel, Clearskin.*

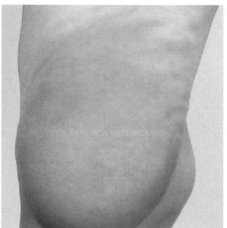

*Photos not retouched.

Pre-Peel Accelerator Mask key ingredients:

Urea – an essential part of the skin's natural moisturizing factor (NMF) and moisturizes the skin.

Malic Acid – an alpha hydroxy acid (AHA) naturally found in apples. This ingredient is also a natural humectant.

Smoothing Body Peel® key ingredients:

Lactic Acid (45%) – an alpha hydroxy acid (AHA) naturally found in milk and sugars. It is part of the skin's natural moisturizing factor (NMF) and moisturizes the skin.

Salicylic Acid (10%) – a calming lipophilic beta hydroxy acid (BHA) that helps promote a clear complexion.

Trichloroacetic Acid (TCA) (10%) – most commonly used as a superficial and medium-depth peeling agent to improve the appearance of fine lines and wrinkles.

Kojic Acid – helps promote an even skin tone.

Arbutin – an antioxidant that also helps promote an even skin tone.

Smoothing Body Peel® Treatment protocol

Cleanse

1. **Facial Wash Oily/Problem** – Cleanse the area of treatment thoroughly. Rinse and pat dry.

Prep/degrease

2. **Smoothing Toner** – Apply with a cotton pad to prep (degrease) the skin. Allow the skin to dry. This product may sting or tingle on some individuals. Assess sensitivity by asking the patient, "On a scale of one to ten, ten being extremely active, how do you rate this sensation (or feeling)?"

Treat

3. **Pre-Peel Accelerator Mask** (Step 1 from the **Smoothing Body Peel® Treatment)** – Apply liberally and massage into the area of treatment. Continue massaging until all product is absorbed, which will be approximately three to five minutes.

   - Ask the patient their sensation level using the scale of 1 to 10 and fan the patient to keep the area cool. Allow the **Pre-Peel Accelerator Mask** (Step 1) to remain on the skin for approximately ten minutes.

   - Remove the **Pre-Peel Accelerator Mask** (Step 1) with cotton pads moistened with warm water. Warm towels may be used for this step. Be certain towels are only warm (not hot). Fan the skin to dry.

   - **Smoothing Body Peel®** (Step 2) – Pour enough peel solution into your peel dish to cover the selected body area (remember not to treat more than 25% of the body at one time). Apply evenly to the area of treatment using a fan brush.

   - Fan the skin to keep the patient cool between layers. Ask their sensitivity level using the scale of 1 to 10. If the patient responds higher than a 6, do not proceed with another layer. If the patient's response is between 1 and 5, proceed with another layer. Wait two to three minutes between layers to ensure penetration.

   - The maximum number of layers is two.

Correct

4. After the peel solution has been absorbed into the skin, customize the protocol with a combination of corrective daily care products to address your patient's particular concerns and skincare goals. Refer to your customization chart on page 286 for suggestions.

Indications:
Fitzpatrick types I–VI
Fine lines and wrinkles
Laxity
Uneven skin tone
Acne
Dehydrated skin
Keratosis pilaris
All body parts (arms, hands, legs, feet, back, etc.)

Maximum Layers (mask): 1
Maximum Layers (peel): 2

Contraindications:
Neck or chest treatments on Fitzpatrick types V – VI
Pregnancy
Lactation
Allergy to aspirin (salicylates)
Treatments covering more than 25% of the body

Retinoid booster (optional)

5. **Advanced Treatment Booster** – Dispense two pumps into gloved hands. Gently spread the product over the area of treatment, keeping application even and thin.

   - Use the scale of 1 to 10 to gauge sensitivity. Most patients will not have any sensitivity to this product.
   - The maximum number of layers is one.

Hydrate & protect

6. **ReBalance** and the appropriate PCA SKIN® broad spectrum SPF product – Complete the treatment with this combination to calm, hydrate and protect the skin from UVA and UVB exposure.

   Tip: When performing the **Smoothing Body Peel**® to areas that will be covered with clothing following treatment, apply a mixture of **ReBalance** and the appropriate PCA SKIN broad spectrum SPF product, and massage in to minimize tackiness. Apply a tissue to the area of treatment prior to having the patient dress to avoid clothing coming in contact with excess residue.

This mask was strategically formulated to soothe and hydrate impaired skin conditions of all kinds. Oat milk, an excellent humectant, is also an antioxidant. This unique treatment mask incorporates advanced botanicals and pro-vitamins such as cucumber, arnica and panthenol to calm and improve the skin's appearance.

Hydrate: Therapeutic Oat Milk Mask

Before
Condition: Rosacea

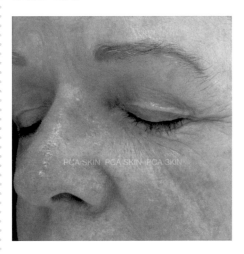

After one treatment
Solution: Hydrate: Therapeutic Oat Milk Mask, Creamy Cleanser, Anti-Redness Serum, Hydrating Serum.*

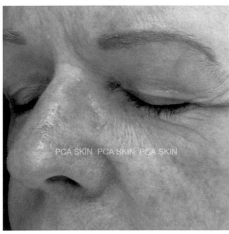

*Photos not retouched.

Key ingredients:

Avena Sativa (Oat) Kernel Extract – oat milk extract high in essential fatty acids (EFA). Oat milk is an antioxidant that soothes and calms the skin, and helps retain vital moisture.

Arnica Montana Flower Extract and Cucumber Fruit Extract – are calming agents.

Panthenol – hydrates the skin.

Glycerin – a humectant and emollient that helps to hydrate skin.

Sodium Hyaluronate – has the ability to hold 1,000 times its weight in water and plays an important role in skin hydration.

Absorb oil and impurities with this balancing mask using Japanese white charcoal. This weekly mask keeps skin clear while minimizing the appearance of pores. For use in the morning or evening. This mask is safe for all skin types, but ideal for oily and breakout-prone skin.

Detoxify: Therapeutic Charcoal Mask

Key ingredients:

Japanese White Charcoal – contains a variety of minerals and works to absorb oil and impurities from the skin. Its structure of very small pores allows it to be highly efficient at skin detoxification.

Kaolin – a type of clay that absorbs oil and impurities helping to clear pores.

Magnesium Aluminum Silicate – a naturally occurring clay-derived mineral that supports skin clearing.

Glycerin – a humectant and emollient that helps to hydrate and sooth skin.

This mask combines a combination of papaya puree and additional fruit extracts from lemon, orange and apple to brighten dull complexions and exfoliate, leaving the skin with a healthy glow. Green tea, vitamin E and honey are moisturizing antioxidants that help keep the skin soft and hydrated. This results-oriented therapeutic mask is appropriate for all skin types and conditions.

Revitalize: Therapeutic Papaya Mask

Before
Condition: fine lines and uneven texture

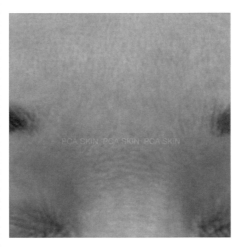

After one treatment
Solution: Revitalize: Therapeutic Papaya mask, BPO 5% Cleanser, Anti-Redness Serum, C&E Strength Max, Acne Gel.*

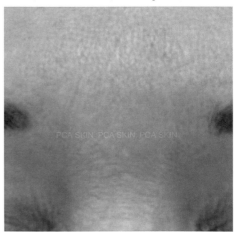

*Photos not retouched.

Key ingredients:

Papaya Fruit – contains the proteolytic fruit enzyme papain, which is widely used for its gentle exfoliating properties. Papaya fruit is also known to be an effective skin purifying ingredient.

Lemon Fruit, Sugar Cane, Orange Fruit and **Apple Fruit Extracts** – sources of naturally occurring alpha hydroxy acids (AHA).

Green Tea Extract – a polyphenolic antioxidant containing beneficial vitamins, minerals and oils.

Honey – a natural humectant that helps moisturize skin.

Orange and **Geranium Oils** – used to stimulate circulation and clear blemishes.

Formulated with the breakout-prone patient in mind, **Clarify: Therapeutic Salicylic Acid Mask** is both purifying and calming to promote a clear complexion.

Before
Condition: acne.*

After one treatment
Solution: Clarify: Therapeutic Salicylic Acid Mask, BPO 5% Cleanser, Pigment Gel®, Intensive Clarity Treatment®: 0.5% pure retinol night.*

Clarify: Therapeutic Salicylic Acid Mask

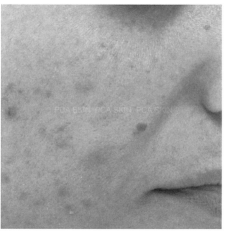

*Photos not retouched.

Key ingredients:

Salicylic Acid (20%) – a calming lipophilic beta hydroxy acid (BHA) that helps promote a clear complexion.

Hydrolyzed Candida Saitoana Extract – a type of fungi that encourages skin detoxification.

Cascarilla Bark and **Wild** and **Sweet Cherry Extracts** – provide excellent calming and antioxidant properties.

Vitamin E (Tocopherol) – a fat-soluble antioxidant vitamin and emollient ingredient.

This nutritive treatment mask addresses thick, resilient skin with acne, sun damage or hyperkeratolytic buildup. **Retexturize: Therapeutic Pumpkin Mask** combines exfoliating pumpkin enzymes and salicylic acid along with a host of antibacterial and antioxidant ingredients to address rough-textured skin caused by keratinization, leaving a healthy complexion following treatment.

Retexturize: Therapeutic Pumpkin Mask

Before
Condition: acne*

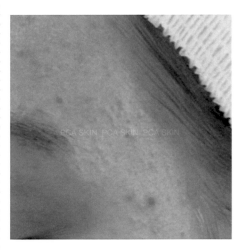

After one treatment
Solution: Retexturize: Therapeutic Pumpkin Mask, BPO 5% Cleanser, Acne Gel, Intensive Clarity Treatment®: 0.5% pure retinol night, Purifying Mask *

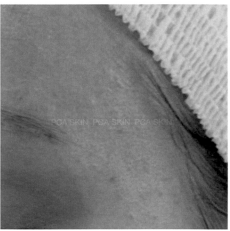

*Photos not retouched.

Key ingredients:

Pumpkin Fruit Enzymes – the proteases from pumpkin that act as exfoliating agents.

Salicylic Acid – a calming lipophilic beta hydroxy acid (BHA) that helps promote a clear complexion.

Glutathione – an endogenous antioxidant that is produced naturally by the body.

Gluconic Acid – an alpha hydroxy acid (AHA) that is calming, moisturizing and promotes a clear complexion.

Indications:
Hydrate: Therapeutic Oat Milk Mask:
Fitzpatrick types I-VI
Sensitive skin
Fine lines
Dry and dehydrated skin
Dull/sallow complexions
Pregnancy
Lactation

Detoxify: Therapeutic Charcoal Mask:
Fitzpatrick types I-VI
Acne or breakout-prone skin
Oily skin
Enlarged pores
Pregnancy (patients should
   check with their obstetrician)
Lactation

Revitalize: Therapeutic Papaya Mask:
Fitzpatrick types I-VI
All skin types and conditions
Fine lines and wrinkles
Dull/sallow complexions
Pregnancy (patients should
   check with their obstetrician)
Lactation

Clarify: Therapeutic Salicylic Acid Mask:
Fitzpatrick types I-VI
Acne or breakout-prone skin
Oily skin
Hyperkeratolytic buildup

Retexturize: Therapeutic Pumpkin Mask:
Fitzpatrick types I-IV
Photodamage
Acne
Dull complexions
Hyperkeratolytic buildup

Maximum Layers: 1

Contraindications:
Hydrate: Therapeutic Oat Milk Mask:
None

Detoxify: Therapeutic Charcoal Mask:
None

Revitalize: Therapeutic Papaya Mask:
None

Clarify: Therapeutic Salicylic Acid Mask:
Pregnancy
Lactation
Hypersensitive skin
Allergy to aspirin (salicylates)

Retexturize: Therapeutic Pumpkin Mask:
Pregnancy
Lactation
Hypersensitive skin
Allergy to aspirin (salicylates)
Fitzpatrick types V-VI

Therapeutic Mask treatment protocol

Cleanse

1. **Facial Wash Oily/Problem** – Cleanse the area thoroughly. Rinse and pat dry.

Prep/degrease

2. **Smoothing Toner** – Apply with a cotton pad to prep (degrease) the skin. Allow the skin to dry. This product may sting or tingle on some individuals. Assess sensitivity by asking the patient, "On a scale of one to ten, ten being extremely active, how do you rate this sensation (or feeling)?"

Treat

3. **Hydrate: Therapeutic Oat Milk Mask** – Apply a generous amount to the area of treatment using gloved hands, enough to cover the face. For the best results, **Hydrate** should be rubbed into the skin. Use the scale of 1 to 10 to gauge sensitivity. Allow the mask to remain on the skin for up to 10 minutes when using **Hydrate**. Remove completely with cotton pads moistened with warm water.

   Detoxify: Therapeutic Charcoal Mask – Apply a generous amount to the area of treatment using gloved hands, enough to cover the face. Use the scale of 1 to 10 to gauge sensitivity. Allow the mask to remain on the skin for 2 to 5 minutes, or until dry when using **Detoxify**. Remove completely with cotton pads moistened with warm water.

   Revitalize: Therapeutic Papaya Mask – Apply a generous amount to the area of treatment using gloved hands, enough to cover the face. Use the scale of 1 to 10 to gauge sensitivity. Allow the mask to remain on the skin for up to 5 minutes when using **Revitalize**. Remove completely with cotton pads moistened with warm water.

   Clarify: Therapeutic Salicylic Acid Mask – Apply a thin layer to the area of treatment using gloved hands, enough to cover the face. Use the scale of 1 to 10 to gauge sensitivity. Allow the mask to remain on the skin for up to 10 minutes when using **Clarify**. Remove completely with cotton pads moistened with warm water.

   Retexturize: Therapeutic Pumpkin Mask – Apply a thin layer to the area of treatment using gloved hands, enough to cover the face. Use the scale of 1 to 10 to gauge sensitivity. Allow the mask to remain on the skin for 30 seconds to 2 minutes when using **Retexturize**. Remove completely with cotton pads moistened with warm water.

   Warning: These masks are not self-neutralizing.

4. **Nutrient Toner** – Apply with a cotton pad to remove any excess. Allow the skin to dry.

Correct

5. After removing the mask, customize the protocol with a combination of corrective daily care products to address your patient's particular concerns and skincare goals. Refer to your customization chart on page 286 for suggestions.

6. **Replenishing Gel** – Use a small amount to massage into the area of treatment. **Replenishing Gel** can be left on the skin for additional hydration, or excess can be removed with cotton pads moistened with **Nutrient Toner**.

7. **Calming Balm** – Using a fan brush or gloved hands, apply a thin layer to the area of treatment to calm and soothe the skin.

Hydrate & protect

8. **ReBalance** and the appropriate PCA SKIN® broad spectrum SPF product – Complete the treatment with this combination to calm, hydrate and protect the skin from UVA and UVB exposure.

9. **Peptide Lip Therapy** – Finish with a liberal application to improve hydration and reduce the appearance of lip lines.

   Note: Apply the appropriate PCA SKIN broad spectrum SPF product prior to applying **Peptide Lip Therapy** to protect the lips from UVA and UVB exposure.

Increase exfoliation, restore keratinization and barrier function, while reducing redness and soothing with this retinoid booster for all skin types.

Advanced Treatment Booster

Before
Condition: Skin in need of increased cell turnover and exfoliation.

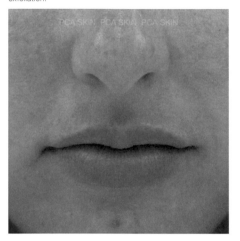

After four days (during the peeling process)
Solution: Received one Ultra Peel® I enhanced with Advanced Treatment Booster.

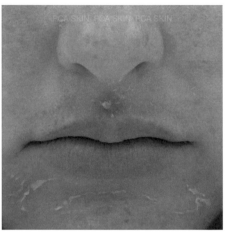

*Photos not retouched.

Key ingredients:

Retinoid Blend (Vitamin A) (10.5%) – converted to retinoic acid in the skin. Vitamin A helps to promote a clear complexion and an even skin tone.

Lens Esculenta (Lentil) Seed Extract (3%) – restores normal keratinization post-treatment, limits pore wall slackening and reduces sebum production.

Panthenol, Escin, Butcher's Broom, Gotu Kola Extract and **Marigold Flower Extract (2%)** – create a skin tolerance enhancement and decrease the stinging response following the application of chemical peels. Highly soothing and an excellent complement to chemical peels.

Panthenol – on its own, panthenol helps restore barrier function and encourage post-treatment re-epithelization.

Vitex Agnus-Castus Extract, Tocopherol and **Ascorbyl Tetraisopalmitate** – work together to provide intense hydration and potent antioxidant action.

Tocopherol – individually, tocopherol provides antioxidant protection against free radicals released during chemical treatment while moisturizing and accelerating epithelization.

Advanced Treatment Booster treatment protocol

Cleanse

1. **Facial Wash Oily/Problem** – Cleanse the area of treatment thoroughly. Rinse and pat dry.

Prep/degrease

2. **Smoothing Toner** – Apply with a cotton pad to prep (degrease) the skin. Allow the skin to dry. This product may sting or tingle on some individuals. Assess sensitivity by asking the patient, "On a scale of one to ten, ten being extremely active, how do you rate this sensation (or feeling)?"

Treat

3. Apply any of the PCA SKIN® professional treatments according to protocol.

Correct

4. At this point, customize the protocol with a combination of corrective daily care products to address your patient's particular concerns and skincare goals. Refer to your customization chart on page 286 for suggestions.

Retinoid booster

5. **Advanced Treatment Booster** – Dispense two pumps into gloved hands. Gently spread the product over the area of treatment, keeping application even and thin.

   - Use the scale of 1 to 10 to gauge sensitivity. Most patients will not have any sensitivity to this product.
   - The maximum number of layers is one.

Hydrate & protect

6. **ReBalance** and the appropriate PCA SKIN broad spectrum SPF product – Complete the treatment with this combination to calm, hydrate and protect the skin from UVA and UVB exposure.

7. **Peptide Lip Therapy** – Finish with a liberal application to improve hydration and reduce the appearance of lip lines.

   Note: Apply the appropriate PCA SKIN broad spectrum SPF product prior to applying **Peptide Lip Therapy** to protect the lips from UVA and UVB exposure.

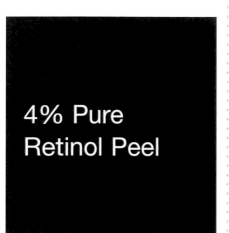

4% Pure Retinol Peel

For skin in need of rejuvenation, this retinoid peel smoothes, brightens and evens skin tone through increased cell turnover and peeling.

Before
Condition: Moderate breakouts, discoloration and uneven surface texture.

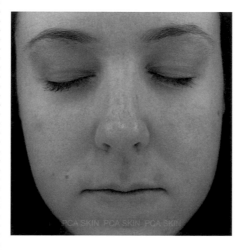

After one treatment (four days)
Solution: 4% Pure Retinol Peel, Facial Wash, Hydrating Serum, Perfecting Protection Broad Spectrum SPF 30 and ReBalance.

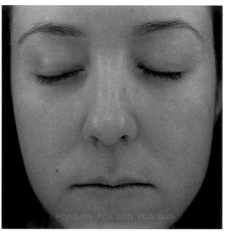

*Photos not retouched.

Key ingredients:

Retinol (4%) – is converted to retinoic acid in the skin. Vitamin A helps to promote a clear complexion and an even skin tone.

Marigold Flower Extract – is a skin calming antioxidant that aids in skin rejuvenation.

Silybum Marianum Fruit Extract – is a powerful antioxidant that helps fight free radical damage.

Olive Fruit Oil – is an antioxidant that also aids in the penetration of other actives within the formula.

Tocopherol (Vitamin E) – is an important antioxidant that also provides emollience.

The most suitable candidates for this more active retinoid treatment are those with normal to resilient skin. **6% Pure Retinol Peel** provides dramatic and rapid rejuvenation of the skin. By providing additional antioxidants within the formula, the skin is further protected from free radical damage. Skin is visibly smoother, brighter and more evenly toned. Note: For physicians' use only.

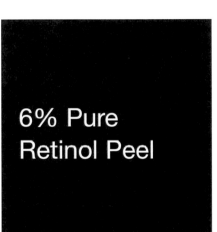

6% Pure Retinol Peel

Before
Condition: melasma.*

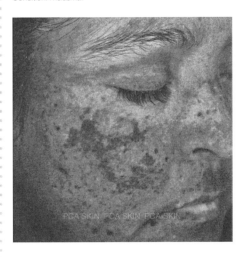

After one treatment
Solution: 6% Pure Retinol Peel, Intensive Brightening Treatment: 0.5% pure retinol night.*

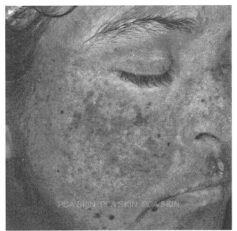

*Photos not retouched.

Key ingredients:

Retinol (6%) – converted to retinoic acid in the skin. Vitamin A helps to promote a clear complexion and an even skin tone.

Calendula Officinalis Flower Extract – a skin calming antioxidant that aids in skin rejuvenation.

Silybum Marianum Fruit Extract – a powerful antioxidant that helps fight free radical damage.

Olea Europaea (Olive) Fruit Oil – an antioxidant that also aids in the penetration of other actives within the formula.

Tocopherol (Vitamin E) – an important antioxidant that also provides emollience.

Fitzpatrick skin types I–III
Aging skin
Pigment disorders
Photodamaged skin

4% Pure Retinol Peel or 6% Pure Retinol Peel protocol

Cleanse

1. **Facial Wash Oily/Problem** – Cleanse the area of treatment thoroughly. Rinse and pat dry.

Prep/degrease

2. **Smoothing Toner** – Apply with a cotton pad to prep (degrease) the skin. Allow the skin to dry. This product may sting or tingle on some individuals. Assess sensitivity by asking the patient, "On a scale of one to ten, ten being extremely active, how do you rate this sensation (or feeling)?"

Correct

3. Customize the protocol with a combination of corrective daily care product to address your patient's particular concerns. Refer to your customization chart on page 286 for suggestions.

Treat

4. Using a cotton-tipped applicator, apply a protective occlusive around the orbital bone, nostrils and the vermillion border to avoid product migration.

5. **4% Pure Retinol Peel** or **6% Pure Retinol Peel** – Open the foil packette and dispense the peel into gloved hands. Gently spread the product over the area of treatment, keeping the application even and thin. Use the scale of 1 to 10 to gauge sensitivity. Fan the skin to keep the patient cool. Most patients will not have any sensitivity to this professional treatment upon application; rather, they will experience a soothing sensation, followed by a higher degree of visible exfoliation for a week to 10 days.

Maximum Layers: 1

Hydrate & protect

6. **ReBalance** and the appropriate PCA SKIN® broad spectrum SPF product – Complete the treatment with this combination to calm, hydrate and protect the skin from UVA and UVB exposure.

7. **Peptide Lip Therapy** – Finish with a liberal application to improve hydration and reduce the appearance of lip lines.

   Note: Apply the appropriate PCA SKIN broad spectrum SPF product prior to applying **Peptide Lip Therapy** to protect the lips from UVA and UVB exposure.

Contraindications:
Hypersensitive skin
Pregnancy
Lactation

This is an excellent choice for detoxifying all skin types. The active blend of lactic, glycolic and salicylic acids exfoliates and promotes a purified and clear complexion. This gentle, deep pore cleansing treatment provides clarifying and antioxidant action.

Detox Gel Deep Pore Treatment

Before
Condition: blackheads.*

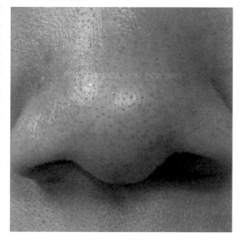

After one treatment
Solution: Detox Gel Deep Pore Treatment.*

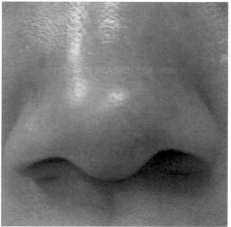

*Photos not retouched.

Key ingredients:

Glycolic Acid (2%) – an alpha hydroxy acid (AHA) that is excellent for oily skin types.

Salicylic Acid (2%) – a calming lipophilic beta hydroxy acid (BHA) that helps promote a clear complexion.

Lactic Acid (2%) – an alpha hydroxy acid (AHA) naturally found in milk and sugars. It is part of the skin's natural moisturizing factor (NMF) and moisturizes the skin.

Totarol – an extract from the New Zealand totara tree that is a gentle antioxidant and purifying agent.

Glutathione – an endogenous antioxidant that is produced naturally by the body.

Hydrogen Peroxide – a topical oxygen source effective in purifying the skin.

Indications:

Fitzpatrick skin types I–VI

Acne and breakout-prone skin

Oily skin

Deep pore cleansing and
    extractions

Pregnancy (patients should
    check with their obstetrician)

Lactation (patients should
    check with their obstetrician)

Maximum Layers: 1

Contraindications:

Allergy to aspirin (salicylates)

Detox Gel Deep Pore Treatment protocol

Cleanse

1. **Facial Wash Oily/Problem** – Cleanse the area of treatment thoroughly. Rinse and pat dry.

Prep/degrease

2. **Smoothing Toner** – Apply with a cotton pad to prep (degrease) the skin. Allow the skin to dry. This product may sting or tingle on some individuals. Assess sensitivity by asking the patient, "On a scale of one to ten, ten being extremely active, how do you rate this sensation (or feeling)?"

Treat

3. **Steam** – You may turn on your steamer at this time and leave it on for the duration of the massage (remember not to combine steam with any other PCA SKIN® peels).

4. **Detox Gel Deep Pore Treatment** – Before using, gently agitate the product. Dispense a generous amount into your peel dish. Using your small fan brush, apply onto the areas of treatment, concentrating on areas of breakouts. Using gloved hands, gently massage the product into the skin for approximately three to five minutes. You may apply more **Detox Gel Deep Pore Treatment** to continue your massage if the product dries on the skin. This is typically not necessary if using in conjunction with steam.

   - Use the scale of 1 to 10 to gauge sensitivity. Fan the skin to keep the patient cool. Allow **Detox Gel Deep Pore Treatment** to penetrate. The skin will have a slightly flushed appearance.

   - The maximum number of layers is one.

5. **Extractions** – If needed, you may now perform gentle extractions. Impurities should be purged from the follicles with ease.

   - Using a cotton pad, swipe the areas of extractions with **Smoothing Toner** to clean and soothe any inflammation that is present.

   Note: You may use **Nutrient Toner** in place of **Smoothing Toner** on sensitive skin types.

Correct

6. After the **Detox Gel Deep Pore Treatment** has been absorbed into the skin or after extractions, customize the protocol with a combination of corrective daily care products to address your patient's particular concerns and skincare goals. Refer to your customization chart on page 286 for suggestions.

Retinoid booster (optional)

7. **Advanced Treatment Booster** – Dispense two pumps into gloved hands. Gently spread the product over the area of treatment, keeping application even and thin.

   - Use the scale of 1 to 10 to gauge sensitivity. Most patients will not have any sensitivity to this product.
   - The maximum number of layers is one.

Hydrate & protect

8. **ReBalance** and the appropriate PCA SKIN® broad spectrum SPF product – Complete the treatment with this combination to calm, hydrate and protect the skin from UVA and UVB exposure.

9. **Peptide Lip Therapy** – Finish with a liberal application to improve hydration and reduce the appearance of lip lines.

   Note: Apply the appropriate PCA SKIN broad spectrum SPF product prior to applying **Peptide Lip Therapy** to protect the lips from UVA and UVB exposure.

This antioxidant therapy supports skin metabolism. This treatment leaves skin purified, glowing and radiant.

Oxygenating Trio®

Before
Condition: acne and diffuse redness.*

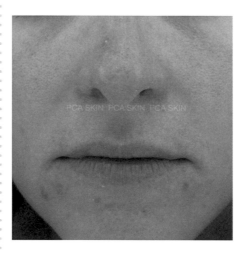

After one treatment
Solution: Oxygenating Trio®, Blemish Control Bar, Acne Gel, Rejuvenating Serum.*

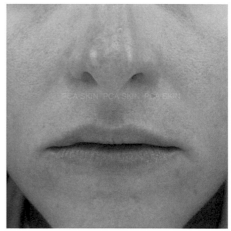

*Photos not retouched.

Key ingredients:

Superoxide Dismutase – an enzyme that supports antioxidant defense.

Fumaric Acid – an antioxidant.

Niacinamide – a form of the B vitamin, niacin (vitamin B3), that hydrates and promotes a clear complexion. It does not cause the flushing response common with niacin.

Hydrolyzed Candida Saitoana Extract – a type of fungi that encourages skin detoxification.

Hydrogen Peroxide – a topical oxygen source effective in purifying the skin.

Lactic Acid – an alpha hydroxy acid (AHA) naturally found in milk and sugars. It is part of the skin's natural moisturizing factor (NMF) and moisturizes the skin.

Glycolic Acid – an alpha hydroxy acid (AHA) that is excellent for oily skin types.

Salicylic Acid – a calming lipophilic beta hydroxy acid (BHA) that helps promote a clear complexion.

Oxygenating Trio® treatment protocol

Cleanse

1. **Facial Wash Oily/Problem** – Cleanse the area of treatment thoroughly. Rinse and pat dry.

Prep/degrease

2. **Smoothing Toner** – Apply with a cotton pad to prep (degrease) the skin. Allow the skin to dry. This product may sting or tingle on some individuals. Assess sensitivity by asking the patient, "On a scale of one to ten, ten being extremely active, how do you rate this sensation (or feeling)?"

Treat

3. **Activator** (Step 1) – Pour a generous amount into a small peel dish. Apply with a brush over the entire area of treatment. Allow to penetrate and dry thoroughly. The patient will feel internal warming as the skin is being stimulated. Fan the patient to keep them cool. You may proceed with the treatment once the product has absorbed and the patient's skin is dry to the touch.

4. **Detoxifier** (Step 2) – Apply with your fingers in a circular motion over the entire treatment area. Take your time with massaging the treatment area. Wait three minutes to allow product to penetrate. Remove any obvious excess by gently blotting with a tissue or with **Nutrient Toner** on a cotton pad.

Correct

5. After performing the first two steps of this trio, customize the protocol with a combination of corrective daily care products to address your patient's particular concerns and skin care goals. Refer to your customization chart on page 286 for suggestions.

Treat

6. **Oxygenator** (Step 3) – Massage a generous amount into the skin with your fingers in a circular motion over the entire area of treatment. A little of this product goes a long way, so do not overuse, avoiding contact with the eyebrows and hair due to possibility of bleaching. Coverage should be thin, even and thorough.

Retinoid booster (optional)

7. **Advanced Treatment Booster** – Dispense two pumps into gloved hands. Gently spread the product over the area of treatment, keeping application even and thin.

   - Use the scale of 1 to 10 to gauge sensitivity. Most patients will not have any sensitivity to this product.

   - The maximum number of layers is one.

Indications:
Fitzpatrick types I–VI
Acne and breakout-prone skin
Asphyxiated skin
Deoxygenated skin
Dull complexions
Pregnancy (patients should
   check with their obstetrician)
Lactation (patients should
   check with their obstetrician)

Maximum Layers (all steps): 1

Contraindications:
Reactive skin
Aggravated rosacea
Vascular weakness
Allergy to aspirin (salicylates)

Hydrate & protect

8. **ReBalance** and the appropriate PCA SKIN® broad spectrum SPF product – Complete the treatment with this combination to calm, hydrate and protect the skin from UVA and UVB exposure.

9. **Peptide Lip Therapy** – Finish with a liberal application to improve hydration and reduce the appearance of lip lines.

Note: Apply the appropriate PCA SKIN broad spectrum SPF product prior to applying **Peptide Lip Therapy** to protect the lips from UVA and UVB exposure.

Replenishing Gel

Replenishing Gel nourishes and supports skin post-treatment with a panel of antioxidants, vitamins and essential fatty acids. This treatment enhancement product also serves as an effective medium for performing circulation-enhancing massage.

Key ingredients:

Magnolia Officinalis Bark Extract – a multi-functional antioxidant ingredient that soothes skin, while also providing support to aging skin.

Grape Seed Extract – rich in polyphenols and proanthocyanidins, which are antioxidants. Grape seed extract contains the antioxidant resveratrol.

Tocopherol and **Tocopheryl Acetate (Vitamin E)** – fat-soluble antioxidant vitamins and emollient ingredients.

Chlorella Vulgaris Extract – a type of algae that is high in antioxidants, vitamins, amino acids and fatty acids.

Calming Balm

Calming Balm is a versatile treatment enhancement that can be used during any protocol to add nutritive and calming benefits to the skin. **Calming Balm** incorporates the advanced soothing botanicals bisabolol, allantoin and aloe with vitamin E, and mushroom extracts for antioxidant benefits.

Key ingredients:

Bisabolol – one of the principal compounds found in chamomile. It is thought to be largely responsible for chamomile's soothing effect on the skin.

Allantoin – an antioxidant that soothes the skin.

Aloe Vera – a purifying ingredient best known for its softening and soothing benefits.

Vitamin E (Tocopherol) – a fat-soluble antioxidant and emollient ingredient.

Cordyceps Sinensis Extract and **Trametes Versicolor Extract** – mushroom-derived soothing and calming ingredients.

alternative protocols

PCA SKIN® facial for men

This facial is designed to clear, hydrate and revitalize men's skin.

Cleanse

1. **Total Wash Face & Body Cleanser** – Cleanse the area of treatment thoroughly. Rinse and pat dry.

Prep/degrease

2. **Nutrient Toner** – Apply with a cotton pad. Allow the skin to dry. This product may sting or tingle on some individuals. Assess sensitivity by asking the patient, "On a scale of one to ten, ten being extremely active, how do you rate this sensation (or feeling)?"

Treat

3. **Gentle Exfoliant** – Apply a small amount to wet fingertips and massage lightly, working in a circular motion. Completely remove from treatment area using cotton pads moistened with warm water.

4. **Steam** – You may turn on your steamer at this time and leave on for the duration of the application of Mask.

5. **Pre-Peel Accelerator Mask** – (Step 1 from the **Smoothing Body Peel®** **Treatment**) – Apply liberally and massage into the area of treatment. Continue massaging until all of the product is absorbed (approximately three to five minutes). This is the exfoliating portion of this protocol. Urea, when used at higher percentages, is an effective keratolytic. This will gently dissolve keratinization and allow for cell renewal. Remove completely with cotton pads moistened with water.

Correct

6. **Total Strength Serum** – Apply one to two pumps amount to the area of treatment to strengthen the skin.

7. **Retinol Treatment for Sensitive Skin** – Apply a pea-sized amount to encourage cell turnover, calm the skin and reduce redness.

8. **Hyaluronic Acid Boosting Serum** and **C&E Strength** – Apply a mixture to minimize the appearance of fine lines and wrinkles, and encourage moisture retention.

9. **Ideal Complex® Revitalizing Eye Gel** – Gently apply around the delicate eye area and directly to the eyelid to reduce the appearance of dark circles, puffiness, fine lines and wrinkles.

Indications:

Fitzpatrick types I-VI

All skin types and conditions

Products:

Total Wash Face & Body Cleanser

Nutrient Toner

Gentle Exfoliant

Pre-Peel Accelerator Mask (step 1)

Total Strength Serum

Retinol Treatment for Sensitive Skin

Hyaluronic Acid Boosting Serum

C&E Strength

Ideal Complex® Revitalizing Eye Gel

Appropriate PCA SKIN® Broad Spectrum SPF

ReBalance

Peptide Lip Therapy

Hydrate & protect

10. **ReBalance** and the appropriate PCA SKIN® broad spectrum SPF product – Complete the treatment with this combination to calm, hydrate and protect the skin from UVA and UVB exposure.

11. **Peptide Lip Therapy** – Finish with a liberal application to improve hydration and reduce the appearance of lip lines.

    Note: Apply the appropriate PCA SKIN broad spectrum SPF product prior to applying **Peptide Lip Therapy** to protect the lips from UVA and UVB exposure.

PCA SKIN® signature facial

The PCA SKIN signature facial is an excellent first-time treatment and a great choice for patients specifically requesting a facial, and for those who do not want to experience peeling. This facial calms, soothes and strengthens all skin types and conditions.

1. **Warm compress** – Begin by applying a warm compress to the décolleté, neck and face, and apply gentle pressure by molding and gently pressing on the towel. Remove the compress.

Cleanse

2. **Facial Wash Oily/Problem** – Cleanse the area of treatment thoroughly. Rinse and pat dry.

Prep/degrease

3. **Smoothing Toner** – Apply with a cotton pad to prep (degrease) the skin. Allow the skin to dry. This product may sting or tingle on some individuals. Assess sensitivity by asking the patient, "On a scale of one to ten, ten being extremely active, how do you rate this sensation (or feeling)?"

   Note: Nutrient Toner may be used in place of **Smoothing Toner** on more sensitive skin types.

Pre-treat

4. **Gentle Exfoliant** – Apply a small amount to wet fingertips and massage lightly, working in a circular motion. Completely remove from treatment area using a cotton pad moistened with water.

5. **Extractions** – Using gloved hands, gentle extractions may be performed at this time.

6. **Nutrient Toner** – With a cotton pad, swipe the areas of extractions to cleanse and soothe.

Treat

7. **Detoxifier** (Step 2 from the **Oxygenating Trio®**) – Apply with your fingers in a circular motion over the entire treatment area. Take your time with massaging the treatment area. Wait three minutes to allow product to penetrate. Remove any obvious excess by gently blotting with a tissue or with **Nutrient Toner** on a cotton pad.

Indications:

Fitzpatrick types I-VI

All skin types and conditions

Pregnant and lactating women (patients should check with their obstetrician)

Products:

Facial Wash Oily/Problem

Smoothing Toner

Gentle Exfoliant

Nutrient Toner

Detoxifier (Step 2 from the Oxygenating Trio®)

ExLinea® Peptide Smoothing Serum

A&C Synergy Serum®

Hyaluronic Acid Boosting Serum

Dual Action Redness Relief

Retinol Treatment for Sensitive Skin

Rejuvenating Serum

C&E Strength

Ideal Complex® Revitalizing Eye Gel

Ideal Complex® Restorative Eye Cream

ReBalance

Peptide Lip Therapy

Correct

8. **ExLinea® Peptide Smoothing Serum** – Apply to areas of apparent laxity and wrinkling.

9. **Hyaluronic Acid Boosting Serum** – Apply one to two pumps to the area of treatment to encourage instant and long-term hydration, and moisture retention.

10. **Dual Action Redness Relief** – Apply one to two pumps to improve the skin's barrier function, calm the skin, and reduce redness and inflammation.

11. **Retinol Treatment for Sensitive Skin** – Apply a pea-sized amount to encourage cell turnover, calm the skin and reduce redness.

12. **Rejuvenating Serum** and **C&E Strength** – Apply a mixture to minimize the appearance of fine lines and wrinkles, while hydrating and brightening the skin.

13. **Perfecting Neck & Décolleté** – Apply a pea-sized amount to the neck and chest for smoother, younger-looking skin.

14. **Ideal Complex® Revitalizing Eye Gel** or **Ideal Complex® Restorative Eye Cream** – Gently apply around the delicate eye area and directly to the eyelid to reduce the appearance of dark circles, puffiness, fine lines and wrinkles.

Hydrate & protect

15. **ReBalance** and the appropriate PCA SKIN® broad spectrum SPF product – Complete the treatment with this combination to calm, hydrate and protect the skin from UVA and UVB exposure.

16. **Peptide Lip Therapy** – Finish with a liberal application to improve hydration and reduce the appearance of lip lines.

    Note: Apply the appropriate PCA SKIN broad spectrum SPF product prior to applying **Peptide Lip Therapy** to protect the lips from UVA and UVB exposure.

Pore Refining Treatment and
Detoxify: Therapeutic Charcoal Mask Protocol

This advanced treatment protocol combines multiple PCA SKIN professional treatment products to deeply purify the pores.

Cleanse

1. **Facial Wash Oily/Problem** – Cleanse the area of treatment thoroughly. Rinse and pat dry.

Prep/degrease

2. **Nutrient Toner** – Apply with a cotton pad. Allow the skin to dry. This product may sting or tingle on some individuals. Assess sensitivity by asking the patient, "On a scale of one to ten, ten being extremely active, how do you rate this sensation (or feeling)?"

Treat

3. **Pore Refining Treatment** and steam – Apply in gentle circular motions, massaging over the face for mechanical, chemical and enzymatic exfoliation. Remove completely with cotton pads moistened with warm water.

4. **Detoxifier** (Step 2 of **Oxygenating Trio®**) — Massage a generous amount into the skin with your fingers in a circular motion for approximately two minutes.

5. **Detoxify: Therapeutic Charcoal Mask** — Apply a generous amount to the area of treatment using a fan brush. Allow the mask to remain on the skin until completely dry. Remove completely with cotton pads moistened with warm water.

6. **Nutrient Toner** – With a cotton pad, swipe the areas of extractions to cleanse and soothe.

7. **Detox Gel Deep Pore Treatment** – Before using, gently agitate the product. Dispense a generous amount into your peel dish. Using your small fan brush, apply onto the areas of treatment, concentrating on areas of breakouts. Using gloved hands, gently massage the product into the skin for approximately three to five minutes. You may apply more **Detox Gel Deep Pore Treatment** to continue your massage if the product dries on the skin. This is typically not necessary if using in conjunction with steam.

   - Use the scale of 1 to 10 to gauge sensitivity. Fan the skin to keep the patient cool. Allow **Detox Gel Deep Pore Treatment** to penetrate. The skin will have a slightly flushed appearance.

   - The maximum number of layers is one.

Correct

8. After performing steps 3 through 7, customize the protocol with a combination of corrective daily care products to address your patient's particular concerns and skincare goals. Refer to your customization chart on page 286 for suggestions.

Indications:

Fitzpatrick types I-VI

Oily skin

Breakout-prone skin

Congested skin

Pregnant and lactating women (patients should check with their obstetrician)

Products:

Facial Wash Oily/Problem

Nutrient Toner

Pore Refining Treatment

Detox Gel Deep Pore Treatment

Detoxifier (Step 2 of Oxygenating Trio®)

Detoxify: Therapeutic Charcoal Mask

ReBalance

Appropriate PCA SKIN broad spectrum SPF

Retinoid booster (optional)

9. **Advanced Treatment Booster** – Dispense two pumps into gloved hands. Gently spread the product over the area of treatment, keeping application even and thin.

   - Use the scale of 1 to 10 to gauge sensitivity. Most patients will not have any sensitivity to this product.

   - The maximum number of layers is one.

Hydrate & protect

10. **ReBalance** and the appropriate PCA SKIN® broad spectrum SPF product – Complete the treatment with this combination to calm, hydrate and protect the skin from UVA and UVB exposure.

business development

building a successful practice

Building a successful practice doesn't have to come with a large price tag. Whether you are an entrepreneur just starting out or an experienced businessperson looking to expand, the secret is to be smart about how and where you are spending your dollars.

Three of the most cost-effective investments you can make in your practice focus on delivering outstanding service, building your patient base, and developing your and your staff's expertise through additional education.

First and foremost, improve your customer service. Find new, innovative ways to interact with your patients, learning their specific wants and needs so you can address them directly. Understand what is important to them and what isn't. Make sure your patients look forward to their next visit by creating valuable and measureable treatment plans that allow them to see and feel results. This will increase their willingness to pay for your services.

By providing a high level of service, you can avoid pricing wars with other practices, seeing who can offer the lowest discount. Deep discounts devalue your offerings and reduce your credibility. Over the long-term your business is better-served by staying true to your pricing strategy while being creative with your customer service.

Next, add to your patient base through networking. The best place to start is with those you treat most frequently. When you offer outstanding customer service and produce visible results for their skincare needs, they will rave about you and your practice. Perhaps they will want to share their experiences with their friends. Design a rewards program for your clients who refer new people to you or who book a small group for a treatment.

But don't stop there. Look to family, friends and acquaintances, and make them ambassadors for you. Go to local social events and popular gathering spots to meet potential clients. If you have the space, organize your own happy hour, inviting key influencers from the community. Some people to identify are socialites, local celebrities and business leaders. You can also reach out to the community and offer workshops and demonstrations focused on caring for your skin, or offer your space and services for fundraising opportunities.

When you do organize compelling events, remember to include the media. Work with a local television or radio station to do a live remote. You will get a tremendous amount of exposure at only a fraction of the cost of advertising.

Finally, invest in training and education for you and your staff. This adds credibility to your practice and gives potential customers confidence in spending their discretionary dollars with you.

This is the time to develop technical skills and expand your knowledge base. Learn new techniques, establishing an expertise in different treatment protocols. Earn certifications demonstrating that your staff has achieved specific training milestones. Help your staff develop other talents that are beneficial to your business such as writing, photography or graphic design. When you support and invest in your staff, you create loyalty, which leads to outstanding customer service and a better network effect.

PCA SKIN® event planning overview

Hosting events is an effective marketing tactic because events bring new and existing patients into your practice to experience samplings of your products and services at little or no cost to them. Events also allow your patients to invite friends and family for an evening out that is fun and educational.

New accounts should wait at least three months before holding an open house or event. This will allow you and your staff time to become familiar with PCA SKIN products and services.

Keep in mind that events take weeks of preparation and careful planning. It is best to contact a member of our Practice Development Group at least eight weeks prior to your event to ensure we can maximize our support.

Marketing your event

Before you can begin marketing your event, you need to decide what it will be. This includes the services you will highlight, the treatments you want to sample and the daily care products you hope to promote.

Reach out to local wine shops, caterers and other merchants, and invite them to co-host. This helps keep your marketing budget in control and exposes each vendor's customer base to your practice. You also may wish to partner with a local charity and donate a percentage of the night's profits to them. This will increase your exposure and help draw more attention to your event.

You will want to start your marketing and invite patients at least four weeks prior to the event. All of your communication needs to focus on what patients can expect when they arrive. If you plan to have gift bags, raffles or special pricing, include it in the invitation and advertising.

In the last 10 days leading up to the event, confirm you have the right amount of food, gift bags, etc., and send reminders to your patients. Online invitation services will assist you with managing this process.

Pre-event training

Hold a pre-event training three to five days prior to the event to review the flow, expectations, goals and responsibilities. Design individual and team goals for sales, new leads, appointments booked and anything else related to the actual event. Establishing these goals keeps everyone focused on the purpose of the event and gives you a definitive way to measure the success.

The event

Do a quick run-through of the event with your team before your guests arrive. Make sure everyone understands their responsibilities and expectations. Set up an easy system for collecting the information you need to follow up with your guests, such as their name, phone number and e-mail address. Remember, the event is about building your business and bringing in new patients, and it is meant to be fun. Put your best foot forward and exceed everyone's expectations.

Following the event

In the first few days after the event, bring the team together to identify what worked well, what needs improvement and what to do better next time. Also, use this time to review how the team did compared to the goals you established. Send out your thank-you notes and start planning for the next one.

Event planning checklist

4 or more months ahead

❏ **Define the goal for the event**
- Possibilities include: client appreciation, grand opening, education, fundraiser, annual event, introducing new services, modalities or products

❏ **Set the date and time**
- Hosting an event one to two times per year is recommended to keep it exclusive; doing so will prevent clients from waiting to purchase products or book services until the next event
- Make sure the date of your event does not conflict with other major events in your area or on a national/religious holiday
- A two- to three-hour time frame is recommended
- Wednesday or Thursday evenings are best; optional weekend date would be Saturday in the late morning or early afternoon

❏ **Determine your budget and the expenses required for the event**

❏ **Set a revenue goal**

❏ **Set the theme for the event**
- Create an atmosphere that is inviting and professional
- Make the theme unique
- Consider tying the theme in with a holiday or season (ex: Mother's Day, Christmas or back to school summer event, etc.)

2-4 months ahead

❏ **Decide how you will publicize the event**

❏ **Consider putting a press release in your local paper**

❏ **Decide which specials or discounts you will offer to guests in order to reach your goal**
- ex: a 20% discount off all products or a signature treatment; bring a friend and receive a complimentary service; raffle gifts; purchase five peels and receive the sixth at no charge; highlighting the retail product or professional treatment being featured in PCA SKIN®'s monthly promotion

❏ **Create Save the Dates or invitations to send out to clients**
- Include special offers, prizes and offerings on your invitation
- The invitation is the first tangible item your guests will see; make a great impression and provide clear RSVP instructions

❏ **Brainstorm your food and beverage menu**

❏ **Consider partnerships with organizations in your area to assist in the execution of the event, such as a local caterer, music, etc.**

❏ **Presentation(s) and Speaker(s)**
- Identify topics to be shared with your guests
- Commit to a specific timeframe and locations for each presentation or speech
- Consider setting up individual appointments for product consultations or treatment demonstrations
- Identify equipment and materials needed

1-2 months ahead

❏ **Consider hosting a PCA SKIN® in-office seminar for your staff before the event**

❏ **Publicize your event on your website, Facebook fan page and any other social media platforms you utilize**

❏ **Create an email blast version of your invitation to email out to clients**
- Send out reminders about event four weeks prior, two weeks prior, the week before and the day of the event

❏ **Place fliers publicizing the event throughout your business**

❏ **Invite nearby businesses to participate to increase your guest list**

❏ **Consider creating a method to drive traffic**
- Stamp cards can be used for each vendor or product station allowing representatives the time to speak with the guests and offer suggestions (ex: the more stamps one receives on their card, the more raffle tickets they receive)

❏ **Finalize food and beverage menu**

2 weeks ahead

❑ Confirm RSVPs

❑ Remember to send out a reminder email and repost on your social media platforms

❑ Check inventory and make sure you have adequate stock for the event

❑ Place order if necessary

❑ Design individual goals for sales, new leads and appointments booked for each staff member

1 week

❑ Send out a one week reminder email and update your social media post

❑ Meet with staff to discuss your vision and goals for the event
- Treating your team to dinner for the meeting can be a great team building opportunity

❑ Communicate specials, discounts, timeline and responsibilities for all involved

❑ Provide vendors or representatives attending the event information on specials and inventory on-hand

❑ Touch base with caterer or purchase food items if you are providing yourself

day before

❑ Decorate your space

❑ Prepare food if you are providing yourself

❑ Do a quick run-through of the event with your team before your guests arrive

❑ Charge your camera

event follow-up

❑ Hold a post-event meeting with your staff to identify what worked well and what needs improvement; also, use this time to review how the team did compared to the goals you established

❑ Post event photos to social media platforms so patients can comment and enjoy!
- Sending out thank you cards to your guests is a nice personal touch following the event

PCA SKIN® practice development tools

In addition to unprecedented customer support from our knowledgeable Practice Development Group, PCA SKIN also offers extensive support to help you build your business. By building a partnership with PCA SKIN, your practice will always be on the cutting edge of skin health science. You can feel a sense of pride knowing your knowledge and expertise are backed by a company with more than 20 years experience in helping patients achieve healthy, beautiful skin. The PCA SKIN marketing package provides you with the tools needed to educate your patients on the features and benefits of our daily care products and professional treatments.

Marketing package

- Acrylic brochure stand
- Aging patient brochure (20)
- Discoloration patient brochure (20)
- Sensitive skin patient brochure (20)
- Acne patient brochure (20)
- Chemical peel patient brochure (100)
- Treat All Eye Concerns 18" x 24" poster
- Get Even Skin Tone 18" x 24" poster
- Clear Stubborn Breakouts 18" x 24" poster
- Even Sensitive Skin 18" x 24" poster
- See the Difference 18" x 24" poster
- Smooth Expression Lines 18" x 24" poster
- Rx Treatment Plans (100)
- Before & After Booklet
- 50 small retail bags
- Tissue paper

marketing and backbar essentials

PCA SKIN® strives to provide all skin health professionals with the tools necessary for safe and effective treatment outcomes. Our Marketing and Backbar Essentials have been designed to support your treatment success and assist you in building your own brand.

PCA SKIN® Retail Logo Bag – large (set of 25 with tissue)

Clear Display with PCA Logo

PCA SKIN® Lab Coat (black or white)

PCA SKIN® Fan

Wood's Lamp

Trial-Size Solutions Clear Travel Bag

Fan Brush (large, medium and small)

Sponges (3)

Cotton Squares (4"x4")

Peel Dish

Disposable Headbands (24)

PCA SKIN® brochure & poster series

Sophisticated design meets science in our new suite of aesthetically pleasing, informational posters and brochures. This new offering will not only help you draw attention to the products, services and results you offer patients, but will also serve as educational resources to set expectations, dispel unnecessary fears and instill trust in what you provide.

This new collection provides a visual reference to the decades of dramatic results PCA Certified Professionals using PCA SKIN products have achieved for their patients. Additionally, aspirational photos of real PCA SKIN patients add an eye-catching element to attract patient attention, and stimulate product and treatment interest.

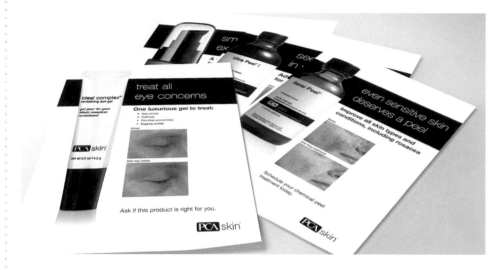

Treat All Eye Concerns

Available in 18" x 24"

See the Difference

Available in 18" x 24"

Clear Stubborn Breakouts

Available in 18" x 24"

Smooth Expression Lines

Available in 18" x 24"

Get Even Skin Tone

Available in 18" x 24"

Even Sensitive Skin

Available in 18" x 24"

Acne patient brochure

(Set of 25)

Aging patient brochure

(Set of 25)

Discoloration patient brochure

(Set of 25)

Sensitive skin patient brochure

(Set of 25)

Product Catalog

Give your patients even more options with the PCA SKIN Patient Brochure that features all of our daily care products. Without having to carry them on your shelf, patients can order any product in the Patient Brochure through your practice.

Available in:
8" x 6"

suggested retail opening order according to skin condition

The skin conditions your practice will see most often depends on many factors, such as skin type, demographics in your area and seasonal changes. Use the suggestions below to purchase the products you are most likely to use in your practice.

Discoloration

	Size	QTY	Price	Total
Facial Wash	7 oz.	3	$ 15.50	$ 46.50
Pigment Bar®	3.3 oz.	1	$ 19.50	$ 19.50
Nutrient Toner	4.4 oz	3	$ 17.50	$ 52.50
C&E Strength Max	1 oz.	3	$ 48.50	$ 145.50
Pigment Gel®	1 oz.	3	$ 27.50	$ 82.50
Pigment Gel® HQ Free	1 oz.	2	$ 27.50	$ 55.00
Intensive Brightening Treatment: 0.5% pure retinol night	1 oz.	2	$ 54.50	$ 109.00
Intensive Pigment Eraser (exclusively sold through physicians)	0.5 oz	2	$ 72.50	$ 145.00
Ideal Complex® Revitalizing Eye Gel	0.5 oz.	3	$ 42.50	$ 127.50
ReBalance	1.7 oz.	3	$ 21.00	$ 63.00
Perfecting Protection Broad Spectrum SPF 30	1.7 oz.	3	$ 17.50	$ 52.50
				$ 898.50

Professional treatments

	Size	QTY	Price	Total
PCA Peel® with Hydroquinone	4 oz	1	$134.00	$ 134.00
4% Pure Retinol Peel (10 packettes/box)		1	$250.00	$ 250.00
6% Pure Retinol Peel (10 packettes/box) (exclusively sold through physicians)		1	$300.00	$ 300.00
Advanced Treatment Booster	1.7 oz	1	$185.00	$ 185.00
				$ 869.00

Total Opening Order $1,767.50

Acne

	Size	QTY	Price	Total
BPO 5% Cleanser	7 oz	3	$ 18.50	$ 55.50
Blemish Control Bar	3.3 oz	1	$ 19.50	$ 19.50
Smoothing Toner	7 oz	3	$ 17.00	$ 51.00
Acne Gel	1 oz	3	$ 22.50	$ 67.50
Acne Cream	0.5 oz	3	$ 13.00	$ 39.00
Intensive Clarity Treatment®: 0.5% pure retinol night	1 oz	2	$ 54.50	$ 109.00
Ideal Complex® Revitalizing Eye Gel	0.5	3	$ 42.50	$ 127.50
Clearskin	1.7 oz	3	$ 21.00	$ 63.00
Weightless Protection Broad Spectrum SPF 45	2.1 oz	3	$ 21.50	$ 64.50
				$ 596.50

Professional treatments

	Size	QTY	Price	Total
Clarify: Therapeutic Salicylic Acid Mask	4 oz	1	$ 46.00	$ 46.00
PCA Peel® with Hydroquinone & Resorcinol	4 oz	1	$134.00	$ 134.00
Advanced Treatment Booster	1.7 oz	1	$185.00	$ 185.00
				$ 365.00

Total Opening Order $ 961.50

Aging

	Size	QTY	Price	Total
Creamy Cleanser	7 oz	3	$15.50	$ 46.50
Nutrient Toner	4.4 oz	3	$17.50	$ 52.50
C&E Strength Max	1 oz	3	$48.50	$ 145.50
ExLinea® Peptide Smoothing Serum	1 oz	3	$54.00	$ 162.00
Total Strength Serum	1 oz	3	$44.50	$ 133.50
Intensive Age Refining Treatment®: 0.5% pure retinol night	1 oz	2	$54.50	$ 109.00
Hyaluronic Acid Boosting Serum	1 oz	3	$57.50	$ 172.50
Ideal Complex® Restorative Eye Cream	0.5 oz	3	$42.50	$ 127.50

	Size	QTY	Price	Total
Perfecting Neck & Décolleté	3 oz	2	$ 39.50	$ 79.00
Collagen Hydrator	1.7 oz	3	$ 21.00	$ 63.00
Hydrator Plus Broad Spectrum SPF 30	1.7 oz	3	$ 17.50	$ 52.50
				$1,143.50
Professional treatments				
Retexturize: Therapeutic Pumpkin Mask	4 oz	1	$ 46.00	$ 46.00
Ultra Peel I®	4 oz	1	$154.00	$ 154.00
Ultra Peel® Forte *(exclusively sold through physicians)*	2 oz	1	$ 93.75	$ 93.75
Advanced Treatment Booster	1.7 oz	1	$185.00	$ 185.00
				$ 478.75
Total Opening Order				$1,622.25

Sensitive Skin

	Size	QTY	Price	Total
Creamy Cleanser	7 oz	3	$ 15.50	$ 46.50
Anti-Redness Serum	1 oz	2	$ 30.50	$ 61.00
Dual Action Redness Relief	1 oz	3	$ 57.50	$ 172.50
Hydrating Serum	1 oz	3	$ 37.00	$ 111.00
Retinol Treatment for Sensitive Skin	1 oz	2	$ 54.50	$ 109.00
Ideal Complex® Revitalizing Eye Gel	0.5 oz	3	$ 42.50	$ 127.50
ReBalance	1.7 oz	3	$ 21.00	$ 63.00
Protecting Hydrator Broad Spectrum SPF 30	1.7 oz	3	$ 17.50	$ 52.50
				$ 743.00
Professional treatments				
Sensi Peel®	4 oz	1	$154.00	$ 154.00
Ultra Peel® I	4 oz	1	$154.00	$ 154.00
Advanced Treatment Booster	1.7 oz	1	$185.00	$ 185.00
				$ 493.00
Total Opening Order				$1,236.00

Preventative

	Size	QTY	Price	Total
Facial Wash	7 oz	3	$ 15.50	$ 46.50
Nutrient Toner	4.4 oz	3	$ 17.50	$ 52.50
C&E Strength	1 oz	3	$ 46.50	$ 139.50
Rejuvenating Serum	1 oz	3	$ 42.50	$ 127.50
Retinol Treatment for Sensitive Skin	1 oz	2	$ 54.50	$ 109.00
Ideal Complex® Revitalizing Eye Gel	0.5 oz	3	$ 42.50	$ 127.50
ReBalance	1.7 oz	3	$ 21.00	$ 63.00
Protecting Hydrator Broad Spectrum SPF 30	1.7 oz	3	$ 17.50	$ 52.50
				$ 718.00
Professional treatments				
Sensi Peel®	4 oz	1	$154.00	$ 154.00
Ultra Peel® I	4 oz	1	$154.00	$ 154.00
Advanced Treatment Booster	1.7 oz	1	$185.00	$ 185.00
				$ 493.00
Total Opening Order				$ 1,211.00

Backbar

	Size	QTY	Price	Total
Facial Wash	16 oz	1	$ 28.00	$ 28.00
Facial Wash Oily/Problem	16 oz	1	$ 28.50	$ 28.50
Smoothing Toner	16 oz	1	$ 30.00	$ 30.00
Nutrient Toner	16 oz	1	$ 50.00	$ 50.00
CliniCalm™ 1%	7 oz	1	$ 58.00	$ 58.00
Weightless Protection Broad Spectrum SPF 45	7 oz	1	$ 58.00	$ 58.00
Perfecting Protection Broad Spectrum SPF 30	7 oz	1	$ 51.00	$ 51.00
Hydrator Plus Broad Spectrum SPF 30	7 oz	1	$ 56.00	$ 56.00
Clearskin	7 oz	1	$ 56.00	$ 56.00
ReBalance	7 oz	1	$ 56.00	$ 56.00

suggested peel charges

When establishing pricing for treatments, it is important to be competitive in your area. This may vary according to specific demographics. For example, prices may be considerably lower in rural areas versus those in a major city. Try not to set your fees too low. It is much easier to lower your charges if you find they are too high. Your patients are usually unhappy with price increases, however small. This is only a guideline.

Initial consultation:	$ 55 (includes trial-size solution)
PCA Peel®	$100 - $175 (1-6 layers)
Sensi Peel®	$100 - $175 (1-4 layers)
Ultra Peel® I	$100 - $175 (1-4 layers)
Ultra Peel Forte®	$150 - $300 (1-3+ layers)
Smoothing Body Peel® Treatment	$150 - $400 (price dependent on body part treated)
Hydrate: Therapeutic Oat Milk Mask	$ 65 - $100
Detoxify: Therapeutic Charcoal Mask	$ 65 - $100
Revitalize: Therapeutic Papaya Mask	$ 65 - $100
Clarify: Therapeutic Salicylic Acid Mask	$ 65 - $100
Retexturize: Therapeutic Pumpkin Mask	$ 65 - $100
Advanced Treatment Booster	$ 20 - $ 30 (optional add-on to other professional treatments)
4% Pure Retinol Peel	$250 - $450
6% Pure Retinol Peel	$300 - $500
Detox Gel Deep Pore Treatment	$ 90 - $110
Oxygenating Trio®	$ 90 - $110

Optional Ideas:

- Charge for five treatments and do the sixth free.
- Alternate different treatments on one patient. Do a promotion, offering one of each treatment.
- Up-charge for add-on/advanced treatments and additional body parts (i.e. neck, chest, hands, lips or arms).
- Promote the **Retexturize: Therapeutic Pumpkin Mask** and **Clarify: Therapeutic Salicylic Acid Mask** during the holidays.
- Take photos of your patients. Use photos of those patients that show the most dramatic improvements (with their written permission) to build your own library of before and after photos.
- Up-charge for added therapeutic massage when incorporated in a peel.

estimating profitability

Daily care products (full-size)	Cost	# of tx	Cost per tx
Facial Wash	$ 15.50	95 - 125	$ .12 - .16
Facial Wash Oily/Problem	$ 15.50	95 - 125	$ .12 - .16
Total Wash Face & Body Cleanser	$ 15.50	95 - 125	$ .12 - .16
Creamy Cleanser	$ 15.50	95 - 125	$ .12 - .16
BPO 5% Cleanser	$ 18.50	95 - 125	$ .14 - .19
Blemish Control Bar	$ 19.50	85 - 115	$ .17 - .22
Dry Skin Relief Bar®	$ 19.50	85 - 115	$ .17 - .22
Pigment Bar®	$ 19.50	85 - 115	$ .17 - .22
Smoothing Toner	$ 17.00	95 - 125	$ .12 - .16
Nutrient Toner	$ 17.50	80 - 110	$ .16 - .22
Gentle Exfoliant	$ 15.50	95 - 125	$ .12 - .16
Pore Refining Treatment	$ 29.00	14 - 20	$1.40 - 2.00
Purifying Mask	$ 29.00	14 - 20	$1.40 - 2.00
Detoxifying Mask	$ 29.00	14 - 20	$1.40 - 2.00
Revitalizing Mask	$ 29.00	14 - 20	$1.40 - 2.00
ExLinea® Peptide Smoothing Serum	$ 54.00	60 - 90	$ .59 - .88
Pigment Gel®	$ 27.50	90 - 120	$ .23 - .30
Pigment Gel® HQ Free	$ 27.50	90 - 120	$ .23 - .30
Acne Gel	$ 22.50	60 - 90	$ .24 - .37
Acne Cream	$ 13.00	90 - 120	$ .10 - .13
C-Quench® Antioxidant Serum	$ 37.50	60 - 90	$ .41 - .62
A&C Synergy Serum®	$ 41.50	60 - 90	$ .46 - .68
Total Strength Serum	$ 44.50	60 - 90	$ .49 - .73
Hydrating Serum	$ 37.50	60 - 90	$ .41 - .62
Rejuvenating Serum	$ 42.50	60 - 90	$ .47 - .70
Anti-Redness Serum	$ 30.50	60 - 90	$ .33 - .49
Retinol Renewal with RestorAtive Complex	$ 45.00	60 - 90	$ .49 - .73
Retinol Treatment for Sensitive Skin	$ 54.50	60 - 90	$ .59 - .88
Intensive Clarity Treatment®: 0.5% pure retinol night	$ 54.50	60 - 90	$ .59 - .88
Intensive Age Refining Treatment®: 0.5% pure retinol night	$ 54.50	60 - 90	$ .59 - .88
Intensive Brightening Treatment: 0.5% pure retinol night	$ 54.50	60 - 90	$ .59 - .88
Intensive Pigment Eraser	$ 72.50	30 - 45	$ .41 - .62
C&E Strength	$ 46.50	60 - 90	$ .51 - .77
C&E Strength Max	$ 48.50	60 - 90	$ .53 - .80
Hyaluronic Acid Boosting Serum	$ 57.50	60 - 90	$ .95 - .63
Dual Action Redness Relief	$ 57.50	60 - 90	$ .95 - .63
Ideal Complex® Revitalizing Eye Gel	$ 42.50	90 - 120	$ .35 - .47
Ideal Complex® Restorative Eye Cream	$ 42.50	90 - 120	$ .35 - .47
EyeXcellence	$ 25.00	90 - 120	$ .20 - .27
Perfecting Neck & Décolleté	$ 39.50	85 - 115	$ .34 - .46
CliniCalm™ 1%	$ 23.50	90 - 120	$ .19 - .25
Peptide Lip Therapy	$ 12.00	85 - 105	$ .11 - .14
Weightless Protection Broad Spectrum SPF 45	$ 21.50	90 - 120	$ .18 - .23
Perfecting Protection Broad Spectrum SPF 30	$ 17.50	85 - 115	$ .15 - .20
Protecting Hydrator Broad Spectrum SPF 30	$ 17.50	85 - 115	$ .15 - .20
Hydrator Plus Broad Spectrum SPF 30	$ 17.50	85 - 115	$ .15 - .20
Active Broad Spectrum SPF 45: Water Resistant	$ 17.50	85 - 115	$ .15 - .20
Sheer Tint Broad Spectrum SPF 45	$ 24.50	85 - 115	$ .29 - .21
Clearskin	$ 21.00	85 - 115	$ .17 - .23
ReBalance	$ 21.00	85 - 115	$ .17 - .23
Après Peel® Hydrating Balm	$ 21.00	85 - 115	$ .17 - .23
Collagen Hydrator	$ 21.00	85 - 115	$ .17 - .23
Silkcoat® Balm	$ 21.00	85 - 115	$ .17 - .23
Body Therapy	$ 30.00	155 - 230	$ .13 - .19

Daily care products (backbar)

Facial Wash (16 oz)	$ 28.00	217 - 286	$ .09 - .12
Facial Wash Oily/Problem (16 oz)	$ 28.50	217 - 286	$ .09 - .12
Smoothing Toner (16 oz)	$ 30.00	217 - 286	$ .09 - .12
Nutrient Toner (16 oz)	$ 50.00	217 - 286	$ .16 - .21
CliniCalm™ (7 oz)	$ 58.00	299 - 399	$ .19 - .15
Weightless Protection Broad Spectrum SPF 45 (7 oz)	$ 58.00	299 - 399	$ .19 - .15
Perfecting Protection Broad Spectrum SPF 30 (7 oz)	$ 51.00	311 - 462	$ .10 - .15
Hydrator Plus Broad Spectrum SPF 30 (7 oz)	$ 56.00	311 - 462	$ .12 - .17
Clearskin (7 oz)	$ 56.00	311 - 462	$ .12 - .17
ReBalance (7 oz)	$ 56.00	311 - 462	$ .12 - .17

Professional treatments

PCA Peel® (2 oz.)	$ 69.50	20 - 30	$ 2.32 - 3.48
PCA Peel® (4 oz.)	$134.00	40 - 60	$ 2.23 - 3.35
Sensi Peel® (2 oz.)	$ 79.50	20 - 30	$ 2.65 - 3.98
Sensi Peel® (4 oz.)	$154.00	40 - 60	$ 2.57 - 3.85
Ultra Peel® I (2 oz.)	$ 79.50	20 - 30	$ 2.65 - 3.98
Ultra Peel® I (4 oz.)	$154.00	40 - 60	$ 2.57 - 3.85
Ultra Peel Forte® (2 oz.)	$ 93.75	15 - 25	$ 3.75 - 6.25
Pre-Peel Accelerator Mask (Step 1) (4 oz.)	$ 83.25	35 - 55	$ 1.51 - 2.38
Smoothing Body Peel® (Step 2) (4 oz.)	$163.25	35 - 55	$ 2.97 - 4.66
Hydrate: Therapeutic Oat Milk Mask (4 oz.)	$ 46.00	35 - 45	$ 1.02 - 1.31
Detoxify: Therapeutic Charcoal Mask (4 oz.)	$ 46.00	35 - 45	$ 1.02 - 1.31
Revitalize: Therapeutic Papaya Acid Mask (4 oz.)	$ 46.00	30 - 40	$ 1.15 - 1.53
Clarify: Therapeutic Salicylic Acid Mask (4 oz.)	$ 46.00	40 - 50	$ .92 - 1.15
Retexturize: Therapeutic Pumpkin Mask (4 oz.)	$ 46.00	50 - 60	$ .77 - .92
Advanced Treatment Booster (1.7 oz.)	$185.00	30 - 50	$ 2.00 - 3.33
4% Pure Retinol Peel (10 packettes per box)	$250.00	10	$25.00
6% Pure Retinol Peel (10 packettes per box)	$300.00	10	$30.00
Oxygenating Trio® (full-size)	$126.00	40 - 50	$ 2.65 - 3.31
Detox Gel Deep Pore Treatment (4 oz.)	$ 87.00	40 - 60	$ 1.45 - 2.18
Replenishing Gel (3.3 oz.)	$ 37.00	50 - 70	$ .53 - .74
Calming Balm (3.3 oz.)	$ 44.00	85 - 95	$ .46 - .52

reference materials

Chart: controlling hyperpigmentation

Gently exfoliate	Increase cell turnover	Inhibit melanogenesis	Protect from UV rays and other inflammatory stimulants
■ AHA ■ Keratolytics ■ Beaded mechanical exfoliation products	■ Retinoids ■ Vigna aconitifolia seed extract ■ AHA	■ Hydroquinone ■ Arbutin ■ Kojic acid ■ Retinoids ■ L-ascorbic acid ■ Lactic acid ■ Azelaic acid ■ Licorice extract ■ Mulberry extract ■ Rumex extracts ■ Phenylethyl resorcinol ■ Resveratrol ■ Phytic acid ■ Niacinamide ■ Hexylresorcinol ■ Hydroxyphenoxy propionic acid	■ Broad spectrum sunscreen products ■ L-ascorbic acid ■ Vitamin E (tocopherol) ■ Glycosamino-glycans (GAG) ■ Epigallocatechin gallate (EGCG) ■ Resveratrol ■ Boldine extract ■ Porphyra umbilicalis extract ■ Glutathione ■ Silybin (milk thistle) ■ Caffeine ■ Niacinamide

K

Chart: controlling acne

	Gently exfoliate and increase cell turnover	Control sebum production	Decrease P. acnes proliferation	Protect from UV rays and other inflammatory stimulants
Topical ingredient recommendations	<ul><li>AHA</li><li>BHA</li><li>PHA</li><li>TCA</li><li>Retinoids</li><li>Azelaic acid</li><li>Sulfur</li><li>Resorcinol</li><li>Gluconolactone</li><li>Benzoyl peroxide</li><li>Vigna aconitifolia seed extract</li><li>Fruit enzymes</li></ul>	<ul><li>Salicylic acid</li><li>Ginger root extract</li><li>Green burnet root</li><li>Licorice extract</li><li>Cucumber extract</li><li>Cinnamon bark</li><li>Astringent toner</li><li>Lilac stem cell extract</li></ul>	<ul><li>Benzoyl peroxide</li><li>Salicylic acid</li><li>Azelaic acid</li><li>Lactic acid</li><li>Kojic acid</li><li>Tea tree oil</li><li>Bakuchiol</li></ul>	<ul><li>Broad spectrum sunscreen products</li><li>Gluconolactone</li><li>Aloe vera</li><li>Bisabolol</li><li>Panthenol</li><li>Licorice extract</li><li>Boldine extract</li><li>Resveratrol</li><li>Epigallocatechin gallate (EGCG)</li><li>Silybin (milk thistle)</li><li>Caffeine</li><li>Niacinamide</li></ul>
Prescription options (Patients should always check with their physician prior to taking any prescription drugs for the treatment of a skin condition.)	<ul><li>Tretinoin (Retin A®)</li><li>Tazarotene (Tazorac®)</li><li>Isotretinoin (Accutane®)</li></ul>	<ul><li>Spironolactone</li><li>Oral contraceptives</li><li>Hormone therapies</li></ul>	<ul><li>Tetracycline (oral)</li><li>Erythromycin (oral or topical)</li><li>Clindamycin (topical)</li><li>Sodium sulfacetamide (topical)</li></ul>	<ul><li>Oral antibiotics that provide anti-inflammatory benefits (e.g. tetracycline and doxycycline)</li></ul>
Lifestyle considerations	<ul><li>Avoid using makeup that is very heavy or contains pore-clogging oils (Note: many oils high in essential fatty acids are good for acne and do not clog pores)</li><li>Mineral powder foundations may provide coverage without blocking the follicle</li><li>Avoid makeup that contains talc</li></ul>	<ul><li>Avoid over-drying and over-stimulating; this will increase oil production</li><li>Always apply a hydrator/ moisturizer after cleansing</li><li>Oil-absorbing papers help to absorb surface oils throughtout the day without reapplying makeup</li></ul>	<ul><li>Wash hands regularly</li><li>Avoid contact with objects that might be bacteria-ridden such as phones, hands, workout clothing, dirty pillowcases, etc.</li><li>Clean objects regularly with alcohol or antibacterial wipes, where applicable</li><li>Wash makeup applicators frequently</li></ul>	<ul><li>Avoid high percentages of aggressive topicals that can induce inflammation</li><li>Do not pick or excoriate blemishes</li><li>Apply a broad spectrum SPF hydrator daily; anti-acne ingredients make the skin more sun-sensitive</li><li>Over-stimulation will increase inflammation and breakouts</li></ul>

K

Chart: controlling sensitive skin

Gently exfoliate and increase cell turnover	Decrease redness and inflammation	Increase hydration to control excessive dryness	Decrease possible bacterial factors	Protect from UV exposure

▪ AHA
▪ BHA
▪ TCA
▪ Gentle retinoids (eg: retinol complexes, retinyl esters)
▪ Papain
	▪ Brown algae
	▪ Red algae
	▪ Caper bud extract
	▪ Hydrocortisone
	▪ Aloe vera
	▪ Panthenol
	▪ Evening primrose seed oil
	▪ Bisabolol
	▪ Menthyl lactate
	▪ Balm mint
	▪ Willow bark
	▪ Niacinamide
		Humectants:
		  ▪ Glycerin
		  ▪ Hyaluronic acid
		  ▪ Sodium PCA
		  ▪ Urea
		  ▪ Honey
		  ▪ Sorbitol
		  ▪ AHA
		  ▪ Pseudoalteromonas ferment
		  ▪ Oat milk
		Occlusives:
		  ▪ Silicones (dimethicone & cyclomethicone)
		  ▪ Plant oils
		  ▪ Squalane
		  ▪ Shea butter
		  ▪ Zinc oxide
		  ▪ Niacinamide
			▪ Azelaic acid
			▪ Lactic acid
			▪ Kojic acid
			▪ Tea tree oil
			▪ Papain
				▪ Broad spectrum sunscreen products
				▪ Caffeine
				▪ Silybin (milk thistle)

K

Chart: controlling aging skin

Gently exfoliate and increase cell turnover	Increase matrix proteins	Inhibit melanogenesis	Increase hydration	Protect from UV rays and other inflammatory stimulants
• AHA • BHA • TCA • Retinoids • Fruit enzymes	• Palmitoyl pentapeptide-4 • Palmitoyl tripeptide-38 • Palmitoyl tetrapeptide-7 • Acetyl hexapeptide-8 • L-ascorbic acid • Retinoids • Vigna aconitifolia seed extract • Calcium hydroxymethionine • Rye seed extract	• Retinoids • Lactic acid • L-ascorbic acid • Licorice extract • Hydroquinone • Kojic acid • Azelaic acid • Phenylethyl resorcinol • Resveratrol • Arbutin • Phytic acid • Lilac stem cell extract • Niacinamide • Hexylresorcinol • Hydroxyphenoxy propionic acid	• Hyaluronic acid • Sodium PCA • Phospholipids • Sphingolipids • Urea • Glycerin • Lactic acid • Lecithin • Ceramides • Retinoids • Oat milk	• Broad spectrum sunscreen products • Resveratrol • Epigallocatechin gallate (EGCG) • Soy isoflavones • Glutathione • Rosehip seed oil • L-ascorbic acid • Vitamin E (tocopherol) • Retinoids • Aloe vera • Caffeine • Silybin (milk thistle) • Grape stem cell extract • Lilac stem cell extract • Ergothioneine • Glycerophospho-inositol lycine

K

Treatment recommendations

	Acne grades I-II [dehydrated]	Acne grades I-II [oily]	Acne grades III-IV [dehydrated]	Acne grades III-IV [oily]	Preventative
Resilient	▪ Sensi Peel® ▪ Ultra Peel® I ▪ Ultra Peel Forte® ▪ Advanced Treatment Booster ▪ 4% Pure Retinol Peel ▪ 6% Pure Retinol Peel ▪ Oxygenating Trio® ▪ Detox Gel Deep Pore Treatment	▪ PCA Peel® with Hydroquinone & Resorcinol ▪ Detoxify: Therapeutic Charcoal Mask ▪ Clarify: Therapeutic Salicylic Acid Mask ▪ Retexturize: Therapeutic Pumpkin Mask ▪ Advanced Treatment Booster ▪ 4% Pure Retinol Peel ▪ 6% Pure Retinol Peel ▪ Oxygenating Trio® ▪ Detox Gel Deep Pore Treatment	▪ Sensi Peel® ▪ Ultra Peel® I ▪ Ultra Peel Forte® ▪ Advanced Treatment Booster ▪ 4% Pure Retinol Peel ▪ 6% Pure Retinol Peel ▪ Detox Gel Deep Pore Treatment	▪ PCA Peel® with Hydroquinone & Resorcinol ▪ Detoxify: Therapeutic Charcoal Mask ▪ Clarify: Therapeutic Salicylic Acid Mask ▪ Retexturize: Therapeutic Pumpkin Mask ▪ Advanced Treatment Booster ▪ 4% Pure Retinol Peel ▪ 6% Pure Retinol Peel ▪ Detox Gel Deep Pore Treatment	
Normal	▪ Sensi Peel® ▪ Ultra Peel® I ▪ Ultra Peel Forte® ▪ Advanced Treatment Booster ▪ 4% Pure Retinol Peel ▪ 6% Pure Retinol Peel ▪ Oxygenating Trio® ▪ Detox Gel Deep Pore Treatment	▪ PCA Peel® with Hydroquinone ▪ Detoxify: Therapeutic Charcoal Mask ▪ Clarify: Therapeutic Salicylic Acid Mask ▪ Advanced Treatment Booster ▪ 4% Pure Retinol Peel ▪ 6% Pure Retinol Peel ▪ Oxygenating Trio® ▪ Detox Gel Deep Pore Treatment	▪ Ultra Peel® I ▪ Advanced Treatment Booster ▪ 4% Pure Retinol Peel ▪ 6% Pure Retinol Peel ▪ Detox Gel Deep Pore Treatment	▪ PCA Peel® with Hydroquinone ▪ Detoxify: Therapeutic Charcoal Mask ▪ Clarify: Therapeutic Salicylic Acid Mask ▪ Retexturize: Therapeutic Pumpkin Mask ▪ Advanced Treatment Booster ▪ 4% Pure Retinol Peel ▪ 6% Pure Retinol Peel	▪ Sensi Peel® ▪ Ultra Peel® I ▪ Revitalize: Therapeutic Papaya Mask ▪ Oxygenating Trio®
Sensitive	▪ Sensi Peel® ▪ Revitalize: Therapeutic Papaya Mask ▪ Advanced Treatment Booster ▪ Oxygenating Trio® ▪ Detox Gel Deep Pore Treatment	▪ PCA Peel® Hydroquinone Free ▪ Detoxify: Therapeutic Charcoal Mask ▪ Revitalize: Therapeutic Papaya Mask ▪ Advanced Treatment Booster ▪ Oxygenating Trio® ▪ Detox Gel Deep Pore Treatment	▪ Sensi Peel® ▪ Revitalize: Therapeutic Papaya Mask ▪ Advanced Treatment Booster ▪ Detox Gel Deep Pore Treatment	▪ PCA Peel® Hydroquinone Free ▪ Detoxify: Therapeutic Charcoal Mask ▪ Revitalize: Therapeutic Papaya Mask ▪ Advanced Treatment Booster	▪ Sensi Peel® ▪ Revitalize: Therapeutic Papaya Mask
Hypersensitive/ reactive	▪ Sensi Peel® ▪ Detox Gel Deep Pore Treatment	▪ Sensi Peel® ▪ Advanced Treatment Booster ▪ Detox Gel Deep Pore Treatment	▪ Sensi Peel®	▪ Sensi Peel® ▪ Advanced Treatment Booster	▪ Revitalize: Therapeutic Papaya Mask

K

Treatment recommendations, continued

	Hyperpigmentation [dry]	Hyperpigmentation [oily]	Sensitive	Age control [dry]	Age control [oily]
Resilient	• Ultra Peel® I • Ultra Peel® Forte® • Ultra Peel® II • 4% Pure Retinol Peel • 6% Pure Retinol Peel	• PCA Peel® with Hydroquinone & Resorcinol • Advanced Treatment Booster • 4% Pure Retinol Peel • 6% Pure Retinol Peel		• Sensi Peel® • Ultra Peel® I • Ultra Peel® Forte® • Ultra Peel® II • 4% Pure Retinol Peel • 6% Pure Retinol Peel	• PCA Peel® with Hydroquinone & Resorcinol • Detoxify: Therapeutic Charcoal Mask • Retexturize: Therapeutic Pumpkin Mask • Advanced Treatment Booster • 4% Pure Retinol Peel • 6% Pure Retinol Peel
Normal	• Ultra Peel® I • Ultra Peel® Forte® • Ultra Peel® II • 4% Pure Retinol Peel • 6% Pure Retinol Peel	• PCA Peel® with Hydroquinone • Detoxify: Therapeutic Charcoal Mask • Advanced Treatment Booster • 4% Pure Retinol Peel • 6% Pure Retinol Peel	• Sensi Peel® • Ultra Peel® I • Hydrate: Therapeutic Oat Milk Mask • Clarify: Therapeutic Salicylic Acid Mask • Ultra Peel® II • Advanced Treatment Booster	• Sensi Peel® • Ultra Peel® I • Revitalize: Therapeutic Papaya Mask • Ultra Peel® II • Advanced Treatment Booster • 4% Pure Retinol Peel • 6% Pure Retinol Peel	• PCA Peel® with Hydroquinone • Detoxify: Therapeutic Charcoal Mask • Revitalize: Therapeutic Papaya Mask • Advanced Treatment Booster • 4% Pure Retinol Peel • 6% Pure Retinol Peel
Sensitive	• Ultra Peel® I • Ultra Peel® II	• PCA Peel® Hydroquinone Free • Advanced Treatment Booster	• Sensi Peel® • Hydrate: Therapeutic Oat Milk Mask • Ultra Peel® II • Advanced Treatment Booster	• Sensi Peel® • Revitalize: Therapeutic Papaya Mask • Ultra Peel® II	• PCA Peel® Hydroquinone Free • Detoxify: Therapeutic Charcoal Mask • Revitalize: Therapeutic Papaya Mask • Advanced Treatment Booster
Hypersensitive/ reactive	• Sensi Peel® • Ultra Peel® II	• Sensi Peel® • Advanced Treatment Booster	• Hydrate: Therapeutic Oat Milk Mask	• Sensi Peel® • Hydrate: Therapeutic Oat Milk Mask • Ultra Peel® II	• Sensi Peel® • Advanced Treatment Booster

Note: You can always consider a less stimulating TCA or Jessner's peel for each category. For example, if **Ultra Peel Forte®** is recommended, you can use **Ultra Peel® I** or **Sensi Peel®** in its place. If any of the above mentioned conditions appear on the body then **Smoothing Body Peel® Treatment** may be used, except for hyper-sensitive skin conditions or impaired barrier function.

Indications

Modified and enhanced Jessner's solutions

	Hyper-pigmenta-tion	Acne	Sensitive skin & rosacea	Visible aging	Dry skin	Oily skin	Dull/sallow complexions	Pregnancy & lactation	Fitz. I-III	Fitz. IV-VI
PCA Peel® Hydroquinone Free	X	X		X		X			X	X (Up to V)
PCA Peel® with Hydroquinone	X	X (When PIH is present)		X (When UV-induced hyper-pigmentation is present)		X			X	X (Up to IV)
PCA Peel® with Hydroquinone & Resorcinol	X	X		X		X			X	

Blended TCA peels

	Hyper-pigmenta-tion	Acne	Sensitive skin & rosacea	Visible aging	Dry skin	Oily skin	Dull/sallow complexions	Pregnancy & lactation	Fitz. I-III	Fitz. IV-VI
Sensi Peel®	X	X (Inflamed and sensitive acne)	X	X (Mild signs)	X		X		X	X
Ultra Peel® I	X	X (Adult and dehydrated acne)	X (Non-inflamed)	X	X				X	X (Up to V)

Indications, continued

	Hyper-pigmentation	Acne	Sensitive skin & rosacea	Visible aging	Dry skin	Oily skin	Dull/sallow complexions	Pregnancy & lactation	Fitz. I-III	Fitz. IV-VI
Ultra Peel Forte®	X	X (Textural scarring)		X	X				X	
Smoothing Body Peel®	X	X	X (Psoriasis and atopic dermatitis)	X	X		X		X	X
Therapeutic masks										
Hydrate: Therapeutic Oat Milk Mask			X	X	X		X	X	X	X
Detoxify: Therapeutic Charcoal Mask		X		X		X		X	X	X
Revitalize: Therapeutic Mask				X			X	X	X	X
Clarify: Therapeutic Salicylic Acid Mask		X				X	X		X	X
Retexturize: Therapeutic Pumpkin Mask		X		X		X	X		X	X (Up to IV)
Retinoid treatments										
Advanced Treatment Booster		X	X	X	X	X	X		X	X
4% Pure Retinol Peel	X	X		X	X	X	X		X	
6% Pure Retinol Peel	X	X		X		X	X		X	
Peel alternatives										
Detox Gel Deep Pore Treatment		X				X		X	X	X
Oxygenating Trio®		X		X			X	X	X	X

K

Layering guidelines

The number of layers of a PCA SKIN® chemical peel to apply depends upon a variety of circumstances such as: advanced preparation of the skin, skin type, skin thickness, use of topical prescription medications, antibiotics, ethnic heritage, etc. Use the sensitivity scale to determine how many layers each individual patient can tolerate.

PCA SKIN professional treatment	Very superficial	Superficial	Medium-depth	Recommended maximum layers
PCA Peel®	1 to 3	4 to 6		6
Sensi Peel®	1 to 2	3 to 4		4
Ultra Peel® I	1	2 to 4		4
Ultra Peel Forte® *For physicians' use only*		1 to 2	Patient dependent	No maximum for physicians when following medium-depth protocol
Smoothing Body Peel® Treatment		I to 2		2
Advanced Treatment Booster				1
4% Pure Retinol Peel				1
6% Pure Retinol Peel				1
Hydrate: Therapeutic Oat Milk Mask	1			1
Detoxify: Therapeutic Charcoal Mask	1			1
Revitalize: Therapeutic Papaya Mask	1			1
Clarify: Therapeutic Salicylic Acid Mask		1		1
Retexturize: Therapeutic Pumpkin Mask		1		1
Oxygenating Trio®	All steps: 1	All steps: 1		N/A
Detox Gel Deep Pore Treatment	1	1		N/A

K

Suggested correctives for customization

	Acne I & II	Acne III &IV	Preventative
Resilient/normal	Acne Gel C-Quench® Antioxidant Serum Rejuvenating Serum Intensive Clarity Treatment®: 0.5% pure retinol night	Acne Cream C-Quench® Antioxidant Serum Anti-Redness Serum Rejuvenating Serum Intensive Clarity Treatment®: 0.5% pure retinol night	Rejuvenating Serum C&E Strength Retinol Treatment for Sensitive Skin EyeXcellence
Sensitive	Acne Gel A&C Synergy Serum® Retinol Treatment for Sensitive Skin	Acne Gel A&C Synergy Serum® Anti-Redness Serum Retinol Treatment for Sensitive Skin	Rejuvenating Serum C&E Strength Retinol Treatment for Sensitive Skin EyeXcellence

	Hyperpigmentation	Sensitive skin	Age control
Resilient/normal	Pigment Gel® C&E Strength Max Intensive Brightening Treatment: 0.5% pure retinol night Intensive Pigment Eraser Ideal Complex® Revitalizing Eye Gel Perfecting Neck & Décolleté		ExLinea® Peptide Smoothing Serum Total Strength Serum C&E Strength Max Intensive Age Refining Treatment®: 0.5% pure retinol night Ideal Complex® Restorative Eye Cream Perfecting Neck & Décolleté
Sensitive	Pigment Gel® HQ Free A&C Synergy Serum® Retinol Treatment for Sensitive Skin C&E Strength Perfecting Neck & Décolleté	C-Quench® Antioxidant Serum Hyaluronic Acid Boosting Serum Rejuvenating Serum Dual Action Redness Relief Retinol Treatment for Sensitive Skin Ideal Complex® Restorative Eye Cream Perfecting Neck & Décolleté	ExLinea® Peptide Smoothing Serum Total Strength Serum C&E Strength Retinol Treatment for Sensitive Skin Ideal Complex® Restorative Eye Cream Perfecting Neck & Décolleté

When applying these products, it is important to layer by consistency: water, gel, cream.

Post-treatment expectations

	Day of treatment	Following morning	Day 2	Day 3 – 5	Day 5+
Skin appearance and feeling	▪ Tight ▪ Moist and dewy appearance ▪ Mild to moderate edema and erythema	▪ Tight ▪ Dry ▪ Mild to moderate edema and erythema	▪ Skin may begin to flake or peel	▪ Heaviest flaking or peeling	▪ Typically peeling is complete
Precautions	▪ Apply products in PCA SKIN® **The Post-Procedure Solution** ▪ Keep cool	▪ Reapply products in PCA SKIN **The Post-Procedure Solution** ▪ Keep cool	▪ Do not pick at loose skin ▪ Reapply products in PCA SKIN **The Post-Procedure Solution**	▪ Reapply products in PCA SKIN **The Post-Procedure Solution** ▪ Avoid direct sun exposure	▪ Restart recommended PCA SKIN daily care

Frequency of treatment

Based on the natural skin cycle

	Day of treatment	Week 1	Week 2	Week 3	Week 4
Normal/ maintenance (Once a month)	X				X
Pigment/melasma (Every three weeks to begin, then once a month)	X			X	
Acne/ blemishes (Every two weeks to begin, then once a month)	X		X		X
Rosacea/ sensitive skin (Once a month)	X				X
Aging skin (Every three weeks to begin, then once a month)	X			X	

Goal: to get everyone to a once-a-month maintenance schedule

ingredient information

a

Acacia Senegal Gum is an effective growth factor alternative to improve skin firmness and elasticity while reducing wrinkles in the crow's feet area.

Acetyl Hexapeptide-8 (Argireline) works by relaxing the facial muscles that cause repeated facial expression wrinkling (crow's feet, laugh lines, etc). It imitates a section of a protein called SNAP-25. This oligopeptide interferes with the assembly of a complex involved in the release of a group of neurotransmitters called catecholamines. Some results indicate that this oligopeptide attenuates wrinkle depth. Argireline is a chain of amino acids linked to each other by peptide bonds: an acetylated glutamic acid, glutamic acid, methionine and arginine.

Acetyl Tetrapeptide-5 is a peptide with anti-edema effects that increases skin elasticity and skin moisturization while improving the appearance of dark circles around the eyes.

Aesculus Hippocastanum (Horse Chestnut) Seed Extract provides aescin, a saponin that has been shown to support healthy circulation.

Albizia Julibrissin Bark Extract reduces upper eyelid sagging, strengthens the dermis and reduces crow's feet wrinkles, while addressing dark circles and puffiness.

Algae (also listed as Algae Extract) detoxifies the skin and helps ease the skin's absorption of amino acids, mineral bioactives and vitamins. Its water-binding property helps maintain the skin's natural moisture balance.

Allantoin can be found in wheat germs, sycamore leaves, the bark of chestnut trees and comfrey root. This antioxidant inhibits the growth of certain strains of bacteria and soothes the skin.

Aloe Barbadensis Leaf Juice is an effective antibacterial agent best known for its softening and soothing benefits. Aloe also acts to suppress the inflammatory response of ultraviolet light exposure.

Aminoguanidine is a compound that assists the skin in its fight against the cross-linking of collagen by inhibiting the build up of glucose (A.G.E.-advanced glycosylation end products). It also protects the skin from free radical damage and helps to keep the skin soft.

Arbutin is found in wheat, pears, bearberries, blueberries and cranberries. Arbutin acts as a melanogenesis inhibitor by suppressing the activity of tyrosinase and by inhibiting melanosome maturation. Arbutin is also an antioxidant and skin conditioner.

Arctium Majus Root Extract is also known as burdock root. Burdock has been used for centuries to treat many internal and external ailments. Its antibacterial and anti-fungal action has made it effective for treating many types of dermatitis.

Arctostaphylos Uva Ursi Leaf Extract is the INCI name for bearberry; a source of arbutin.

Ascophyllum Nodosum Extract is also known as brown algae. When combined with asparagopsis armata extract (red algae), it inhibits VEGF (vascular endothelial growth factor), which encourages microcapillary hyperpermeability (leakiness). It also suppresses PGE_2 activity (prostaglandin E_2), which induces microcapillary dilation (enlargement of capillary diameter).

Asiaticoside is a novel ingredient that helps inhibit MMP1 to reduce collagen degradation while supporting dermal regeneration.

L-Ascorbic Acid is a powerful water-soluble antioxidant that is the only bio-available form of vitamin C for the skin. It is also a cofactor for an enzyme crucial in the synthesis of collagen (prolyl hydrolase) and is an antioxidant agent that provides important protection against damage induced by UV radiation. Vitamin C also improves skin elasticity and decreases wrinkles by stimulating collagen synthesis. Additionally, it reduces erythema and acts as a melanogenesis inhibitor. It functions as an MMPi by controlling the expression of inflammatory enzymes (matrix metalloproteinases).

Asparagopsis Armata Extract is also known as red algae. When combined with ascophyllum nodosum extract (brown algae), it inhibits VEGF (vascular endothelial growth factor) expression, which encourages microcapillary hyperpermeability (leakiness). It also suppresses PGE_2 activity (prostaglandin E_2), which induces microcapillary dilation (enlargement of capillary diameter).

Avena Sativa (Oat) Kernel Extract is a superb moisturizer, as well as an anti-irritant and anti-inflammatory agent.

Avobenzone is a UVA sunscreen ingredient. Avobenzone is combined with UVB filters (e.g. benzophenone-3 or oxybenzone) to form effective, broad spectrum sunscreens.

Azelaic Acid is a melanogenesis inhibitor that suppresses tyrosinase production and also kills malfunctioning melanocytes without injuring healthy surrounding cells. This ingredient also provides bactericidal and antimicrobial action, and helps to normalize keratinization in the skin.

b

Bakuchiol is a natural meroterpene phenol, antimicrobial and anti-inflammatory.

Bentonite is an absorbent clay that helps pull unwanted dirt, oil and debris from the pores.

Beta-Carotene is a fat-soluble antioxidant that scavenges singlet oxygen radicals. It has a characteristic yellow-orange pigment. It is widely found in carrots, squash and pumpkin. Beta-carotene is converted to vitamin A in the body.

Beta-Glucan is derived from oat; this ingredient reduces irritation while also stimulating the strengthening of damaged skin.

Betula Alba Bark Extract is sourced from many varieties of birch trees. It provides potent anti-inflammatory benefits because of its high concentrations of betulinic acid and flavanoids.

Bisabolol is one of the principal active compounds found in chamomile. It is largely responsible for chamomile's anti-inflammatory effects. Topically, alpha bisabolol has been found to be one of the most potent topical ingredients for treating skin inflammation.

Borago Officinalis (Borage) Seed Oil is an excellent source of the omega-3 essential fatty acid (EFA) gamma linolenic acid (GLA). GLA provides the skin with potent anti-inflammatory action. EFAs are major components in cellular membranes and allow the cells to remain flexible and functional. This is a beneficial oil for acneic skin due to its high EFA content.

Boron Nitride is a naturally occurring mineral that reflects light away from the eye area, leaving dark circles and under-eye bags immediately brighter.

Butyrospermum Parkii (Shea Butter) is butter from the nut of the Mangifolia tree in Central Africa. It's also called Karite Butter or African Shea Nut Butter. Shea butter is high in triglycerides and gamma linolenic acid (GLA), and it has a high content of vitamins A and E. It softens the skin and maintains moisture without greasiness.

C

Caffeine has demonstrated the ability to force damaged skin cells into apoptosis (death), which inhibits the potential for skin carcinogenesis. Caffeine is also a powerful antioxidant that is capable of reducing several UV-induced free radicals, including hydroxyl radicals, hydrogen peroxide, peroxyl radicals and singlet oxygen.

Calcium Hydroxymethionine was tested specifically on neck tissue; this ingredient fortifies and restructures thin, fragile skin.

Calendula Officinalis Flower Extract is a calming antioxidant that aids in skin rejuvenation.

Camellia Oliferia (Green Tea) Leaf Extract has more health benefits than black tea, as the leaves are not fermented, so all of the active ingredients remain unchanged. Green tea contains vitamins, minerals and oils. One of the most important components are the catechin polyphenols (e.g. epigallocatechin gallate [EGCG]), which are thought to be responsible for most of the antioxidant properties in green tea.

Capparis Spinosa Fruit Extract is commonly known as caper bud extract. It contains capparenols that act as anti-inflammatory agents by inhibiting the production of cytokines, immune activated cells involved in inflammatory reactions.

Carica Papaya (Payaya) Fruit contains the enzyme papain, an effective keratolytic. Papaya fruit is also an antibacterial agent and possesses wound healing capabilities.

Carnitine is an amino acid derivative found in nearly every cell in the body. Carnitine has demonstrated excellent antioxidant benefits, and encourages healthy cell proliferation and desquamation.

Cassia Angustifolia Leaf Extract has a calming and hydrating effect on the skin. The polysaccharides in this extract function similarly in plants as hyaluronic acid does in animals, by increasing the skin's ability to retain moisture.

Ceramides are complex lipids. Ceramides exert important biological effects, but they are found in minute concentrations in most tissues. The exception is the stratum corneum of the skin, which contains relatively high levels of distinctive ceramides, together with free fatty acids and cholesterol. The specific function of these lipids is still a matter of speculation, but clearly they have a role in the barrier properties of the skin. They limit the loss of water and solutes and, at the same, time prevent the entry of harmful substances into the skin. Topical application of ceramides is an effective way of replenishing the skin's endogenous lipids, thus repairing cell membranes and helping it in its fundamental role as a barrier.

Chamomilla Recutita (Matricaria) Flower Extract is a variety of chamomile, a strong anti-inflammatory.

Chlorella Vulgaris Extract is a skin conditioning and protecting agent. It is also a rich source of carotenoids; amino acids such as lysine, proline, glycine and alanine; and methyl-cobolamine, the most bioavailable form of B_{12}. Science suggests that chlorella vulgaris extract may also stimulate collagen production and increase skin firmness.

Cinchona Succiruba Bark Extract is a potent antibacterial agent that is naturally found in the leaves of the cinchona plant and is a source of quinine.

Cinnamomum Cassia (Cinnamon) Bark Extract contains many antimicrobial, anesthetic and anti-inflammatory chemicals. It is used as a blend with green burnet and ginger root to reduce the appearance of pores and control sebum production.

Citric Acid is an alpha hydroxy acid (AHA) found in citrus fruits. It increases the hyaluronic acid content in the dermis and epidermis to help the skin attract and hold moisture more effectively. It also exfoliates dead skin cells and is a natural skin brightener.

Citrus Aurantium Dulcis Callus Culture Extract (Orange Stem Cell Extract) increases the production of collagen and elastin; and organizes and redensifies the dermal structure to reduce fine lines and wrinkles, and increase elasticity and firmness.

Citrus Grandis (Grapefruit) Peel Oil is effective in fighting bacteria due to its antiseptic, astringent and detoxifying action. This oil is naturally found in the peels of ripe grapefruits. This is a beneficial oil in the treatment of acne.

Cocos Nucifera (Coconut) Fruit Juice is naturally found in the milk or coconut water inside the hard exterior that is the endosperm (food) for the germination of the plant. It is highly nutritive, containing amino acids, sugars, vitamins and plant growth factors.

Cordyceps Sinensis Extract is a mushroom-derived anti-inflammatory and calming ingredient.

Crocus Chrysanthus Bulb Extract is an effective growth factor alternative to improve skin firmness and elasticity while reducing wrinkles in the crow's feet area.

Croton Glabellus (Cascarilla) Bark Extract is a potent anti-inflammatory and antioxidant.

Collagen is a fibrous protein that makes up the connective tissue in the body. In cosmetic products, it is used as an emollient and humectant agent that is able to draw moisture from the dermis into the epidermis.

Colloidal Sulfur is a form of sulfur that is comprised of finely divided particles that are dispersed in a manner that keeps them from being filtered easily or settled rapidly. Sulfur is a heavy ingredient and this form of sulfur stays emulsified within a product more evenly.

Cucumis Sativa (Cucumber) Fruit Extract is an anti-inflammatory that reduces skin oiliness, tightens skin and is even thought to help minimize the appearance of enlarged pores.

Cucurbita Pepo (Pumpkin) Extract provides the hundreds of beneficial components in pumpkin to the skin.

Curcuma Longa (Turmeric) Root Extract is made up of primarily tetrahydrocurcuminoids that are potent antioxidants. It also provides anti-inflammatory benefits and is thought to be a possible skin brightener.

Cymbopogon Schoenanthus Extract is lemongrass extract. It helps reduce inflammation and control oil production. It also helps to contract weak connective tissue to tone the skin.

d

Decylene Glycol is an effective antibacterial agent that also helps to control sebum production.

Dimethicone is a silicone derivative that acts as a light occlusive agent and increases the ability of hyaluronic acid to link to protein in connective tissue and skin.

Dimethyl Sulfone improves skin brightening and helps other ingredients penetrate the skin better.

Dipeptide-2 improves lymphatic circulation to effectively remove toxins from the skin.

Dipeptide Diaminobutyroyl Benzylamide Diacetate is a next generation peptide that has a fast-acting wrinkle smoothing effect around the eyes, diminishing wrinkles and expression lines.

Dipotassium Glycyrrhizinate is a form of licorice extract that is widely used as an anti-inflammatory and anti-irritant. It also improves the appearance of dry or damaged skin by increasing hydration.

e

Epidermal Growth Factor (EGF) aids in the healthy proliferation of skin cells and the repairing of skin damage from aging. Our EGF protein is a product of yeast metabolism.

Epigallocatechin Gallate (EGCG) is a polyphenol that is naturally found in green tea. It is an extremely effective antioxidant and anti-inflammatory. It protects the skin from UV-induced damage.

Ergothioneine is a superior antioxidant naturally found in many plant species. It helps to boost the protective capabilities of traditional antioxidants, such as L-ascorbic acid. Ergothioneine corrects and prevents free radical damage.

Eucalyptus Globulus Leaf Oil is made up of predominantly eucalyptol. Eucalyptol is an antiseptic, astringent and antibacterial agent. This is a beneficial oil in the treatment of acne.

f

Folic Acid is also known as vitamin B9. Folic acid plays a critical role in healthy cell proliferation throughout the body, including the skin. Folic acid deficiencies have been linked to many skin conditions, including seborrheic dermatitis.

Fraxinus Excelsior Bark Extract reduces eye puffiness, dark circles and eye bags while infusing antioxidants into the skin.

Fructan works to condition skin and helps to retain moisture.

Fumaric Acid is found in mosses and lichens. It is an antioxidant and helps to promote cell oxygenation. It helps to establish pathways of absorption for ingredients into the skin.

g

Galactoarabinan is the INCI name for arabinogalactan proteins, which are found throughout the plant kingdom. These proteins play an important role in healthy cell proliferation.

Gluconolactone, aka Gluconic Acid, is an polyhydroxy acid precursor. It has strong anti-inflammatory effect and significantly improves acne by reducing the number of both inflamed and non-inflamed lesions, while providing moisturizing and barrier strengthening properties. Gluconolactone may also function by scavenging free radicals, thereby protecting skin from the damaging effects of UV radiation. Gluconolactone is also used in small amounts as a part of a gentle preservative blend.

Glutathione is a combination of three amino acids: cystine, glutamic acid and glycine. Glutathione is found in the tissues of all plants and animals. It is a strong antioxidant thought to be a key ingredient in slowing the aging process because of its ability to strengthen and rebuild collagen bonds.

Glycerin is a humectant and emollient that helps to bind water to the skin. Glycerin is one of the most effective topical hydrators, as it is readily accepted by the aquaporins (water channels) in the skin cells. It also improves the appearance and function of the skin by assisting in the healthy maturation of keratinocytes.

Glycerophoshoinositol Lysine, found in sunflowers, is a semisynthetic derivative of glycerophoshoinositol and a strong anti-inflammatory agent.

Glycine is an amino acid that has demonstrated antioxidant activity. It is found in a number of proteins and makes up 35% of collagen. Glycine is also used as a hydrator and skin conditioning agent.

Glycolic Acid is an AHA that helps to break down the bonds between the cells (desmosomes) and acts as a strong degreasing agent. It is best used short-term on very oily skin types. Overuse can cause dehydration and overproduction of sebum.

Glycosaminoglycans (GAG) GAG are responsible for keeping collagen and elastin fibers in good condition, as well as promoting their ability to hold moisture. GAG are also essential to the epidermal and dermal cells' metabolism. GAG consist of hyaluronic acid, mucopolysaccharides and chondroiton sulphates. Their main function is to maintain and support the collagen, elastin and turgor within cellular spaces.

Glycyrrhiza Glabra (Licorice) Root Extract has anti-inflammatory and antihistamine properties. Licorice preserves the effect of the body's hormone cortisol, allowing it to maintain extended anti-inflammatory action. It is also an effective melanogenesis inhibitor. Certain components of licorice also reduce sebum production, inhibit 5 alpha-reductase and fight lipase, the enzyme produced by the acne bacteria that cause local irritation and inflammation.

Gynostemma Pentaphyllum Extract has been used over centuries to reduce skin irritation, and enhance circulation and oxygenation. This action helps to keep the skin healthy and protected from oxidative damage. Gypenosodes, the active component in this botanical, also exhibit strong antioxidant and anti-inflammatory effects.

h

HA-Pro Complex™ is a PCA SKIN proprietary blend that works to stimulate the production of the skin's own hyaluronic acid. As the skin ages, natural production of hyaluronic acid slows. HA-Pro Complex™ delivers 24-hours moisturization through all levels of the skin, smoothing fine lines and wrinkles, and plumping and firming the skin.

Hamamelis Virginiana (Witch Hazel) Extract is anti-inflammatory. Tannins and volatile oils are the main active constituents in witch hazel, giving it a strong astringent effect.

Helianthus Annuus (Sunflower) Seed Oil is high in essential fatty acids (EFA). It improves barrier function, and is an antioxidant and lubricant.

Hesperidin Methyl Chalcone is an antioxidant that has been shown to prevent fluid from collecting in the skin, making it effective for use under the eyes.

Hexylresorcinol helps to promote an even skin tone and reduce inflammation that can lead to discoloration.

Hordeum Distichon (Barley) Extract is used to help improve the barrier function of skin. It is also used with tomato extract to make up BMX Complex, which aids in the reduction of lip flakiness, and helps to increase lipid retention and accumulation.

Hyaluronic Acid is a naturally occurring glycosaminoglycan (GAG) that helps retain water in the skin. This ingredient can hold up to 1,000 times its weight in water. It typically exists as a sodium salt (sodium hyaluronate), with exceptional lubricating qualities. It plays an important role in cell protection and lubrication, and maintenance of the structural integrity of tissues. The amount of this protein depletes as we age. The natural source of hyaluronic acid is often rooster combs. We have our hyaluronic acid synthesized to mirror that naturally found in animals to avoid using animal sources.

Hydrastis Canadensis (Goldenseal) Root Extract was used by the early Americans as a medicinal herb. Goldenseal root extract is an antibacterial and astringent agent.

Hydrocortisone (1%) is a corticosteroid hormone used to relieve topical itching, irritation and discomfort.

Hydrolyzed Candida Saitoana Extract is a type of fungi that encourages skin cell autophagy (the skin's natural detoxification process). Studies show that topical application rids the skin cells of toxins and reduces free radical damage.

Hydrolyzed Ceratonia Siliqua Seed Extract accelerates the recovery of stressed skin and improves barrier function.

Hydrolyzed Silk is a product of hydrolyzing silk protein. When hydrolyzed, silk releases amino acids and peptides for the biosynthesis of dermal proteins. It strengthens the skin and speeds post-procedure recovery.

Hydrolyzed Wheat Protein is a hydrating agent that significantly enhances epidermal moisture.

Hydroquinone (HQ) is naturally found in wheat, berries, coffee and tea, or produced synthetically. We use synthesized HQ to ensure purity. This ingredient helps to inhibit the binding of copper to tyrosinase and induces melanocyte-specific cytotoxicity, lightening existing and preventing future hyperpigmentation.

Hydroxyphenoxy Propionic Acid helps to promote an even skin tone and leave the skin radiant.

Hydroxypropyl Beta-Cyclodextrin (HPBCD) is a starch derivative ideally suited for molecular encapsulation of a variety of lipid compounds that are not soluble in water. Encapsulation enhances solubility, bioavailability and the stability of reactive compounds. HPBCD acts to carry the oil-soluble ingredients through a water environment and into the skin.

I

Inflacin® (PEG-23 Glyceryl Distearate) prevents subclinical inflammation by stopping the inflammatory pathway that results in redness, topical irritation and signs of aging.

J

Japanese White Charcoal contains a variety of minerals and absorbs impurities from the skin. It's structure of very small pores allows it to be highly efficient in detoxification by trapped dirt and oil in the molecule and sweeping unwanted debris away.

K

Kaolin is an absorbent clay that helps draw impurities and excess oil out of the pores.

Kojic Acid is an antibacterial agent and melanogenesis inhibitor. Its ability to chelate copper away from tyrosinase and decrease the number of melanosomes and dendrites makes it very effective in reducing hyperpigmentation.

L

L-Ascorbic Acid is a powerful water-soluble antioxidant that is the only bio-available form of vitamin C for the skin. It is also a cofactor for an enzyme crucial in the synthesis of collagen (prolyl hydrolase) and is an antioxidant agent that provides important protection against damage induced by UV radiation. Vitamin C also improves skin elasticity and decreases wrinkles by stimulating collagen synthesis. Additionally, it reduces erythema and acts as a melanogenesis inhibitor. It functions as an MMPi by controlling the expression of inflammatory enzymes (matrix metalloproteinases).

Lactic Acid is an alpha hydroxy acid naturally found in milk and sugars. It breaks down bonds (desmosomes) between cells to allow for easier exfoliation of dead surface cells and hydrates the skin. Lactic acid also inhibits skin discoloration.

Lactobacillus/Pumpkin Ferment Extract is pumpkin wine that is produced by fermenting whole pumpkin. This fermentation releases the nutrients and many benefits of pumpkin.

Lavendula Angustifolia (Lavender) Extract is an antiseptic, antibacterial agent and analgesic.

Lavendula Hybrida (Lavandin) Oil is an aromatic antioxidant that provides antiseptic and anti-inflammatory action.

Lecithin is a lipid that is required by every cell in the body. The cell membranes in the body are composed largely of lecithin. These membranes handle the flow of nutrients into and out of the cell.

Limnanthes Alba (Meadowfoam) Seed Oil is a botanical source of essential fatty acids (EFA). EFA are lipids that are necessary for healthy skin function.

m

Magnesium Aluminum Silicate is a naturally occurring clay-derived mineral that supports skin clearing.

Magnolia Officinalis Bark Extract is well-known in Traditional Chinese Medicine and is used primarily for the two active components, magnolol and honokoi, both potent anti-inflammatory and anti-aging agents.

Mandelic Acid is an alpha hydroxy acid derived from bitter almonds. It has been shown to improve photoaging, pigmentation, acne and is often used as a peeling agent in professional treatments. It's a gentler alternative to glycolic acid.

Melaleuca Alternifolia (Tea Tree) Leaf Oil contains the active components terpinen-4-ol, alpha-terpineol and alpha-pinene. In vitro antimicrobial activity has been demonstrated against candida albicans, escherichia coli (e. coli), taphylococcus aureus, pseudomonas aeruginosa, staphylococcus epidermidis and propionibacterium acnes (P. acnes). This is a beneficial oil in the treatment of acne as it helps to bring oxygen to the skin cells and reduces the P. acnes population.

Menthyl Lactate has a cooling and soothing effect on the skin.

Methylsulfonylmethane (MSM) is the main biologic source of sulfur. MSM is a small molecule containing 34% elemental sulfur and is readily absorbed by the skin. Sulfur is responsible for the flexible bond between cells, including those that make up the skin. When the body is deficient in sulfur, sulfur bonds between proteins are not optimal, and cross-linking between protein (collagen, elastin and keratin) fibers occurs. Regular topical use of MSM has shown softer, more pliable skin with fewer wrinkles.

Morus Alba Root Extract is also known as mulberry root extract. It assists in the correction of hyperpigmentation by inhibiting the conversion of tyrosinase to L-DOPA.

Myristoyl Hexapeptide-4 is a peptide that stimulates collagen synthesis and tissue repair, and provides an effective alternative to human growth factor.

Myristoyl Nonapeptide-3 is a novel peptide that mimics retinoic acid (vitamin A) to increase cell turnover and collagen synthesis without causing negative side effects, such as irritation and stinging.

Myristoyl Pentapeptide-8 is a peptide that stimulates collagen synthesis and tissue repair, and provides an effective alternative to human growth factor.

n

Niacin is vitamin B3. It is shown to improve blood flow.

Niacinamide is a form of the B vitamin, niacin (vitamin B3). When used topically it has been shown to help reduce breakouts, rosacea-like symptoms and the yellowing of the skin due to glycation and melanosome transfer. Niacinamide does not have the flushing response of niacin. Niacinamide increases ceramide and fatty acid levels in the skin to provide maximum hydration. Studies have shown that niacinamide hydrates, reduces transepidermal water loss (TEWL) and maintains hydration in the stratum corneum more effectively than the common occlusive agent petrolatum.

Octinoxate is a UVB filter commonly used in sun protection products.

Oenothera Biennis (Evening Primrose) Seed Oil is an excellent source of gamma linolenic acid (GLA) and a high source of omega 6 essential fatty acid (EFA). It has an anti-inflammatory effect, is a vasoconstrictor, and is used to treat dermatitis and any other irritated or inflamed conditions. Its anti-inflammatory capabilities and high EFA content make it beneficial in the treatment of acne.

Olea Europaea (Olive) Fruit Extract is an antioxidant that also aids in the penetration of other actives within the formula.

Origanum Vulgare (Oregano) Leaf Extract is an anti-inflammatory and antiseptic agent.

Oryza Sativa (Rice) Bran Wax helps to moisturize and smooth the skin while improving barrier function.

Palmaria Palmata Extract promotes an even skin tone.

Palmitoyl Tripeptide-5 stimulates collagen production to strengthen skin and minimize wrinkling.

Palmitoyl Tripeptide-38 is the newest generation of messenger peptides that instigates the synthesis of matrix proteins to minimize the appearance of fine lines and wrinkles.

Pantothenic Acid is vitamin B5. It acts as a humectant while promoting healthy cell regeneration.

Panthenol is pro-vitamin B5, a vitamin precursor that is converted into vitamin B5 in the skin. It improves and increases the moisture-retention capacity of the skin, and it has anti-inflammatory and anti-itching effects.

Pelargonium Graveolens Oil (geranium oil) boosts circulation, thus reducing acne breakouts, and helps to regulate sebum production while improving skin's elasticity. Geranium oil also improves the lymphatic system by relieving water retention.

Peptides are compounds consisting of two or more amino acids, the building blocks of proteins. Peptides act as transmitters from the brain to the body, telling muscles and nerves to perform specific functions. There are multiple peptides available that will achieve different topical results.

Peumus Boldus (Boldine) Extract is a natural alkaloid from the Chilean boldo tree. It acts as an anti-inflammatory, a cell protector and a powerful antioxidant.

Phenylethyl Resorcinol is a synthetically produced resorcinol derivative that acts as an antioxidant and a potent melanogenesis inhibitor. It prevents the conversion of tyrosinase to L-DOPA, aiding in the clearing of discolorations. Studies demonstrate comparable results to kojic acid and hydroquinone with no irritation.

Phospholipids are the fats that make up cell membranes. Topical use helps to strengthen and improve the integrity of the cell walls, and improve emolliency and barrier function.

Phytic Acid is an exfoliating and keratolytic agent thought to be gentler than AHAs. Used at low percentages it does not cause peeling, but helps with clearing impacted surface cells.

Phytosterols provide antioxidant, anti-inflammatory, anti-aging, moisturizing and skin-smoothing benefits. They also work to improve the skin's barrier function. Our phytosterols are naturally found in rice bran.

Pogostemom Cablin Leaf Oil (patchouli) encourages wound healing and stimulates cell regeneration.

Porphyra Umbilicalis Extract is a form of red algae that exhibits strong antioxidant properties.

Poterium Officinale (Green Burnet) Root is an effective botanical astringent used to control sebum production.

Prasterone is DHEA (dehydroepiandrosterone), an adrenal hormone precursor that softens the skin and protects cells from thermal injury. It is also one of the substances responsible for regulating sebum production and is useful in treating aging skin. DHEA depletes with age, contributing to dry skin.

Prunus Serotina (Wild Cherry) Extract is a strong anti-inflammatory that reduces redness. It is also a source of flavonoids, natural antioxidant compounds that contribute to the integrity of capillaries and collagen structures. The anthocyanidin and proanthocyanidin flavonoids in cherries disarm the free radicals that damage healthy cells.

Prunus Serotina (Wild Cherry) Bark Extract is a soothing, anti-inflammatory and emollient ingredient.

Pseudoalteromonas Ferment Extract is a glycoprotein containing three amino acids: glycine, histidine and lysine. It's believed to encourage collagen and elastin production and protect moisture in the skin.

Pyrus Malus (Apple) Fruit Extract is a natural source of malic acid, an AHA that helps to reduce hyperkeratinized cells. It is also an antioxidant and skin conditioning agent.

r

Resorcinol is a flaking agent and keratolytic. In low concentrations, it is antiseptic and an anti-itch agent.

RestorAtive Complex is a potent combination of stabilized retinol and vigna aconitifolia seed extract.

Resveratrol is a phytoalexin from red grape skins. Phytoalexins are potent polyphenol antioxidants and are a plant's protective mechanism against harsh conditions. It is excellent in controlling acute and chronic inflammation. Resveratrol acts as an MMPi by preventing the production of cyclooxygenase (COX), the key enzyme in the inflammatory response.

Retinol is a form of vitamin A that is converted to retinoic acid in the skin. It works to repair photodamaged skin, acne and other sluggish skin conditions. It helps to normalize cell turnover, increase collagen deposition and bind moisture in the skin. It inhibits melanogenesis by limiting the transfer of melanosomes from the melanocytes to the keratinocytes.

Retinyl Palmitate is retinol esterified with palmitic acid. Its benefits are similar to retinol.

Rice Powder is a physical exfoliating agent.

Rosa Rubiginosa and **Rosa Canina Seed Oil** are forms of rose hip seed oil. They contain high concentrations of essential fatty acids (EFA) that are found in the structural lipids of the cell, but are not produced by the human body. Rose hip seed oil provides hydration by bolstering the skin's epidermal lipids with EFA. Rose hip seed oil is a natural source of trans-retinoic acid. In clinical studies with humans, it was shown to achieve similar benefits to retinoic acid, including increasing collagen and elastin production, and aiding in cell turnover, without irritation

Rosmarinus Officinalis (Rosemary) Leaf Extract is an antioxidant and anti-inflammatory. Its numerous components make it useful in fighting breakouts.

Saccharide Isomerate (Pentavitin®) is a marine exopolysaccharide that increases skin renewal and exfoliation while reducing skin sensitivity and the appearance of pores. Pentavitin helps generate a moisture reserve in the skin.

Saccharomyces Ferment is a humectant ingredient used to increase hydration.

Saccharomyces Lysate Extract is closely related to yeast. It is an effective humectant and antioxidant.

Saccharum Officinarum (Sugar Cane) Extract is a naturally occurring form of glycolic acid. Sugar cane extract is moisturizing, while offering anti-aging benefits.

Salicylic Acid is a beta hydroxy acid (BHA) and a keratolytic. Due to its lipophyllic nature, it is able to penetrate through oil-filled pores, making it an excellent anti-acne ingredient. Salicylic acid reduces the shedding of cells within the follicles, reducing impactions and microcomedo formation. It is also a potent anti-inflammatory agent.

Scrophularia Nodosa Extract is figwort extract. It is frequently used as a natural remedy for several types of dermatitis. Figwort extract exhibits strong anti-inflammatory properties because of a high content of betulinic acid.

Secale Cereale (Rye) Seed Extract stimulates the synthesis of stress fibers to reduce laxity in the skin.

Silanetriol reduces eye puffiness, dark circles and eye bags while infusing antioxidants into the skin.

Silybum Marianum Fruit Extract reduces stress in the skin.

Silymarin is a powerful antioxidant, provides anti-inflammatory action and has a protective effect against UVA-induced oxidative stress. It suppresses UVB-induced skin edema and the formation of sunburn cells.

Simmondsia Chinensis (Jojoba) Seed Oil is a skin moisturizer that also helps strengthen the elastin network in the skin. It is used for its ability to penetrate into the skin while still providing light occlusion. It is thought to reduce irritation in the skin by inhibiting the production of pore-clogging sebum. This is a beneficial oil for acneic skin.

Sodium Cocoyl Glutamate is a gentle cleansing agent.

Sodium Chondroitin Sulfate acts to inhibit the matrix metalloproteinase enzymes (MMP) that degrade and destroy the skin's collagen network. Protecting the skin's extracellular matrix (collagen, elastin, proteoglycans, fibronectin and other glycoproteins) is important in maintaining healthy and younger-looking skin.

Sodium Hyaluronate is the sodium salt of hyaluronic acid, which is a naturally occurring glycosaminoglycan with exceptional lubricating qualities. Its ability to hold 1,000 times its weight in water plays an important role in cell protection, hydration, lubrication and maintenance of the structural integrity of tissues.

Sodium Laureth Sulfate is a gentle surfactant that is often used in baby shampoos.

Sodium Methyl Cocoyl Taurate is naturally found in oleic acid. It is often used as a gentle emulsifier and foaming agent.

Sodium PCA is a naturally occurring humectant in human skin. It can attract and hold 250 times its weight in water. This is an important ingredient for healthy skin function.

Solanum Lycopersicum (Tomato) Extract is combined with barley extract to make up BMX Complex, which aids in the reduction of lip flakiness, and helps to increase lipid retention and accumulation.

Soy Isoflavones are a rich source of the anitoxidant phytohormone genistein that helps to build collagen and improve the overall condition of aging skin. Isoflavones may increase the hyaluronic acid content in the skin, making it more able to attract and hold moisture.

Sphingolipids are the fats that make up cell membranes. Topical use helps to strengthen and improve the integrity of the cell walls, and improve emolliency and barrier function.

Squalane is a naturally occurring oil found in such foods as olives and wheat germ. It helps to keep the skin moist.

Superoxide Dismutase is an enzyme that protects oxygen-metabolizing cells against the harmful effects of superoxide free radicals.

Syringa Vulgaris (Lilac) Leaf Cell Culture Extract is the most active component of Lilac Leaf. Its major component is verbascoside. This potent antioxidant is derived from the stem cells of the lilac plant. Lilac stem cells have an unsurpassed oxygen radical absorbance capacity (ORAC) value of 28,166. In addition, they are exceptional at inhibiting P. acnes bacteria, supporting wound healing action and inhibiting collagenase.

Thymus Vulgaris (Thyme) Leaf is an anti-inflammatory, antimicrobial, antiseptic and astringent.

Tocopherol, the pure form of vitamin E, is an excellent antioxidant and emollient. Vitamin E is a fat-soluble vitamin and the major antioxidant that protects the lipids in the body, including cell membranes, from oxidation.

Tocotrienols are forms of vitamin E that are more powerful antioxidants than pure tocopherol and penetrate into our cells more effectively. There are alpha, gamma and delta tocotrienols. We use all three in combination.

Totarol is an extract from the New Zealand totara tree. It has potent antibacterial and antioxidant properties while being gentle and non-irritating.

Trametes Versicolor Extract is a mushroom-derived anti-inflammatory and calming ingredient.

Trichloroacetic Acid (TCA) can be used in many concentrations, but it is most commonly used for superficial and medium-depth peeling to remove fine lines and wrinkles, and acne scarring. TCA can be a very aggressive agent when not used in a formulation with other ingredients. TCA is the result of a chlorine and acetic acid chemical reaction, and is generally produced synthetically.

U

Ubiquinone (CoEnzyme Q10) is a powerful antioxidant that fights free radical damage. It easily penetrates the skin and has shown an ability to improve collagen and elastin.

Undecylenoyl Phenylalanine is a synthetic amino acid. It assists in reducing skin discolorations by suppressing the formation of melanocyte stimulating hormone (MSH) and, as a result, the formation of tyrosinase, and the transfer of melanin and melanosomes.

Urea comprises an essential part of the natural moisture factor (NMF) of human skin. It is responsible for the re-hydration of the epidermis and increases the skin's ability to retain moisture. In higher percentages, urea acts as a keratolytic to soften skin. Urea is one of the most effective topical hydrators, as it readily moves through the aquaporins, or water channels, in the skin cells.

V

Vigna Aconitifolia Seed Extract is a botanical that has demonstrated activity in stimulating the growth factors that increase epidermal cell turnover. It is also effective in the protection of the dermis from age-related breakdown, as well as stimulating the fibroblasts to produce collagen.

Vitex Agnus Castus Extract is a botanical extract that imitates the action of the hormone progesterone. Topically applied, phytohormones help to plump and hydrate the skin.

Vitis Vinifera (Grape) Fruit Cell Extract is a unique antioxidant that derives its potency from the stem cells of grapes. It helps to prevent free radical damage in the stem cells of human skin and acts as UV absorber, protecting epidermal stem cells from UV damage.

Vitis Vinifera (Grape) Seed Extract is rich in polyphenols and proanthocyanidins, including resveratrol, which are powerful antioxidants that fight free radicals and improve circulation. Grape seed has also been shown to assist in cell regeneration and the strengthening of capillaries.

Wheat Germ Oil is an exceptional source of vitamin E and essential fatty acids (EFA). It is an antioxidant and emollient.

Wheat Amino Acid is a natural growth factor for the skin, used for its softening properties. This is an excellent source of plant-derived protein, which is highly moisturizing.

Yeast Polysaccharides are a natural source of beta-glucan and provide excellent water-binding action. These polysaccharides increase skin elasticity, smoothe wrinkles and protect the skin from irritation.

Yucca Schidigera Extract is a foaming agent that offers antibacterial and anti-inflammatory benefits.

Zinc Oxide is an excellent broad spectrum UV protection agent and a powerful anti-inflammatory ingredient. It reduces inflammation and inhibits melanogenesis.

Zingiber Officinale (Ginger) Root Oil is an effective antioxidant and antimicrobial agent. It acts as a powerful astringent to reduce the appearance of pores and control sebum production, when used as a blend with green burnet and cinnamon.

K

daily care product ingredient list

Cleanse

Facial Wash
Water/Aqua/Eau, Sodium C14-16 Olefin Sulfonate, Cocamidopropyl Betaine, Lactic Acid, Sodium Cocoamphoacetate, Sodium Chloride, Propanediol, Sodium Hydroxide, Phenoxyethanol, Cocamidopropyl Hydroxysultaine, Ethylhexylglycerin, Sodium Benzoate, Caprylyl Glycol, Chlorphenesin, Potassium Sorbate, Allantoin, Aloe Barbadensis Leaf Juice, Salix Nigra (Willow) Bark Extract, Amorphophallus Konjac Root Powder

Facial Wash Oily/Problem
Water/Aqua/Eau, Lauramidopropyl Betaine, Sodium Laurylglucosides Hydroxypropylsulfonate, Gluconolactone, Glycerin, Sodium Lauroyl Sarcosinate, Sodium Hydroxide, Lactic Acid, PEG-150 Distearate, Sodium Hydroxymethylglycinate, Aloe Barbadensis Leaf Juice

Total Wash Face & Body Cleanser
Water/Aqua/Eau, Sodium C14-16 Olefin Sulfonate, Glycerin, Sodium Cocoamphoacetate, Cocamide MIPA, Sodium Chloride, Propanediol, Cocamidopropyl Hydroxysultaine, Phenoxyethanol, Panthenol, Ethylhexylglycerin, Guar Hydroxypropyltrimonium Chloride, Menthyl Lactate, Potassium Sorbate, Sodium Benzoate, Sodium Hydroxide, Lavandula Angustifolia (Lavender) Oil, Citric Acid, Allantoin, Caprylyl Glycol, Phytic Acid, Lactic Acid, Chlorphenesin, Mentha Piperita (Peppermint) Oil, Opuntia Ficus-Indica Stem Extract, Aloe Barbadensis Leaf Juice, Dipotassium Glycyrrhizate, Melaleuca Alternifolia (Tea Tree) Leaf Oil, Bisabolol, Carthamus Tinctorius (Safflower) Seed Oil, Tocopherol

Creamy Cleanser
Water/Aqua/Eau, Glycerin, Caprylic/Capric Triglyceride, Behenyl Alcohol, Sodium Methyl Cocoyl Taurate, Cocamidopropyl Betaine, Helianthus Annuus (Sunflower) Seed Oil, Phenoxyethanol, Acrylates/C10-30 Alkyl Acrylate Crosspolymer, Aminomethyl Propanol, Disodium Cocoyl Glutamate, Rosa Canina Fruit Oil, Caprylyl Glycol, Sucrose Distearate, Sucrose Stearate, Xanthan Gum, Ethylhexylglycerin, Sodium Cocoyl Glutamate, Tocopherol, Hexylene Glycol, Lavandula Angustifolia (Lavender) Oil, Yucca Schidigera Leaf/Root/Stem Extract, Aloe Barbadensis Leaf Juice

BPO 5% Cleanser
Active Ingredient: Benzoyl Peroxide (5%)

Other Ingredients: Water/Aqua/Eau, Gluconolactone, Sodium C14-16 Olefin Sulfonate, Aminomethyl Propanol, Glycerin, Cocamidopropyl Betaine, Acrylates/C10-30 Alkyl Acrylate Crosspolymer, Phenoxyethanol, Polyacrylate-13, Citrus Grandis (Grapefruit) Peel Oil, Caprylyl Glycol, Polyisobutene, Ethylhexylglycerin, Allantoin, Aloe Barbadensis Leaf Juice, Simmondsia Chinensis (Jojoba) Seed Oil, Tocopheryl Acetate, Triticum Vulgare (Wheat) Germ Oil, Hexylene Glycol, Panthenol, Sodium PCA, Polysorbate 20, Butylene Glycol, Phytic Acid, Algae Extract, Anthemis Nobilis Flower Extract, Arnica Montana Flower Extract, Cucumis Sativus (Cucumber) Fruit Extract, Vitis Vinifera (Grape) Seed Extract

Blemish Control Bar
Active Ingredient: Salicylic Acid (2%)

Other Ingredients: Glycerin, Cocos Nucifera (Coconut) Oil, Elaeis Guineensis (Palm) Kernel Oil, Ricinus Communis (Castor) Seed Oil, Water/Aqua/Eau, Sodium Hydroxide, Carthamus Tinctorius (Safflower) Seed Oil, Sorbitan Oleate, Sorbitol, Azelaic Acid, Eucalyptus Globulus Leaf Oil, Tsuga Canadensis Leaf Oil, Glycine Soja (Soybean) Protein, Aloe Barbadensis Leaf Juice Powder, Tocopherol, Glycine Soja (Soybean) Oil

Dry Skin Relief Bar®
Active Ingredient: Salicylic Acid (3%)

Other Ingredients: Glycerin, Cocos Nucifera (Coconut) Oil, Elaeis Guineensis (Palm) Kernel Oil, Ricinus Communis (Castor) Seed Oil, Water/Aqua/Eau, Sodium Hydroxide, Carthamus Tinctorius (Safflower) Seed Oil, Sorbitan Oleate, Sorbitol, Glycine Soja (Soybean) Protein, Foeniculum Vulgare (Fennel) Oil, Lecithin, Lavandula Angustifolia (Lavender) Oil, Hamamelis Virginiana (Witch Hazel) Water, Aloe Barbadensis Leaf Juice Powder, Camellia Sinensis Leaf Extract, Cucurbita Pepo (Pumpkin) Seed Oil, Honey/Mel/Miel, Phenylethyl Resorcinol, Alcohol, Tocopherol, Evernia Prunastri (Oakmoss) Extract, Glycine Soja (Soybean) Oil

Pigment Bar®
Glycerin, Cocos Nucifera (Coconut) Oil, Elaeis Guineensis (Palm) Kernel Oil, Ricinus Communis (Castor) Seed Oil, Water/Aqua/Eau, Sodium Hydroxide, Carthamus Tinctorius (Safflower) Seed Oil, Sorbitan Oleate, Sorbitol, Azelaic Acid, Kojic Acid, Hamamelis Virginiana (Witch Hazel) Water, Glycine Soja (Soybean) Protein, Camellia Sinensis Leaf Extract, Alcohol, Calcium Ascorbate, Glucosamine HCl, Maltose, Niacinamide, Sodium Lactate, Tannic Acid, Aniba Rosodora (Rosewood) Wood Oil

Tone

Smoothing Toner
Water/Aqua/Eau, Lactic Acid, Citric Acid, Glycerin, Arctium Lappa Root Extract, Calendula Officinalis Flower Extract, Cucumis Sativus (Cucumber) Fruit Extract, Hedera Helix (Ivy) Leaf/Stem Extract, Hydrastis Canadensis (Goldenseal) Extract, Paullinia Cupana Seed Extract, Salvia Officinalis (Sage) Leaf Extract, Tetrasodium EDTA, Aloe Barbadensis Leaf Juice

Nutrient Toner
Water/Aqua/Eau, Lactobacillus/Pumpkin Ferment Extract, Sucrose, Propylene Glycol, Lactic Acid, Citric Acid, Cinnamomum Cassia Leaf Oil, Eugenia Caryophyllus (Clove) Leaf Oil, Zingiber Officinale (Ginger) Root Oil, Alcohol Denat., Aminoguanidine HCl, Glutathione, Yeast

Correct

Gentle Exfoliant
Water/Aqua/Eau, Butylene Glycol, Polyethylene, Isopropyl Palmitate, Glyceryl Stearate SE, Carbomer, Glycolic Acid, Sodium Hydroxide, Phenoxyethanol, Caprylyl Glycol, Stearyl Alcohol, Simmondsia Chinensis (Jojoba) Seed Oil, Ethylhexylglycerin, Aloe Barbadensis Leaf Juice, Disodium EDTA, Hexylene Glycol

Pore Refining Treatment
Water, Kaolin, Bentonite, Glycerin, Neopentyl Glycol Diethylhexanoate, Pumice, Isopropyl Palmitate, Mandelic Acid, Oryza Sativa (Rice) Powder, Panthenol, Phenoxyethanol, Oleth-10, Tocopheryl Acetate, Sodium Hydroxide, Bisabolol, Ethylhexylglycerin, Rosmarinus Officinalis (Rosemary) Leaf Oil, Xanthan Gum, Carrageenan, Glucose, Camellia Oleifera Leaf Extract, Saccharide Isomerate, Papain

Purifying Mask
Water/Aqua/Eau, Pumice, Glycine Soja (Soybean) Oil, Glycerin, Kaolin, Montmorillonite, Cetyl Alcohol, Glyceryl Stearate, PEG-100 Stearate, Helianthus Annuus (Sunflower) Seed Oil, Hydroxypropyl Starch Phosphate, Vitis Vinifera (Grape) Seed Oil, Olivoyl Hydrolyzed Wheat Protein, Phenoxyethanol, Decyl Glucoside, Xanthan Gum, Caprylyl Glycol, Citric Acid, Ethylhexylglycerin, Disodium EDTA, Hexylene Glycol, Carrageenan, Citrus Aurantium Dulcis (Orange) Peel Oil, Citrus Paradisi (Grapefruit) Peel Oil, Eucalyptus Globulus Leaf Oil, Lavandula Angustifolia (Lavender) Oil, Mentha Viridis (Spearmint) Leaf Oil, Thymus Zygis Flower Oil, Melaleuca Alternifolia (Tea Tree) Leaf Oil, Tocopheryl Acetate, Glucose, Sodium PCA

Detoxifying Mask
Water/Aqua/Eau, Kaolin, Charcoal Powder, Glycerin, Magnesium Aluminum Silicate, Phenoxyethanol, Xanthan Gum, Citric Acid, Disodium EDTA, Ethylhexylglycerin.

Revitalizing Mask
Carica Papaya (Papaya) Fruit, Water/Aqua/Eau, Glycerin, Hydroxyethyl Acrylate/Sodium Acryloyldimethyl Taurate Copolymer, Squalane, Phenoxyethanol, Saccharum Officinarum (Sugarcane) Extract, Chlorophyllin-Copper Complex, Xanthan Gum, Polysorbate 60, Ethylhexylglycerin, Honey/Mel/Miel, Potassium Sorbate, Tocopheryl Acetate, Pelargonium Graveolens Flower Oil, Foeniculum Vulgare (Fennel) Oil, Pogostemon Cablin Oil, Camellia Sinensis Leaf Extract, Citrus Aurantium Dulcis (Orange) Fruit Extract, Citrus Limon (Lemon) Fruit Extract, Pyrus Malus (Apple) Fruit Extract, Sucrose, Glycine Soja (Soybean) Oil, Aniba Rosodora (Rosewood) Wood Oil, Citrus Aurantifolia (Lime) Fruit Extract, Citrus Aurantium Dulcis (Orange) Peel Oil

ExLinea® Peptide Smoothing Serum
Water/Aqua/Eau, Aloe Barbadensis Leaf Juice, Hydroxyethyl Acrylate/Sodium Acryloyldimethyl Taurate Copolymer, Gluconolactone, Aminomethyl Propanol, Dipotassium Glycyrrhizate, Sodium Benzoate, 1,2 - Hexanediol, Caprylyl Glycol, Acrylates/C10-30 Alkyl Acrylate Crosspolymer, Santalum Austrocaledonicum Wood Oil, Aniba Rosaeodora (Rosewood) Wood Oil, Sodium Hyaluronate, Phenoxyethanol, Citrus Grandis (Grapefruit) Peel Oil, Citrus Nobilis (Mandarin Orange) Peel Oil, Tropolone, Mentha Piperita (Peppermint) Oil, Potassium Sorbate, Acetyl Hexapeptide-8, Phytosterols, Tocopherol, Tocotrienols, Oryza Sativa (Rice) Bran Wax, Squalene

Pigment Gel®
Active Ingredient: Hydroquinone (2%)

Other Ingredients: Water/Aqua/Eau, SD Alcohol 40-B, Butylene Glycol, Alcohol, Lactic Acid, Azelaic Acid, Kojic Acid, Hamamelis Virginiana (Witch Hazel) Water, Hydroxyethylcellulose, Phenylethyl Resorcinol, BHT, Glutathione, Silybum Marianum Fruit Extract

Pigment Gel® HQ Free
Water/Aqua/Eau, SD Alcohol 40-B, Hamamelis Virginiana (Witch Hazel) Water, Lactic Acid, Butylene Glycol, Kojic Acid, Azelaic Acid, Alcohol, Hydroxyethylcellulose, Phenylethyl Resorcinol, BHT, Glutathione, Silybum Marianum Fruit Extract

Acne Gel
Active Ingredient: Salicylic Acid (2%)

Other Ingredients: Water/Aqua/Eau, SD Alcohol 40-B, Ethoxydiglycol, Azelaic Acid, Pentylene Glycol, Glycerin, Hydroxyethylcellulose, Butylene Glycol, Potassium Hydroxide, Glycyrrhiza Glabra (Licorice) Root Extract, Cinnamomum Cassia Bark Extract, Poterium Officinale Root Extract, Zingiber Officinale (Ginger) Root Extract

Acne Cream
Active Ingredient: Benzoyl Peroxide (5%)

Other Ingredients: Water/Aqua/Eau, Gluconolactone, Glycerin, Caprylic/Capric Triglyceride, Cetyl Alcohol, Vitis Vinifera (Grape) Seed Oil, Aminomethyl Propanol, Lactic Acid, Aloe Barbadensis Leaf Juice, Cyclopentasiloxane, Dimethicone, Glyceryl Stearate, PEG-100 Stearate, Polyacrylate-13, Phenoxyethanol, Polyisobutene, Caprylyl Glycol, Ammonium Acryloyldimethyltaurate/VP Copolymer, Potassium Cetyl Phosphate, Ethylhexylglycerin, Allantoin, Tocopheryl Acetate, Hexylene Glycol, Citrus Grandis (Grapefruit) Peel Oil, Polysorbate 20, Melaleuca Alternifolia (Tea Tree) Leaf Oil, Panthenol, Butylene Glycol, Anthemis Nobilis Flower Extract, Ascorbic Acid, Retinyl Palmitate

C-Quench® Antioxidant Serum

Water/Aqua/Eau, Hamamelis Virginiana (Witch Hazel) Water, Ascorbic Acid, Alcohol, Hydroxyethyl Acrylate/Sodium Acryloyldimethyl Taurate Copolymer, Glycerin, Squalane, Maltodextrin, Sodium Citrate, Ribes Nigrum (Black Currant) Seed Oil, Pseudoalteromonas Ferment Extract, Phytosterols, Cassia Angustifolia Seed Polysaccharide, Glutathione, Resveratrol, Xanthan Gum, Tocopherol, Tocotrienols, Citrus Aurantium Dulcis (Orange) Peel Oil, Citrus Grandis (Grapefruit) Peel Oil, Oryza Sativa (Rice) Bran Wax, Squalene, Caprylyl Glycol, Syringa Vulgaris (Lilac) Leaf Cell Culture Extract, Ethylhexylglycerin, Sodium Hyaluronate, Alanine, Proline, Serine, Sodium Phosphate, Sodium Hydroxide, Ergothioneine

A&C Synergy Serum®

Hamamelis Virginiana (Witch Hazel) Water, SD Alcohol 40-B, Alcohol, Glycerin, Ascorbic Acid, Water/Aqua/Eau, Benzyl Alcohol, Butylene Glycol, Lactic Acid, Polyacrylate Crosspolymer-6, Hydroxyethyl Acrylate/Sodium Acryloyldimethyl Taurate Copolymer, Isohexadecane, Alpha-Arbutin, Caprylic/Capric Triglyceride, Kojic Acid, Resveratrol, Retinyl Palmitate, Polysorbate 60, Arginine, Allyl Methacrylates Crosspolymer, Glycyrrhiza Glabra (Licorice) Root Extract, Polygonum Cuspidatum Root Extract, Aminoguanidine HCl, Decarboxy Carnosine HCl, Peumus Boldus Leaf Extract, Retinol, Polysorbate 20

Total Strength Serum

Water/Aqua/Eau, Hamamelis Virginiana (Witch Hazel) Water, Glycerin, Glycosaminoglycans, Alcohol, Alcohol Denat., Gluconolactone, Hydroxypropyl Cyclodextrin, Ammonium Acryloyldimethyltaurate/VP Copolymer, Sodium Benzoate, Xanthan Gum, Lonicera Caprifolium (Honeysuckle) Flower Extract, Cocos Nucifera (Coconut) Fruit Juice, Adenosine, Aesculus Hippocastanum (Horse Chestnut) Seed Extract, Lavandula Hybrida Oil, Lonicera Japonica (Honeysuckle) Flower Extract, Melaleuca Alternifolia (Tea Tree) Leaf Oil, Menthyl Lactate, Santalum Austrocaledonicum Wood Oil, Silybum Marianum Extract, Sodium Hyaluronate, Totarol, Tocotrienols, Elaeis Guineensis (Palm) Oil, Citric Acid, Phospholipids, Potassium Sorbate, Tocopherol, sh-Oligopeptide-1, Palmitoyl Tripeptide-38

Hydrating Serum

Water/Aqua/Eau, Glycerin, Sodium Polyacrylate, Sodium PCA, Aloe Barbadensis Leaf Juice, Sodium Lactate, Gluconolactone, Sodium Hyaluronate, Wheat Amino Acids, Triticum Vulgare (Wheat) Germ Extract, Sodium Benzoate, Panthenol, Symphytum Officinale Leaf Extract, Saccharomyces Lysate Extract, Hydroxyproline, Fructose, Glycine, Inositol, Niacinamide, Urea

Rejuvenating Serum

Water/Aqua/Eau, Alcohol Denat., Glycerin, Hydroxyethyl Acrylate/Sodium Acryloyldimethyl Taurate Copolymer, Aminomethyl Propanol, Gluconolactone, Acrylates/C10-30 Alkyl Acrylate Crosspolymer, Polysorbate 20, Bisabolol, Isomalt, Sodium Benzoate, Sodium Lactate, Sodium PCA, Caprylyl Glycol, 1,2-Hexanediol, Mentha Piperita (Peppermint) Oil, Tocopherol, Citrus Paradisi (Grapefruit) Peel Oil, Glutathione, Squalane, Oryza Sativa (Rice) Bran Oil, Citrus Aurantium Dulcis (Orange) Peel Oil, Phospholipids, Tropolone, Tocotrienols, Camellia Sinensis Leaf Extract, Epigallocatechin Gallate, Aloe Barbadensis Leaf Juice Powder, Fructose, Glycine, Niacinamide, Urea, Inositol, Lecithin, Vitis Vinifera (Grape) Fruit Cell Extract, sh-Oligopeptide-1

Anti-Redness Serum
Water/Aqua/Eau, Sorbitol, Cyclomethicone, Glycerin, Butylene Glycol, Caprylic/
Capric Triglyceride, Octyldodecyl Myristate, Dimethicone, Ethoxydiglycol, Sodium
Polyacrylate, Capparis Spinosa Fruit Extract, Phenoxyethanol, Hydrogenated
Polydecene, Caprylyl Glycol, Bisabolol, Panthenol, Sodium PCA, Steareth-21,
Aminomethyl Propanol, Steareth-2, Disodium EDTA, Trideceth-6, Sorbic Acid,
Ascophyllum Nodosum Extract, Potassium Sorbate, Asparagopsis Armata Extract

Retinol Renewal with RestorAtive Complex
Water/Aqua/Eau, Polymethylsilsesquioxane, Glycerin, Butylene Glycol, Polyacrylate-13,
Phenoxyethanol, Vigna Aconitifolia Seed Extract, Polyisobutene, Caprylic/Capric
Triglyceride, Caprylyl Glycol, Panthenol, Lecithin, Tocopherol, Sodium Ascorbate,
Ethylhexylglycerin, Disodium EDTA, Hexylene Glycol, Polysorbate 20, Retinol, Sodium
Citrate, Superoxide Dismutase, Hydrogenated Castor Oil, Sodium Hyaluronate,
Phytosterols,Tocotrienols, Oryza Sativa (Rice) Bran Wax, Squalene

Retinol Treatment For Sensitive Skin
Water/Aqua/Eau, Isododecane, Caprylic/Capric Triglyceride, Niacinamide, Glycerin,
Isoamyl Laurate, Tapioca Starch Polymethylsilsesquioxane, Dimethicone, PEG-8,
Panthenol, Cetearyl Alcohol, Glyceryl Stearate, PEG-100 Stearate, Polysilicone-11,
Hexylresorcinol, PEG-23 Glyceryl Distearate, Phenoxyethanol, Coco-Caprylate/
Caprate, Bisabolol, Tocopherol, Ammonium Acryloyldimethyltaurate/VP Copolymer,
Sodium Polyacrylate, Butylene Glycol, PEG-12 Glyceryl Dimyristate, Caprylyl Glycol,
Isoamyl Cocoate, Ethylhexyl Stearate, Ceramide NP, Xanthan Gum, Chlorphenesin,
Propyl Gallate, Retinol, Polysorbate 20, Citric Acid, Sodium Phytate, Trideceth-6,
Avena Sativa (Oat) Kernel Extract, Decyl Glucoside, Potassium Sorbate

Intensive Clarity Treatment®: 0.5% pure retinol night
Active Ingredient: Salicylic Acid (2%)

Other Ingredients: Water/Aqua/Eau, Glycerin, PEG-12 Glyceryl Dimyristate,
Cyclopentasiloxane, Isododecane, Niacinamide, Butylene Glycol, Dimethicone,
Ammonium Acryloyldimethyltaurate/VP Copolymer, Cetearyl Alcohol, Isoamyl Laurate,
Sodium Polyacrylate, Glyceryl Stearate, PEG-100 Stearate, Polysilicone-11, Bakuchiol,
Caprylic/Capric Triglyceride, Hexylresorcinol, Maltodextrin, Phenoxyethanol, Coco-
Caprylate/Caprate, Ethyl Linoleate, Ethylhexyl Stearate, Retinol, Polysorbate 20,
Dipotassium Glycyrrhizate, Caprylyl Glycol, Xanthan Gum, Chlorphenesin, Trideceth-6,
Pentylene Glycol, Isoamyl Cocoate, Disodium EDTA, Sodium Citrate, Syringa Vulgaris
(Lilac) Leaf Cell Culture Extract, Decyl Glucoside, Myristoyl Nonapeptide-3, Citric Acid

Intensive Age Refining Treatment®: 0.5% pure retinol night
Water/Aqua/Eau, Cyclopentasiloxane, Glycerin, Niacinamide, Cetearyl Alcohol,
Isosorbide Dicaprylate, Isoamyl Laurate, Glyceryl Stearate, PEG-100 Stearate,
Panthenol, PEG-23 Glyceryl Distearate, Dimethicone, Phenoxyethanol, PEG-12
Glyceryl Dimyristate, Polysilicone-11, Retinol, Terminalia Chebula Fruit Extract,
Polysorbate 20, Sodium Polyacrylate, Butylene Glycol, Citrus Aurantium Dulcis
(Orange) Callus Culture Extract, Phytosterols, Ammonium Acryloyldimethyltaurate/
VP Copolymer, Caprylyl Glycol, Xanthan Gum, Ethylhexylglycerin, Hexylene Glycol,
Ethylhexyl Stearate, Tocopherol, Tocotrienols, Lecithin, Oryza Sativa (Rice) Bran Wax,
Pentylene Glycol, Squalene, Isoamyl Cocoate, Disodium EDTA, Sodium Citrate, Avena
Sativa (Oat) Kernel Extract, Trideceth-6, Superoxide Dismutase, Decyl Glucoside, Citric
Acid, Potassium Sorbate, Sodium Hyaluronate, Myristoyl Nonapeptide-3

Intensive Brightening Treatment: 0.5% pure retinol night
Water/Aqua/Eau, Isododecane, Cyclopentasiloxane, Niacinamide, Propanediol, Dimethicone, PEG-12 Glyceryl Dimyristate, Glycerin, Tapioca Starch Polymethylsilsesquioxane, Cetearyl Alcohol, Hydroxyphenoxy Propionic Acid, Pentylene Glycol, Polysilicone-11, Glyceryl Stearate, PEG-100 Stearate, Hexylresorcinol, CocoCaprylate/Caprate, Resveratrol, Phenoxyethanol, Retinol, Polysorbate 20, Butylene Glycol, Sodium Polyacrylate, Caprylyl Glycol, Ethylhexyl Stearate, Ammonium Acryloyldimethyltaurate/VP Copolymer, Xanthan Gum, Chlorphenesin, Sodium Citrate, Tocopheryl Acetate, Trideceth-6, Disodium EDTA, Decyl Glucoside, Aminomethyl Propanol

Intensive Pigment Eraser
Active Ingredient: Hydroquinone (2%)

Other Ingredients: Water/Aqua/Eau, PEG-12 Glyceryl Dimyristate, Isododecane, Niacinamide, Propanediol, Glycerin, Caprylic/Capric Triglyceride, Dimethicone, PEG-8, Tapioca Starch Polymethylsilsesquioxane, Panthenol, Cetearyl Alcohol, Glyceryl Stearate, PEG-100 Stearate, Polysilicone-11, Hexylresorcinol, PEG-23 Glyceryl Distearate, Retinol, Polysorbate 20, Phenoxyethanol, Coco-Caprylate/Caprate, Bisabolol, Tocopherol, Sodium Polyacrylate, Ammonium Acryloyldimethyltaurate/VP Copolymer, Butylene Glycol, Palmaria Palmata Extract, Caprylyl Glycol, Mentha Piperita (Peppermint) Extract, Ceramide NP, Xanthan Gum, Chlorphenesin, Ethylhexyl Stearate, Hydrolyzed Ceratonia Siliqua Seed Extract, Citrus Grandis (Grapefruit) Peel Oil, Propyl Gallate, Citric Acid, Avena Sativa (Oat) Kernel Extract, Trideceth-6, Sodium Phytate, Decyl Glucoside

C&E Strength
Cyclopentasiloxane, Ascorbic Acid, Polymethylsilsesquioxane, Polysilicone-11, Ethylhexyl Hydroxystearate, Tocopherol, Hordeum Distichon (Barley) Extract, Citrus Aurantium Dulcis (Orange) Oil, Phellodendron Amurense Bark Extract, Santalum Album (Sandalwood) Wood Extract, Bisabolol, Retinyl Palmitate

C&E Strength Max
Cyclopentasiloxane, Ascorbic Acid, Polymethylsilsesquioxane, Ethylhexyl Hydroxystearate, Polysilicone-11, Tocopherol, Hordeum Distichon (Barley) Extract, Citrus Aurantium Dulcis (Orange) Oil, Phellodendron Amurense Bark Extract, Santalum Album (Sandalwood) Wood Extract, Bisabolol, Retinyl Palmitate

Hyaluronic Acid Boosting Serum
Water/Aqua/Eau, Propanediol, Glycerin, Niacinamide, Dimethicone, Hydrolyzed Yeast Extract, Polyglyceryl-3 Beeswax, Coconut Alkanes, Phenoxyethanol, Isododecane, Jojoba Esters, Dimethicone Crosspolymer, Polysilicone-11, Sodium Hyaluronate, Sodium Benzoate, Carbomer, Xanthan Gum, Hydrolyzed Hyaluronic Acid, Cetyl Alcohol, Polyglyceryl-6 Distearate, Sodium Lauroyl Lactylate, Disodium Acetyl Glucosamine Phosphate, Hydrolyzed Glycosaminoglycans, Ethylhexylglycerin, Sodium Hydroxide, Hexylene Glycol, Polygonum Bistorta Root Extract, Cetyl Hydroxyethylcellulose, Rosmarinus Officinalis (Rosemary) Leaf Oil, Aroma, Polyglucuronic Acid, Ceramide NP, Hyaluronic Acid, Sodium Carrageenan, Ceramide AP, Phytosphingosine, Caprylyl Glycol, Cholesterol, Lecithin, Maris Sal, Ceramide EOP

Dual Action Redness Relief
Water/Aqua/Eau, Isododecane, Cyclopentasiloxane, Niacinamide, Dimethicone, Glycerin, PEG-12 Glyceryl Dimyristate, Tapioca Starch Polymethylsilsesquioxane, Ammonium Acryloyldimethyltaurate/VP Copolymer, Cetearyl Alcohol, Dimethyl Sulfone, Pentylene Glycol, Polysilicone-11, Panthenol, Glyceryl Stearate, PEG-100 Stearate, Coco-Caprylate/Caprate, PEG-23 Glyceryl Distearate, Silybum Marianum Fruit Extract, Phenoxyethanol, Bisabolol, Tocopheryl Acetate, Butylene Glycol, Sodium Polyacrylate, Caprylyl Glycol, Ethylhexyl Stearate, Ceramide NP, Xanthan Gum, Chlorphenesin, Citrus Grandis (Grapefruit) Peel Oil, Sodium Citrate, Trideceth-6, Disodium EDTA, Decyl Glucoside, Aminomethyl Propanol

Ideal Complex® Revitalizing Eye Gel

Water/Aqua/Eau, Cyclopentasiloxane, Glycerin, Propanediol, Butylene Glycol, Dimethicone, Polysilicone-11, Ethylhexyl Hydroxystearate, Hydroxyethyl Acrylate/ Sodium Acryloyldimethyl Taurate Copolymer, Acacia Senegal Gum, Niacinamide, Albizia Julibrissin Bark Extract, Caprylyl Glycol, Isohexadecane, Citrus Aurantium Dulcis (Orange) Callus Culture Extract, Phenoxyethanol, Fraxinus Excelsior Bark Extract, Carbomer, Hydroxyethylcellulose, Decyl Glucoside, Hexylene Glycol, Pentylene Glycol, Aminomethyl Propanol, Polysorbate 60, Potassium Citrate, Silanetriol, Hydroxypropyl Cyclodextrin, Xanthan Gum, Myristoyl Nonapeptide-3, Crocus Chrysanthus Bulb Extract, Myristoyl Hexapeptide-4, Myristoyl Pentapeptide-8, Dipeptide Diaminobutyroyl Benzylamide Diacetate, Acetyl Tetrapeptide-5, Darutoside, Palmitoyl Tripeptide-38

Ideal Complex® Restorative Eye Cream

Water/Aqua/Eau, Glycerin, Cetearyl Ethylhexanoate, Ethylhexyl Palmitate, Pentylene Glycol, Boron Nitride, Cetearyl Alcohol, Butylene Glycol, Butyrospermum Parkii (Shea) Butter, Dimethicone, Myristyl Myristate, Squalane, Vitis Vinifera (Grape) Seed Oil, Glyceryl Stearate Citrate, Glyceryl Stearate, PEG-12 Dimethicone, Acacia Senegal Gum, Niacinamide, Albizia Julibrissin Bark Extract, Titanium Dioxide, Caprylyl Glycol, Carbomer, Citrus Aurantium Dulcis (Orange) Callus Culture Extract, Fraxinus Excelsior Bark Extract, Phenoxyethanol, Citrus Grandis (Grapefruit) Peel Oil, Sodium Hydroxide, Hexylene Glycol, Aloe Barbadensis Leaf Juice, Tocopheryl Acetate, Potassium Citrate, Silanetriol, Hydroxypropyl Cyclodextrin, Xanthan Gum, Alumina, Myristoyl Nonapeptide-3, Crocus Chrysanthus Bulb Extract, Myristoyl Hexapeptide-4, Myristoyl Pentapeptide-8, Silica, Dipeptide Diaminobutyroyl Benzylamide Diacetate, Acetyl Tetrapeptide-5, Darutoside, Polyquaternium-7, Palmitoyl Tripeptide-38

EyeXcellence

Water/Aqua/Eau, Isononyl Isononanoate, Vitis Vinifera (Grape) Seed Oil, Glycerin, Butylene Glycol, Cetyl Alcohol, Squalane, Glyceryl Stearate, PEG-100 Stearate, Cetyl Esters, Dimethicone, Panax Ginseng Root Extract, Cetearyl Alcohol, Yeast Polysaccharides, Caprylyl Glycol, PEG-12 Dimethicone, Polyglyceryl-3 Beeswax, Tocopheryl Acetate, Phenoxyethanol, Carbomer, Ceteareth-20, Triethanolamine, Gynostemma Pentaphyllum Extract, Hesperidin Methyl Chalcone, Hexylene Glycol, Aloe Barbadensis Leaf Juice, Disodium EDTA, Steareth-20, Glycyrrhiza Glabra (Licorice) Root Extract, Polysorbate 20, Dipeptide-2, Palmitoyl Pentapeptide-4, Palmitoyl Tetrapeptide-7

Perfecting Neck & Décolleté

Water/Aqua/Eau, Glycerin, Caprylic/Capric Triglyceride, C12-15 Alkyl Benzoate, Isopropyl Palmitate, Niacinamide, Stearyl Alcohol, Cetyl Alcohol, Dimethicone, Cyclopentasiloxane, Glycol Distearate, Potassium Cetyl Phosphate, Stearic Acid, Phenoxyethanol, Cetearyl Alcohol, Tocopheryl Acetate, Citrus Aurantium Dulcis (Orange) Oil, Pentylene Glycol, Polysorbate 60, Prunus Amygdalus Dulcis (Sweet Almond) Oil, Butyrospermum Parkii (Shea) Butter, Carbomer, Xanthan Gum, Sodium Hydroxide, Allantoin, Ethylhexylglycerin, Tetrasodium EDTA, Isomalt, Polysorbate 20, Citrus Grandis (Grapefruit) Peel Oil, 3-Aminopropane Sulfonic Acid, Calcium Hydroxymethionine, Citrus Aurantifolia (Lime) Leaf Oil, Zingiber Officinale (Ginger) Root Oil, Secale Cereale (Rye) Seed Extract, Hydroxyethylcellulose, Palmitoyl Tripeptide-5, Retinol, Hydroxypropyl Cyclodextrin, Citrus Aurantium Bergamia (Bergamot) Fruit Oil, Hydrolyzed Silk, Kaempferia Galanga Root Extract, Mentha Piperita (Peppermint) Oil, Sclareolide, Camellia Oleifera Leaf Extract, Glycyrrhiza Glabra (Licorice) Root Extract, Silybum Marianum Extract, Morus Alba Root Extract, Oenothera Biennis (Evening Primrose) Root Extract, Lecithin, Vitis Vinifera (Grape) Fruit Cell Extract, Sodium Benzoate, Sodium Hyaluronate, Palmitoyl Tripeptide-38

15100.14
© 2017 Physicians Care Alliance, LLC

K

CliniCalm™ 1%
Active Ingredient: Hydrocortisone (1%)

Other ingredients: Water/Aqua/Eau, Glycerin, Caprylic/Capric Triglyceride, Alcohol Denat., Cetearyl Olivate, Squalane, Olea Europaea (Olive) Fruit Oil, Sorbitan Olivate, Caprylyl Glycol, Phenoxyethanol, Pentylene Glycol, Linum Usitatissimum (Linseed) Seed Oil, Xanthan Gum, 4-t-Butylcyclohexanol, 1,2-Hexanediol, Honey/Mel/Miel, Carbomer, Phospholipids, Asiaticoside, Beta-Glucan, Bisabolol, Lysine HCl, Sodium Hydroxide, Aloe Barbadensis Leaf Juice Powder, Ceramide NP, Sorbic Acid, Trisodium Ethylenediamine Disuccinate, Helianthus Annuus (Sunflower) Seed Oil, Butylene Glycol, Hyaluronic Acid, Sphingolipids, Tocopherol, Tropolone, Hydroxyphenyl Propamidobenzoic Acid

Peptide Lip Therapy
Ricinus Communis (Castor) Seed Oil, Hydrogenated Castor Oil, Ozokerite, Sorbitan Oleate, Euphorbia Cerifera (Candelilla) Wax, Carthamus Tinctorius (Safflower) Seed Oil, Squalane, Butyrospermum Parkii (Shea) Butter, Cetearyl Ethylhexanoate, Mentha Piperita (Peppermint) Oil, Hordeum Distichon (Barley) Extract/Hordeum Distichon/Extrait d'orges à deux rangs, Phenoxyethanol, Bisabolol, Tocopheryl Acetate, Sorbitan Isostearate, Solanum Lycopersicum (Tomato) Fruit/Leaf/Stem Extract, Sucralose, Helianthus Annuus (Sunflower) Seed Oil, Aloe Barbadensis Leaf Extract, Portulaca Pilosa Extract, Rosmarinus Officinalis (Rosemary) Leaf Extract, Sucrose Cocoate, Palmitoyl Tripeptide-38

Hydrate & protect

Weightless Protection Broad Spectrum SPF 45
Active ingredients: Zinc Oxide (9.0%), Octinoxate (7.5%)

Other ingredients: Butylene Glycol, Caffeine, Cyclopentasiloxane, Hydroxyethyl Acrylate/Sodium Acryloyldimethyl Taurate Copolymer, Iodopropynyl Butylcarbamate, Lactic Acid, Octyldodecyl Neopentanoate, Oleth-3 Phosphate, PEG-7 Trimethylolpropane Coconut Ether, Phenoxyethanol, Polyisobutene, Silybum Marianum Extract, Sodium Hyaluronate, Tocopheryl Acetate, Triethoxycaprylylsilane, Water/Aqua/Eau

Perfecting Protection Broad Spectrum SPF 30
Active Ingredients: Zinc Oxide (9.8%), Octinoxate (7.5%)

Other Ingredients: Aloe Barbadensis Leaf Juice, Arctostaphylos Uva Ursi Leaf Extract, Arginine, Butylene Glycol, C20-22 Alcohols, C20-22 Alkyl Phosphate, Caffeine, Caprylyl Glycol, Cellulose Gum, Cetearyl Alcohol, Cetearyl Glucoside, Citrus Grandis (Grapefruit) Peel Oil, Cyclopentasiloxane, Dimethicone, Ethylhexyl Palmitate, Ethylhexylglycerin, Glycerin, Glycyrrhiza Glabra (Licorice) Root Extract, Hexylene Glycol, Isononyl Isononanoate, Kojic Acid, Lactic Acid, Magnesium Ascorbyl Phosphate, Microcrystalline Cellulose, Morus Alba Root Extract, Phenoxyethanol, Polyacrylate-13, Polyisobutene, Polysorbate 20, SD Alcohol 40-B, Silybum Marianum Fruit Extract, Sodium Hyaluronate, Sodium PCA, Tetrasodium EDTA, Tocopheryl Acetate, Triethoxycaprylylsilane, Water/Aqua/Eau

Protecting Hydrator Broad Spectrum SPF 30
Active Ingredients: Octinoxate (7.5%), Zinc Oxide (4.3%), Octisalate (3.6%)

Other Ingredients: Allantoin, Aloe Barbadensis Leaf, Butylene Glycol, Caffeine, Cetearyl Glucoside, Cetyl Alcohol, Ethylhexyl Isononanoate, Glycerin, Glyceryl Stearate, Hydroxyethyl Acrylate/Sodium Acryloyldimethyl Taurate Copolymer, Iodopropynyl Butylcarbamate, Lactic Acid, Panthenol, PEG-100 Stearate, PEG-7 Trimethylolpropane Coconut Ether, Phenoxyethanol, Polyether-1, Polyisobutene, Silybum Marianum Extract, Titanium Dioxide, Tocopheryl Acetate, Triethoxycaprylylsilane, Water/Aqua/Eau

Hydrator Plus Broad Spectrum SPF 30
Active Ingredients: Octinoxate (7.5%), Zinc Oxide (4.3%), Octisalate (3.6%)

Other Ingredients: Allantoin, Aloe Barbadensis Leaf, Butylene Glycol, Caffeine, Cetearyl Glucoside, Cetyl Alcohol, Dimethicone, Ethylhexyl Isononanoate, Glycerin, Glyceryl Stearate, Hydroxyethyl Acrylate/Sodium Acryloyldimethyl Taurate Copolymer, Iodopropynyl Butylcarbamate, Lactic Acid, Panthenol, PEG-100 Stearate, PEG-7 Trimethylolpropane Coconut Ether, Phenoxyethanol, Polyether-1, Polyisobutene, Silybum Marianum Extract, Sodium Hyaluronate, Sodium PCA, Stearic Acid, Tocopheryl Acetate, Triethoxycaprylylsilane, Water/Aqua/Eau

Active Broad Spectrum SPF 45: Water Resistant
Active ingredients: Zinc Oxide (8.0%), Octinoxate (7.5%), Octisalate (3.0%)

Other ingredients: Ascorbyl Palmitate, Butylene Glycol, Caffeine, Cyclopentasiloxane, Dimethicone, Dimethicone/PEG-10/15 Crosspolymer, Dimethicone/Vinyl Dimethicone Crosspolymer, Ethylhexyl Isononanoate, Iodopropynyl Butylcarbamate, Lauryl PEG-9 Polydimethylsiloxyethyl Dimethicone, Phenoxyethanol, Silybum Marianum Extract, Sodium Chloride, Triethoxycaprylylsilane, Water/Aqua/Eau

Sheer Tint Broad Spectrum SPF 45
Active ingredients: Titanium Dioxide (6.0%), Zinc Oxide (8.0%)

Other ingredients: Aluminum Hydroxide, Butyloctyl Salicylate, C12-15 Alkyl Benzoate, Caprylyl Glycol, Cyclopentasiloxane, Dimethicone, Dimethicone/ PEG-10/15 Crosspolymer, Dimethicone/Vinyl Dimethicone Crosspolymer, Ethylhexylglycerin, Hexylene Glycol, Iron Oxides, Isododecane, Methyl Methacrylate/Glycol Dimethacrylate Crosspolymer, PEG-9 Polydimethylsiloxyethyl Dimethicone, Phenoxyethanol, Polyglyceryl-3 Polydimethylsiloxyethyl Dimethicone, Polymethylsilsesquioxane, Sodium Chloride, Stearic Acid, Triethoxysilylethyl Polydimethylsiloxyethyl Hexyl Dimethicone, Ubiquinone, Water/Aqua/Eau

Clearskin
Water/Aqua/Eau, Ethylhexyl Isononanoate, Niacinamide, Glycereth-26, Hydroxyethyl Acrylate/Sodium Acryloyldimethyl Taurate Copolymer, Butylene Glycol, Phenoxyethanol, Carbomer, Polyisobutene, Caprylyl Glycol, Bisabolol, PEG-7 Trimethylolpropane Coconut Ether, Sodium Hydroxide, Ethylhexylglycerin, Hexylene Glycol, Borago Officinalis Seed Oil, Aloe Barbadensis Leaf Juice, Sodium Hyaluronate, Retinyl Palmitate, Glycerin, Calendula Officinalis Flower Extract, Cucumis Sativus (Cucumber) Fruit Extract

ReBalance
Water/Aqua/Eau, Ethylhexyl Isononanoate, Glycereth-26, Butylene Glycol, Hydroxyethyl Acrylate/Sodium Acryloyldimethyl Taurate Copolymer, Phenoxyethanol, Niacinamide, Carbomer, Polyisobutene, Caprylyl Glycol, Bisabolol, Sodium Hydroxide, Ethylhexylglycerin, Hexylene Glycol, PEG-7 Trimethylolpropane Coconut Ether, Tocopheryl Acetate, Oenothera Biennis (Evening Primrose) Oil, Borago Officinalis Seed Oil, Aloe Barbadensis Leaf Juice, Sodium Hyaluronate

Après Peel® Hydrating Balm
Water/Aqua/Eau, Glycerin, Olea Europaea (Olive) Fruit Oil, Caprylic/Capric Triglyceride, Coco-Caprylate/Caprate, Triticum Vulgare (Wheat) Germ Oil, Cetearyl Alcohol, Cetearyl Glucoside, Glyceryl Stearate, Xanthan Gum, Caprylyl Glycol, Hydrolyzed Milk Protein, Phenoxyethanol, 1,2-Hexanediol, Alcohol Denat., Allantoin, Aloe Barbadensis Leaf Juice Powder, Ammonium Acryloyldimethyltaurate/VP Copolymer, Fructooligosaccharides, Polysorbate 80, Vitex Agnus Castus Extract , Benzyl Alcohol, Citrus Limon (Lemon) Peel Oil, Lecithin, Potassium Sorbate, Prunus Armeniaca (Apricot) Kernel Oil, Tropolone, Soy Isoflavones

Collagen Hydrator
Water/Aqua/Eau, Glycerin, C12-15 Alkyl Benzoate, Glyceryl Stearate, Cetearyl Alcohol, Isopropyl Palmitate, Butyrospermum Parkii (Shea) Butter, Cyclopentasiloxane, Dimethicone, Cetyl Alcohol, Polysorbate 60, Phenoxyethanol, Tetrahexyldecyl Ascorbate, Allantoin, Glycol Distearate, Helianthus Annuus (Sunflower) Seed Oil, Hydrolyzed Wheat Protein, Olea Europaea (Olive) Fruit Oil, Potassium Cetyl Phosphate, Prunus Amygdalus Dulcis (Sweet Almond) Oil, Carbomer, Xanthan Gum, Sodium PCA, Tocopherol, Cucumis Sativus (Cucumber) Fruit Extract, Ethylhexylglycerin, Tetrasodium EDTA, Aloe Barbadensis Leaf Extract, Chamomilla Recutita (Matricaria) Flower Extract, Sodium Hydroxide, Sodium Hyaluronate

Silkcoat® Balm
Water/Aqua/Eau, Glycerin, Butyrospermum Parkii (Shea) Butter, Caprylic/Capric Triglyceride, Cetyl Alcohol, Glyceryl Stearate, Cyclopentasiloxane, Dimethicone, Theobroma Cacao (Cocoa) Seed Butter, C12-15 Alkyl Benzoate, Stearic Acid, Potassium Cetyl Phosphate, Cetearyl Alcohol, Phenoxyethanol, Polysorbate 60, Allantoin, Simmondsia Chinensis (Jojoba) Seed Oil, Squalane, Tocopheryl Acetate, Hydrolyzed Silk, Acrylates/C10-30 Alkyl Acrylate Crosspolymer, Ethylhexylglycerin, Hydrastis Canadensis (Goldenseal) Extract, Lavandula Angustifolia (Lavender) Flower Extract, Rosmarinus Officinalis (Rosemary) Leaf Extract, Thymus Vulgaris (Thyme) Flower/Leaf Extract, Sodium Hydroxide

Body Therapy
Water/Aqua/Eau, Lactic Acid, Glycerin, Jojoba Esters, Cyclopentasiloxane, Behenyl Alcohol, Isopropyl Jojobate, Jojoba Alcohol, Hordeum Distichon (Barley) Extract/Hordeum Distichon/Extrait d'orges à deux rangs, Butyrospermum Parkii (Shea) Butter, Dimethicone, Glyceryl Stearate, Polyacrylate-13, Ammonia, Arachidyl Alcohol, Gluconolactone, C20-22 Alkyl Phosphate, Sodium Hyaluronate, Galactoarabinan,Tocopheryl Acetate, C20-22 Alcohols, Polyisobutene, Phellodendron Amurense Bark Extract, Santalum Album (Sandalwood) Wood Extract, Sodium Benzoate, Xanthan Gum, Arachidyl Glucoside, Sodium PCA, Wheat Amino Acids, Citrus Grandis (Grapefruit) Peel Oil, Arginine, Panthenol, Symphytum Officinale Leaf Extract, Polysorbate 20, Phytic Acid, Hydroxyproline

PCA SKIN® professional product ingredient listings

PCA Peel® Hydroquinone Free
Alcohol Denat., Lactic Acid (14%), Salicylic Acid (14%), Citric Acid, Kojic Acid (3%), Water/Aqua/Eau

2 oz. – approximately 20-30 treatments; 4 oz. – approximately 40-60 treatments

PCA Peel® with Hydroquinone
Alcohol Denat., Lactic Acid (14%), Salicylic Acid (14%), Citric Acid, Kojic Acid (3%), Hydroquinone (2%), Water/Aqua/Eau

2 oz. – approximately 20-30 treatments; 4 oz. – approximately 40-60 treatments

PCA Peel® with Hydroquinone & Resorcinol
Alcohol Denat., Lactic Acid (14%), Resorcinol (14%), Salicylic Acid (14%), Kojic Acid (3%), Hydroquinone (2%), Citric Acid, Water/Aqua/Eau

2 oz. – approximately 20-30 treatments; 4 oz. – approximately 40-60 treatments

Sensi Peel®
Water/Aqua/Eau, Alcohol Denat., Glycerin, Hamamelis Virginiana (Witch Hazel) Water, Lactic Acid (12%), Trichloroacetic Acid (TCA) (6%), Azelaic Acid, Alpha-Arbutin, Kojic Acid, Alcohol, Linum Usitatissimum (Linseed) Seed Oil, Xanthan Gum, Limnanthes Alba (Meadowfoam) Seed Oil, Ascorbic Acid, Althaea Officinalis Root Extract, Prunus Amygdalus Dulcis (Sweet Almond) Fruit Extract, Calcium Gluconate, Carrageenan, Glucosamine HCl, Hydrolyzed Actin, Mannitol, Sodium Chloride, Sodium Glucuronate, Sorbitol, Vitex Agnus Castus Extract

2 oz. – approximately 20-30 treatments; 4 oz. – approximately 40-60 treatments

Ultra Peel® I
Hamamelis Virginiana (Witch Hazel) Water, Lactic Acid (20%), Trichloroacetic Acid (TCA) (10%), Alcohol, Azelaic Acid, Alcohol Denat., Ascorbic Acid, Kojic Acid, Linum Usitatissimum (Linseed) Seed Oil, Glycerin, Ricinus Communis (Castor) Seed Oil, Hydroxypropyl Methylcellulose, Xanthan Gum, Althaea Officinalis Root Extract, Prunus Amygdalus Dulcis (Sweet Almond) Fruit Extract, Calcium Gluconate, Carrageenan, Glucosamine HCl, Hydrolyzed Actin, Mannitol, Sodium Chloride, Sodium Glucuronate, Sorbitol, Vitex Agnus Castus Extract

2 oz. – approximately 20-30 treatments; 4 oz. – approximately 40-60 treatments

Ultra Peel Forte®
Hamamelis Virginiana (Witch Hazel) Water, Alcohol Denat., Trichloroacetic Acid (TCA) (20%), Lactic Acid (10%), Azelaic Acid, Alcohol, Ascorbic Acid, Kojic Acid, Vitex Agnus Castus Extract, Linum Usitatissimum (Linseed) Seed Oil, Glycerin, Hydroxypropyl Methylcellulose, Limnanthes Alba (Meadowfoam) Seed Oil, Ricinus Communis (Castor) Seed Oil, Althaea Officinalis Root Extract, Prunus Amygdalus Dulcis (Sweet Almond) Fruit Extract, Calcium Gluconate, Carrageenan, Glucosamine HCl, Hydrolyzed Actin, Mannitol, Sodium Chloride, Sodium Glucuronate, Sorbitol, Xanthan Gum

2 oz. – approximately 20-30 treatments

K

Smoothing Body Peel®
Pre-Peel Accelerator Mask (Step 1) - Water/Aqua/Eau, Hamamelis Virginiana (Witch Hazel) Water, Urea, Alcohol, Malic Acid, Butylene Glycol, Glycol Distearate, Cetyl Alcohol, Stearic Acid, Xanthan Gum, Glycerin, Cetearyl Alcohol, Polysorbate 60

4 oz. – approximately 35-55 treatments

Smoothing Body Peel® (Step 2) – Lactic Acid (45%), Alcohol Denat., Salicylic Acid (10%), Trichloroacetic Acid (TCA) (10%), Arbutin, Kojic Acid, Xanthan Gum.

4 oz. – approximately 35-55 treatments

Hydrate: Therapeutic Oat Milk Mask
Avena Sativa (Oat) Kernel Extract, Glycerin, Water/Aqua/Eau, Glycine Soja (Soybean) Oil, Carthamus Tinctorius (Safflower) Seed Oil, Honey/Mel/Miel, Glyceryl Stearate SE, Pectin, Phenoxyethanol, Xanthan Gum, Styrax Tonkinensis Resin Extract, Aniba Rosaeodora (Rosewood) Wood Oil, Carrageenan, Ethylhexylglycerin, Potassium Sorbate, Panthenol, Sodium Hyaluronate, Glucose, Anacyclus Pyrethrum Root Extract, Arnica Montana Flower Extract, Cucumis Sativus (Cucumber) Fruit Extract

Detoxify: Therapeutic Charcoal Mask
Water/Aqua/Eau, Kaolin, Charcoal Powder, Glycerin, Magnesium Aluminum Silicate, Phenoxyethanol, Xanthan Gum, Citric Acid, Disodium EDTA, Ethylhexylglycerin.

Revitalize: Therapeutic Papaya Mask
Carica Papaya (Papaya) Fruit, Water/Aqua/Eau, Glycerin, Hydroxyethyl Acrylate/ Sodium Acryloyldimethyl Taurate Copolymer, Squalane, Phenoxyethanol, Saccharum Officinarum (Sugarcane) Extract, Chlorophyllin-Copper Complex, Xanthan Gum, Polysorbate 60, Ethylhexylglycerin, Honey/Mel/Miel, Potassium Sorbate, Tocopheryl Acetate, Pelargonium Graveolens Flower Oil, Foeniculum Vulgare (Fennel) Oil, Pogostemon Cablin Oil, Camellia Sinensis Leaf Extract, Citrus Aurantium Dulcis (Orange) Fruit Extract, Citrus Limon (Lemon) Fruit Extract, Pyrus Malus (Apple) Fruit Extract, Sucrose, Glycine Soja (Soybean) Oil, Aniba Rosodora (Rosewood) Wood Oil, Citrus Aurantifolia (Lime) Fruit Extract, Citrus Aurantium Dulcis (Orange) Peel Oil

Clarify: Therapeutic Salicylic Acid Mask
Water/Aqua/Eau, Salicylic Acid, Hamamelis Virginiana (Witch Hazel) Water, Glycerin, Caprylic/Capric Triglyceride, Cetyl Alcohol, Alcohol, Croton Glabellus Bark Oil, Hydrolyzed Candida Saitoana Extract, Titanium Dioxide, Glycol Distearate, Dimethicone, Allantoin, Tocopherol, Benzyl Alcohol, Helianthus Annuus (Sunflower) Seed Oil, Prunus Avium (Sweet Cherry) Fruit Extract, Prunus Serotina (Wild Cherry) Bark Extract, Fragrance/Parfum

Retexturize: Therapeutic Pumpkin Mask
Cucurbita Pepo (Pumpkin), Lactobacillus/Pumpkin Ferment Extract, Propanediol, Water/Aqua/Eau, Salicylic Acid, Gluconic Acid, Phenoxyethanol, Caprylyl Glycol, Eugenia Caryophyllus (Clove) Leaf Oil, Hydroxypropyl Methylcellulose, Cinnamomum Cassia Leaf Oil, Zingiber Officinale (Ginger) Root Oil, Alcohol Denat., Fructooligosaccharides, Glutathione, Sucrose, Yeast

Advanced Treatment Booster
Water/Aqua/Eau, Gelatin, Caprylic/Capric Triglyceride, Glycerin, PPG-2 Myristyl Ether Propionate, Hamamelis Virginiana (Witch Hazel) Water, Zea Mays (Corn) Starch, Cyclopentasiloxane, Cetearyl Alcohol, Retinyl Acetate, Stearic Acid, Sucrose, Butylene Glycol, Ascorbic Acid, Olea Europaea (Olive) Fruit Oil, Polysorbate 60, Potassium Cetyl Phosphate, Stearyl Alcohol, Phenoxyethanol, Retinyl Palmitate, BHT, Sodium Hydroxide, Allantoin, Panthenol, Potassium Sorbate, Disodium EDTA, Lens Esculenta (Lentil) Seed Extract, Tocopherol, Ethylhexylglycerin, Glycine Soja (Soybean) Oil, Hydrogenated Lecithin, Magnesium Ascorbyl Phosphate, Escin, Ruscus Aculeatus Root Extract, Calendula Officinalis Flower Extract, Althaea Officinalis Leaf/Root Extract, Ammonium Glycyrrhizate, Alcohol, Aloe Barbadensis Leaf Juice, Centella Asiatica Extract, Hydrolyzed Yeast Protein, Lecithin, Vegetable Oil, Vitex Agnus-Castus Extract, Ascorbyl Tetraisopalmitate, Cyclodextrin, Glycine Soja (Soybean) Seed Extract, Xanthan Gum

4% Pure Retinol Peel
Water/Aqua/Eau, Glycerin, Polysorbate 20, Retinol, Caprylic/Capric Triglyceride, PPG-2 Myristyl Ether Propionate, Stearyl Alcohol, Cetearyl Alcohol, Cetyl Alcohol, Cyclopentasiloxane, Potassium Cetyl Phosphate, BHT, Dimethicone, Ethylhexyl Methoxycrylene, Hamamelis Virginiana (Witch Hazel) Water, Phenoxyethanol, Xanthan Gum, Polysorbate 60, Calendula Officinalis Flower Extract, Tocopheryl Acetate, Allantoin, Sodium Metabisulfite, Disodium EDTA, Sodium Ascorbyl Phosphate, Tocopherol, BHA, Ethylhexylglycerin, Sodium Hydroxide, Silybum Marianum Fruit Extract, Olea Europaea (Olive) Fruit Oil, Vitex Agnus Castus Extract

6% Pure Retinol Peel
Water/Aqua/Eau, Retinol, Polysorbate 20, Glycerin, Caprylic/Capric Triglyceride, PPG-2 Myristyl Ether Propionate, Stearyl Alcohol, Cetearyl Alcohol, Cetyl Alcohol, Cyclopentasiloxane, Potassium Cetyl Phosphate, BHT, Dimethicone, Hamamelis Virginiana (Witch Hazel) Water, Phenoxyethanol, Polysorbate 60, Calendula Officinalis Flower Extract, Ethylhexyl Methoxycrylene, Tocopheryl Acetate, Allantoin, Xanthan Gum, Sodium Metabisulfite, Alcohol, BHA, Disodium EDTA, Sodium Ascorbyl Phosphate, Tocopherol, Ethylhexylglycerin, Sodium Hydroxide, Silybum Marianum Fruit Extract, Olea Europaea (Olive) Fruit Oil, Vitex Agnus Castus Extract

Oxygenating Trio®
Activator (Step 1) – Water/Aqua/Eau, Hamamelis Virginiana (Witch Hazel) Water, SD Alcohol 40-B, Alcohol, Propylene Glycol, Polysorbate 20, Niacinamide, Phenoxyethanol, Fumaric Acid, Hamamelis Virginiana (Witch Hazel) Extract, Niacin, Phospholipids, Superoxide Dismutase

Detoxifier (Step 2) – Cucurbita Pepo (Pumpkin) Seed Oil, Hydrolyzed Candida Saitoana Extract, Fragrance/Parfum, Phenethyl Alcohol, Caprylyl Glycol, Alcohol Denat., Prunus Avium (Sweet Cherry) Fruit Extract

Oxygenator (Step 3) – Water/Aqua/Eau, Hydrogen Peroxide, Glyceryl Stearate, PEG-100 Stearate, Cetyl Alcohol, Hydroxypropyl Starch Phosphate, Carthamus Tinctorius (Safflower) Seed Oil, Glycerin, Salicylic Acid, Helianthus Annuus (Sunflower) Seed Oil, Glycolic Acid, Polysorbate 20, Sorbitol, Phenoxyethanol, Disodium EDTA, Coconut Alkanes, Eucalyptus Citriodora Oil, Coco-Caprylate/Caprate, Lactic Acid, Retinyl Palmitate

Detox Gel Deep Pore Treatment
Water/Aqua/Eau, Alcohol Denat., Hydrogen Peroxide, Glycerin, Glycolic Acid, Lactic Acid, Salicylic Acid, Aloe Barbadensis Leaf Juice Powder, Eucalyptus Globulus Leaf Oil, Glutathione, Totarol, Xanthan Gum

Replenishing Gel
Water/Aqua/Eau, Caprylic/Capric Triglyceride, Isopropyl Myristate, Butylene Glycol, Glycerin, Hamamelis Virginiana (Witch Hazel) Water, Phenoxyethanol, Acrylates/C10-30 Alkyl Acrylate Crosspolymer, Alcohol, Hydroxyethyl Acrylate/Sodium Acryloyldimethyl Taurate Copolymer, Squalane, Sodium Hydroxide, Allantoin, Ethylhexylglycerin, Potassium Sorbate, Prunus Amygdalus Dulcis (Sweet Almond) Oil, Tocopheryl Acetate, Maltodextrin, Aloe Barbadensis Leaf Juice, Chlorella Vulgaris Extract, Polysorbate 60, Lecithin, Magnolia Officinalis Bark Extract, Tocopherol, Vitis Vinifera (Grape) Seed Extract

Calming Balm
Water/Aqua/Eau, Caprylic/Capric Triglyceride, Glycerin, Pentylene Glycol, Pichia/Resveratrol Ferment Extract, 4-t-Butylcyclohexanol, Bisabolol, Allantoin, Aloe Barbadensis (Aloe Vera) Leaf Juice, Glycine Soja (Soybean) Oil, Rosa Canina Seed, Cordyceps Sinensis Extract, Trametes Versicolor Extract, Butylene Glycol, Sodium Polyacrylate, Xanthan Gum, Tocopherol, Phenoxyethanol, Ethylhexylglycerin, Potassium Sorbate

K

commonly used medical terms

Acid Mantle – describes the portion of the skin that helps to retard bacterial growth.

Acne – is a skin disease that arises due to a combination of four well-known factors: increased sebum production as a result of increased androgen production; abnormal keratinization within the follicles resulting in obstruction; proliferation of propionibacterium acnes and inflammation.

Acne rosacea – is another term for papulopustular rosacea. See papulopustular rosacea for definition.

Acute – describes conditions having severe symptoms with rapid onset. Acute reactions are typically short-lived.

Alopecia – is a disease present as a deficiency of hair or total baldness.

Antioxidant – describes a molecule that can safely terminate an oxidation chain reaction before cells incur damage.

Asphyxiated – describes the impairment or absence of oxygen. Asphyxiated skin is marked by a dry surface with oil trapped under the surface that feels bumpy to the touch.

Astringent – describes a substance that causes contraction of the tissues, controls bleeding and lowers secretions.

Atopic dermatitis – is also referred to as eczema. It is a congenital inflammatory skin condition characterized by dry, itchy skin.

Chloasma – is synonymous with melasma. It is hyperpigmentation characterized by large patches with jagged irregular borders.

Chronic – describes a condition having long duration and is the opposite of acute.

Collagen – is a fibrous protein that is a constituent of the dermal matrix, connective tissue, cartilage and bone.

Comedogenic – refers to ingredients or products that tend to promote the formation of comedones.

Comedone – describes a dilated hair follicle filled with keratin, bacteria and sebum, but free of inflammation.

Comedone extractor – is an instrument used for the removal of comedones (a small blade lancet may also be used for this purpose).

Corneocyte – is a flattened dead keratinocyte that is found in the stratum corneum.

Couperose – is a condition that is characterized by broken capillaries and an overall florid complexion.

Cutaneous – refers to anything pertaining to the skin (e.g. subcutaneous is below the skin's surface).

Dehydrated – describes skin that is lacking in or deprived of water.

Dermabrasion – is an operative procedure to treat acne scars or pits performed with sandpaper, revolving wire brushes or other abrasive materials.

Dermatitis – is a condition that is characterized by any inflammation of the skin.

Dermatosis – is a non-specific term used to denote any cutaneous abnormality.

Dyschromia – describes abnormal pigmentations of the skin.

Eczema – is also referred to as atopic dermatitis. It is a congenital inflammatory skin condition characterized by dry, itchy skin.

Edema – is swelling as a result of an accumulation of watery fluid in cells or intercellular tissues.

Effleurage – is a gentle, relaxing stroking movement used in massage.

Elasticity – describes the quantity and quality of the elastin fibers in the dermis; dictates how well the skin is allowed to stretch and return to its former shape.

Emollient – is an agent that softens or soothes the surface of the skin that typically contains oils.

Epidermal growth factor – are agents used topically to stimulate healthy cell proliferation.

Erythema – is redness due to capillary dilation.

Erythematotelangiectatic rosacea – is the technical name for subtype I rosacea. It is characterized by flushing and persistent redness of the central third of the face, broken capillaries, discomfort and roughness.

Extracellular matrix (ECM) – is a complex group of biomolecules designed to support and protect the cells.

Exudate – describes any fluid that has leaked out of tissue or its capillaries. It may be a result of injury, inflammation or aggressive medical device treatments.

Herpes simplex – is a virus that produces fever blisters and cold sores.

Inflammation – describes any reaction the body has to external or internal irritation that presents with redness, pain, heat and swelling.

Keloid – is a nodular, firm mass of hyperplastic scar tissue that is often tender or painful. Keloids consist of wide, irregularly distributed bands of collagen.

Keratin – is the collective name for a group of proteins that form the intermediate filaments in epithelial cells.

Keratinocytes – are the major cell type of the epidermis, making up about 90% of epidermal cells. They originate in the basal layer from the division of keratinocyte stem cells. They are pushed up through the layers of the epidermis, undergoing gradual differentiation until they reach the stratum corneum, where they form a layer of enucleated, flattened, highly keratinized cells called corneocytes. This layer forms an effective barrier to the entry of foreign matter and infectious agents into the body, and minimizes moisture loss. Keratinocytes are shed and replaced continuously from the stratum corneum. The time of transit from basal layer to shedding is approximately one month, although this can be accelerated in conditions of keratinocyte hyperproliferation, such as psoriasis.

Laser – is the acronym for Light Amplification by Stimulated Emission of Radiation. Lasers are a source of intense radiation of the visible, ultraviolet or infrared portions of the electromagnetic spectrum.

Lesion – describes any structural tissue change caused by injury or disease.

Macule – describes any flat spot of discoloration level with the skin (e.g. a freckle).

Matrix metalloproteinases (MMP) – are enzymes (e.g. collagenase or elastase) responsible for the breakdown and recycling of old and unusable protein fragments (e.g. collagen or elastin). They can also be excessively stimulated by internal and external factors to breakdown needed, healthy proteins.

Melanin – is the protein that is triggered by an inflammatory response (e.g. heat, trauma, sun or any cutaneous inflammation). Groups of these darkly pigmented granules are collected into melanosomes (packets of pigment) and deposited over the nucleus of the affected keratinocytes to protect its DNA.

Melanocyte – is the term for the pigment producing-cells that are located in the basal layer of the epidermis.

Melanosome – describes the generally oval collections of pigment granules produced by melanocytes to be distributed to keratinocytes over their nuclei to protect the bodies' DNA.

Milia – is a small subepidermal keratinous cyst that typically appears on the face and is not in an open follicle.

Monochromatic – describes something that has only one color.

Natural Moisturizing Factor (NMF) – is an important skin component that is a combination of several low molecular weight and water soluble compounds formed within corneocytes (dead cells in the stratum corneum). These substances include amino acids, pyrrolidone carboxylic acid, lactate, urea, ammonia, uric acid, glucosamine, creatinine, citreate, sodium, postassium, calcium, magnesium, phosphate, chlorine, sugar, organic acids, peptides and other unidentified substances.

Neutralization – is the act of changing the reaction of a solution from acid or alkaline to neutral.

Nevus – is a circumscribed abnormality of the skin that is often discolored by hyperpigmentation (e.g. a birthmark or mole).

Occlusion – can be accomplished by a dressing or topical substance that prevents air from reaching a wound/lesion. Occlusion is the act of retaining moisture, heat, bodily fluids and medications in the skin.

Ocular rosacea – is the technical name for subtype IV rosacea that affects the eyes. It leaves them with a watery or bloodshot appearance and stinging, dryness, itching, light sensitivity, frequent styes and blurred vision.

Oxidation – is a reaction that occurs by combining oxygen with another substance

Papulopustular rosacea – is the technical name for subtype II rosacea. It is sometimes referred to as acne rosacea, and is characterized by persistent central facial erythema with papules and pustules.

pH – indicates "potential of hydrogen" concentration and states the relative degree of acidity or alkalinity of a substance.

Phymatous rosacea – is the technical name for subtype III rosacea. It most commonly presents on the nose (rhinophyma), but may also affect the chin, forehead, cheeks and ears. It is characterized by thickening skin, irregular surface nodules and enlargement.

Pigment – describes any organic coloring matter, such as that of red blood cells, hair, skin or the iris.

Pigmentation – is the deposition of pigment in the skin or tissues.

Pore – describes small openings of the sweat glands or hair follicles of the skin.

Post-inflammatory hyperpigmentation (PIH) – is a type of hyperpigmentation that occurs as a result of any inflammatory incident in the skin, and results in the deposition of protective melanin and dark spots of pigmentation.

Prophylactic – describes the use of any preventative measure.

Psoriasis – is a common, inherited skin disease that is characterized by circumscribed red patches covered with adherent white silver scales.

Rhytid – is the medical term for a skin wrinkle.

Sebaceous cyst – describes a sac or cyst found beneath the surface of the skin that is filled with sebum and keratin.

Sebaceous glands – are the oil producing glands of the skin.

Seborrhea – is an oily skin condition caused by the over-activity of the sebaceous glands.

Sebum – is the fatty or oily secretions of the sebaceous glands.

Slough – refers to the separation of dead cells from living tissues.

Steatoma – is a sebaceous cyst or a fatty tumor.

Systemic – refers to things pertaining to a system or to the body as a whole.

Transepidermal water loss (TEWL) – describes moisture loss through the stratum corneum. This movement of water from the lower tissues through the epidermis and then through evaporation from the stratum corneum can be accelerated with the use of harsh topical agents, and may lead to dehydration and irritation.

Verruca – is a wart or flesh-colored growth of the papillae and epidermis.

commonly used medical abbreviations

prn	as needed
tx	treatment
bid	twice daily
tid	three times a day
qid	four times a day
qd	daily
qod	every other day
qhs	at bedtime
qam	in the morning
qpm	in the evening
rx	prescription
hx	history of

recommended reading

Aloe Vera

Dal' Belo SE, Rigo-Gaspar L, et al. (2006) "Moisturizing Effect of Cosmetic Formulations Containing Aloe Vera Extract in Different Concentrations Assessed by Skin Bioengineering Techniques." *Skin Research and Technology*, volume 12: pp. 241-246

Byeon SW, Pelley RP, Ullrich SE, et al. (1998) "Aloe Barbadensis Extracts Reduce the Production of Interleukin-10 After Exposure to Ultraviolet Raditation." *Journal Investigative Dermatology*, volume 110: pp. 811-817

Chithra P, Sajithlal GB, Chandrakasan G. (1998) "Influence of Aloe Vera on the Glycoaminoglycans in the Matrix of Healing Dermal Wounds in Rats." *Journal of Ethnopharmacology*, volume 59: pp. 179-186

Heggers JP, Kucukcelebi A, et al. (1996) "Beneficial Effect of Aloe on Wound Healing in an Excisional Wound Model." *Journal of Alternative and Complimentary Medicine*, volume 2: pp. 271-277

Acne Treatment

Baldwin H, Berman B, et al. (2008) "Act on Acne™: Evolutionary and Revolutionary Approaches to Treatment – Proceedings from a Scientific Roundtable." *PROCEEDINGS,* SynerMed Communications, pp. 1-11

Aquaporins

Diabas AI, Mia AJ, Yorio T (1998) "Aquaporins (Water Channels): Role in Vasopressin-Activated Water Transport." *Proceedings of the Society for Experimental Biology and Medicine*, volume 219: pp. 183-199

Hara M, Ma T, Verkman AS (2002) Selectively Reduced Glycerol in the Skin of Aquaporin-3-Deficient Mice may Account for Impaired Skin Hydration, Elasticity and Barrier Recovery. Journal of Biological Chemistry, volume 277: pp. 46,616-46,621

Hara M, Verman AS (2003) "Glycerol Replacement Corrects Defective Skin Hydration, Elasticity and Barrier Function in Aquaporin-3-Deficient Mice." *Proceedings of the National Academy of Sciences*, volume 100: pp. 7,360-7,365

Zheng X, Bollag WB. (2003) "Aquaporin 3 Colocates with Phospholipase D2 in Caveolin-Rich Membrane Microdomains and Is Downregulated upon Keratinocyte Differentiation." *Journal of Investigative Dermatology*, volume 121: pp. 1487-1495

Hara-Chikuma M, Verkman AS. (2005) "Aquaporin-3 Functions as a Glycerol Transporter in Mammalian Skin." *Biology of the Cell*, volume 97: pp. 479-496

Benzoyl Peroxide

Del Rosso J. (2003) "Keeping it Clean." *Skin & Aging*, volume 11: pp. 82-88

Dreno B. (2004) "Topical Antibacterial Therapy for Acne Vulgaris." *Drugs*, volume 64: pp. 2,389-2,397

Chemical Peels

Tosti, A, Grimes, PE, et al. Color Atlas of Chemical Peeling. Berlin, Germany: Springer-Verlag; 2007

Citric Acid

Bernstein EF, Underhill CB, Lakkakorpi J, et al. (1997) "Citric Acid Increases Viable Epidermal Thickness and Glycosaminoglycan Content of Sun-Damaged Skin." *Dermatologic Surgery*, volume 23: pp. 659-694

Enzymatic Exfoliation
Smith WP, Bishop M, Gillis G, et al. (2007) "Topical Proteolytic Enzymes Affect Epidermal and Dermal Properties." *International Journal of Cosmetic Science*, volume 29: pp. 15-21

Essential Fatty Acids
Letawe C, Boone M, Piérard GE. (1998) "Digital Image Analysis of the Effect of Topically Applied Linoleic Acid on Acne Microcomedones." *Clinics and Experimental Dermatology*, volume 23: pp. 56-58

Garrow JS, James WPT, Ralph A. *Human Nutrition and Dietetics*, 10th ed. Edinburgh, U.K.: Churchill Livingstone: 2000. pp. 741-742

Boelsma E, Tanojo H, Bodde HE, et al. (1996) "Assessment of the Potential Irritancy of Oleic Acid on Human Skin: Evaluation In Vitro and In Vivo." *Toxicol In Vitro*, volume 10: pp. 729-742

Puglia C, Tropea S, Rizza L, et al. (2005) "In Vitro Percutaneous Absorption Studies and In Vivo Evaluation of Anti-Inflammatory Activity of Essential Fatty Acids (EFA) from Fish Oil Extracts." *International Journal of Pharmacology*, volume 299: pp. 41-48

James MJ, Gibson RA, Cleland LG. (2000) "Dietary Polyunsaturated Fatty Acids and Inflammatory Mediator Production." *American Journal of Clinical Nutrition*, volume 71: pp. 343S-348S

Terano T, Salmon JA, Higgs GA, et al. (1986) "Eicosapentaenoic Acid as a Modulator of Inflammation Effect on Prostaglandin and Leukotriene Synthesis." *Biochemical Pharmacology*, volume 35: pp. 779-785

Ethnic Skin:
Grimes P. Aesthetics and Cosmetic Surgery for Darker Skin Types, Philadelphia: Lippincott Williams & Wilkins, 2008

General Ingredient Information:
Dweck A. (2003) "The Role of Natural Ingredients in Anti-Aging of the Skin." Australian Society of Cosmetic Chemists: pp. 1-21 http://www.naturalingredient.org/Articles/ASCC_paper.pdf (July 2007)

Thornfeldt C (2005) "Cosmeceuticals Containing Herbs: Fact, Fiction and Future." *Dermalologic Surgery*, volume 31: pp. 873-880

Bennett S, Chaudhuri RK, et al. *Anti-aging: Physiology to Formulation*, Carol Stream, Illinois: Allured Publishing Corporation, 2006

Grape Seed Polyphenols:
Mei-Hua L, Jung-Hee J, Buxiang S, et al. (2004) "Protective Effects of Oligomers of Grape Seed Polyphenols Against ß-Amyloid-Induced Oxidative Cell Death." *Annals of the New York Academy of Sciences*, volume 1030: pp. 317-329

Baxter RA. "Anti-aging Properties of Resveratrol; Review and Report of a Potent New Antioxidant Formulation." *Journal of Cosmetic Dermatology*, volume 7: pp. 2-7

Green Tea/EGCG:

Hsu S, Bollag WB, Lewis J et al. (2003) "Green Tea Polyphenols Induce Differentiation and Proliferation in Epidermal Keratinocytes." *JPET*, volume 306: pp. 29-34

Mui Y, We D, Liu J. (2005) "Reversal of Multidrug Resistance in KB Cells with Tea Polyphenol Antioxidant Capacity." *Cancer Biology and Therapy*, volume 4: pp. 468-473

Elmets CA, Singh D, et al. (2001) "Cutaneous Photoprotection from Ultraviolet Injury by Green Tea Polyphenols." *Journal of American Academy of Dermatology*, volume 44: pp. 425-432

Lactic Acid:

Smith W. (1996) "Epidermal and Dermal Effects of Topical Lactic Acid." *Journal of American Academy of Dermatology*, volume 35: pp 388-391

Sharquie KE, Al-Tikreety MM, et al. (2005) "Lactic Acid as a New Therapeutic Peeling Agent in Melasma." *Dermatologic Surgery*, volume 31: pp. 149-154

Orth DS, Kabara JJ. *Cosmetic and Drug Microbiology*, New York: Informa Healthcare; 2005: pp. 163-184

Usuki A, Ohashi A, et al. (2003) "The Inhibitory Effect of Glycolic Acid and Lactic Acid on Melanin Synthesis in Melanoma Cells." *Experimental Dermatology*, volume 12: pp. 43-50

Leyden JJ, Rawlings AV. *Skin Moisturization*, New York: Marcel Dekker, Inc; 2002: pp. 323-352

Brody HJ. *Chemical Peeling and Resurfacing Second Edition*, St. Louis: Mosby-Year Book, Inc; 1992: pp. 73-108

Modified and Enhanced Jessner's Solutions:

Fulton JE Jr. "Jessner's Peels." in: Dover JS, Alam M, Rubin M. *Chemical Peels*. New York, NY: Elsevier Inc; 2006: pp. 57-71

Niacinamide:

Gehring W. (2004) "Nicotinic Acid/Niacinamide and the Skin." *Journal of Cosmetic Dermatology*, volume 3: pp. 88-93

Parabens:

U.S. Food and Drug Administration. (2006) "Parabens." Center for Food Safety and Applied Nutrition: http://www.cfsan.fda.gov/~dms/cos-para.html (July 2007)

Weil A. (2004) "Ask the Expert: Parabens Paranoia?" health.yahoo.com http://health.yahoo.com/ate/drweil/alldaily/2004/08/20040823;_ylt=AuNQGGrz87pc7cKynScKZJpLvs8F (July 2007)

Golden R, Gandy J, Vollmer G. (2005) "A Review of the Endocrine Activity of Parabens and Implications for Potential Risks to Human Health." *Critical Reviews in Toxicology*, volume 35: pp. 435-458

Peptides:

Blanes-Mira C, Clemente J, Jodas G, et al. (2002) "A Synthetic Hexapeptide (Argireline) with Anti-Wrinkle Activity." *International Journal of Cosmetic Science*, volume 24: pp. 303-310

Katayama K, Armendariz-Borunda J, Raghow R, et al. (1993) "A Pentapeptide from Type I Pro-Collagen Promotes Extracellular Matrix Production." *The Journal of Biological Chemistry*, volume 268: pp. 9941-9944

Farris P. (2004) "Cosmeceutical Critique: Peptides." *Skin & Allergy News*, volume 35: pp. 30

Lupo MP, Cole AL. (2007) "Cosmeceutical Peptides." *Dermatologic Therapy*, volume 20: pp. 343-349

Pigment Control:

Nordlund JJ, Grimes PE, Ortonne JP. (2006) "The Safety of Hydroquinone." *JEADV*, volume 20: pp. 781-787

Maeda K, Fukuda M. (1996) "Arbutin: Mechanism of its Depigmenting Action in Human Melanocyte Culture." *Journal of Pharmacology and Experimental Therapeutics*, volume 276: pp. 765-769

Nazarro-Porro, M. (1987) "Azelaic Acid." *J Am Acad Dermatol*, volume 17: pp. 1033-1041

Yokota T, Nishio H, Kubota Y, et al. (1998) "The Inhibitory Effects of Glabridin from Licorice Extracts on Melanogenesis and Inflammation." *Pigment Cell Research*, volume 11: pp. 356-361

Kahn, V. (1995) "Effect of Kojic Acid on the Oxidation of DL-DOPA, Norepinephrine, and Dopamine by Mushroom Tyrosinase." *Pigment Cell Research*, volume 8: pp. 234-240

Lotti T, Theirs, BH, et al. *Dermatologic Clinics: Pigmentary Disorders*, Philadelphia: Elsevier Saunders, 2007

Draelos ZD. *Cosmetic Formulation of Skin Care Products*, New York: Taylor and Francis Group LLC, 2006

Badreshia-Bansal S, Draelos ZD. "Insight into Skin Lightening Cosmeceuticals for Women of Color." *Journal of Drugs in Dermatology*, volume 6: pp. 32-39

James AJ. (2006) "Skin Lightening and Depigmenting Agents." emedicine from WebMD: http://www.emedicine.com/derm/topic528.htm (July 2008)

Rendon, MI, Gaviria JI. (2005) "Review of Skin Lightening Agents." *Dermatologic Surgery*, volume 31: pp. 886–890

Vallero-Rowell VM, Verallo V, et al. (1989) "Double-Blind Comparison of Azelaic Acid and Hydroquinone in the Treatment of Melasma." *Acta Dermato-Venereologica Suppl*, volume 143: pp. 58-61

Fitton A, Goa KL. (1991) "Azelaic Acid: A Review of its Pharmacological Properties and Theraputic Efficacy in Acne and Hyperpigmentary Disorders." *Drugs*, volume 4: pp. 780-798

K

Retinol:
Elder JT, Kaplan A. (1996) "Retinoid Induction of CRABPII mRNA in Human Dermal Fibroblasts: Use as a Retinoid Bioassay." *J Invest Dermatol*, volume 106: pp. 517-521

Draelos Z. (2005) "Retinoids in Cosmetics." *Cosmetic Dermatology*, volume 18: pp. 3-5

Kang S. (2005) "Mechanism of Action of Retinol." *Cosmetic Dermatology*, volume 18: pp. 6-8

Del Rosso JQ. (2002) "Topical Retinoid Therapy." *Skin & Aging*, volume 10

Rosehip Seed Oil:
Concha J, Soto C, Chamy R, et al. (2006) "Effect of Rosehip Extraction Process on Oil and Defatted Meal Physicochemical Properties." *Journal of the American Oil Chemists' Society*, volume 83: pp. 771-775

Salicylic Acid:
Baumann L. (2001) "Cosmeceutical Critique: Salicylic Acid." *Skin & Allergy News*, volume 32, issue 9: pp. 33

Lee H, Kim I. (2003) "Salicylic Acid Peels for the Treatment of Acne Vulgaris in Asian Patients." *Dermatol Surg*, volume 29: pp. 1196-1199

Del Rosso J. (2005) "The Many Roles of Salicylic Acid." *Skin & Aging*, volume 13: pp. 38-42

Soy Isoflavones:
Baumann L. (2001) "Cosmeceutical Critique: Soy and Its Isoflavones." *Skin & Allergy News*, volume 32, issue 8: pp. 17

Kawai N. (2003) "Phytoestrogens: Applications of Soy Isoflavones in Skin Care." *Cosmetics and Toiletries*, volume 118: pp. 73-80

Sunscreens:
Maier H, Schauberger G, Brunnhofer K, et al. (2001) "Change of Ultraviolet Absorptions of Sunscreens by Exposure to Solar Simulated Radiation." *Journal of Investigative Dermatology*, volume 117: pp. 256-262

Tarras-Wahlberg N, Stenhagen G, Larkö O, et al. (1999) "Changes in Ultraviolet Absorption of Sunscreens After Ultraviolet Irradiation." *Journal of Investigative Dermatology*, volume 113: pp. 547-553

Glaser DA, Waldorf HA. "Sunscreens." Dover JS, Alam M, Draelos ZD *Cosmeceuticals*. New York, NY: Elsevier Inc; 2005: pp. 139-147

Trichloroacetic Acid (TCA):
Leonhardt J, Lawrence N. "Trichloroacetic Acid (TCA) Peels." Dover JS, Alam M, Rubin M. *Chemical Peels*. New York, NY: Elsevier Inc; 2006: pp. 73-86

Vitamins C and E:
Pinnell S, Huanshu Y, Omar M, et al. (2001) "Topical L-Asocorbic Acid: Percutaneous Absorption Studies." *Dermatologic Surgery*, volume 27: pp 137-142

Lin J, Selim MA, Shea CR, et al. (2003) "UV Photoprotection by Combination Topical Antioxidants Vitamin C and Vitamin E." *Journal of American Academy of Dermatology*, volume 48: pp 866-874

Heber, G Markovic B, Hayes A. (2006) "Anhydrous Topical Ascorbic Acid On Human Skin." *Journal of Cosmetic Dermatology*, volume 5: pp 150-156

Kobayashi S, Takehana M, Itoh S, et al. (1996) "Protective Effect of Magnesium-L-ascorbyl-2 Phosphate Against Skin Damage Induced by UVB Radiation." *Photochemical Photobiology*, volume 64: pp. 224-228

shelf life/pH

A "best by" date is printed on all non-OTC products to help you determine the time frame during which a product is most effective. OTC products will not have the 'best by' date, as they already carry an expiration date. Please always feel free to contact us with any questions.

	pH	Shelf life (years/post-production date)
Facial Wash	3.3 - 4.3	3
Facial Wash Oily/Problem	4.5 - 5.5	2
Total Wash Face & Body Cleanser	6.0 - 7.0	3
Creamy Cleanser	5.67 - 6.67	3
BPO 5% Cleanser	5.5 - 6.5	2
Blemish Control Bar	N/A	3
Dry Skin Relief Bar®	N/A	3
Pigment Bar®	N/A	3
Smoothing Toner	1.76 - 2.76	3
Nutrient Toner	2.0 - 2.4	3
Gentle Exfoliant	5.8 - 7.0	3
Pore Refining Treatment	5.5	2
Purifying Mask	5.5 - 7.5	3
Revitalizing Mask	3.0 - 4.0	2
Detoxifying Mask	4.5	2
ExLinea® Peptide Smoothing Serum	5.3 - 6.3	3
Pigment Gel®	2.0 - 3.0	2
Pigment Gel® HQ Free	2.0 - 3.0	3
Acne Gel	3.29 - 4.29	2
Acne Cream	3.06 - 4.06	2
C-Quench® Antioxidant Serum	2.42 - 3.42	1
A&C Synergy Serum®	2.6 - 3.6	1.5
Total Strength Serum	4.9 - 5.3	1
Hydrating Serum	4.49 - 5.49	3
Rejuvenating Serum	4.65 - 5.65	3
Anti-Redness Serum	4.95 - 5.95	3
Retinol Renewal With RestorAtive Complex	5.24 - 6.24	1.5
Retinol Treatment for Sensitive Skin	5.36	1.5
Intensive Clarity Treatment®: 0.5% pure retinol night	2.57 - 3.57	1.5
Intensive Age Refining Treatment®: 0.5% pure retinol night	4.61 - 5.61	1.5
Intensive BrighteningTreatment: 0.5% pure retinol night	5.82 - 6.82	1.5
Intensive Pigment Eraser	4.74 - 5.74	1.5
C&E Strength	N/A	2
C&E Strength Max	N/A	2
Hyaluronic Acid Boosting Serum	5.5 - 6.5	2
Dual Action Redness Relief	6.08	2
Ideal Complex® Revitalizing Eye Gel	5.0 - 6.0	2
Ideal Complex® Restorative Eye Cream	5.5 - 6.5	2
EyeXcellence	5.33 - 6.33	2
Perfecting Neck & Décolleté	6.0 - 7.0	3
CliniCalm™ 1%	5.65 - 6.65	2
Peptide Lip Therapy	N/A	3
Weightless Protection Broad Spectrum SPF 45	7.0 - 8.0	3
Perfecting Protection Broad Spectrum SPF 30	6.6 - 7.6	3
Protecting Hydrator Broad Spectrum SPF 30	7.3 - 8.3	3
Hydrator Plus Broad Spectrum SPF 30	7.2 - 8.0	3
Active Broad Spectrum SPF 45: Water Resistant	N/A	3
Sheer Tint Broad Spectrum SPF 45	N/A	3

	pH	Shelf life (years/post-production date)
Clearskin	6.0 - 6.5	3
ReBalance	5.0 - 6.5	3
Après Peel® Hydrating Balm	5.8 - 6.2	1.5
Collagen Hydrator	4.87 - 5.87	3
Silkcoat® Balm	5.74 - 6.74	3
Body Therapy	2.85 - 3.85	3
PCA Peel® Hydroquinone Free	1.55 - 1.95	3
PCA Peel® with Hydroquinone	1.55 - 1.95	2
PCA Peel® with Hydroquinone & Resorcinol	1.65 - 2.05	2
Sensi Peel®	0.9 - 1.1	2
Advanced Treatment Booster	5.0 - 6.0	1.5
Ultra Peel Forte®	0.6 - 0.7	2
Pre-Peel Accelerator Mask (Step 1)	2.9 - 3.3	2
Smoothing Body Peel® (Step 2)	0.25 - 0.65	2
Hydrate: Therapeutic Oat Milk Mask	5.5 - 6.5	2
Detoxify: Therapeutic Charcoal Mask	4.5	2
Revitalize: Therapeutic Papaya Mask	3.0 - 4.0	2
Clarify: Therapeutic Salicylic Acid Mask	3.0 - 3.6	2
Retexturize: Therapeutic Pumpkin Mask	2.0 - 2.6	3
Ultra Peel® II	4.81 - 5.21	1
4% Pure Retinol Peel	5.5 - 6.5	1.5
6% Pure Retinol Peel	6.5 - 7.5	1.5
Oxygenating Trio® - Step 1 Activator	2.0 - 4.0	3
Oxygenating Trio® - Step 2 Detoxifier	N/A	3
Oxygenating Trio® - Step 3 Oxygenator	2.0 - 3.5	1.5
Detox Gel Deep Pore Treatment	1.9 - 2.3	1
Replenishing Gel	5.5 - 6.5	3
Calming Balm	5.5 - 6.0	3

15100.14